WITHDRAWN

GEOCHEMISTRY
OF
SEDIMENTS

A Brief Survey

Geheimnisvoll am lichten Tag
lässt sich Natur des Schleiers nicht berauben,
und was sie Deinem Geist nicht offenbaren mag,
das zwingst Du ihr nicht ab mit Hebeln
und mit Schrauben

GOETHE, FAUST I

GEOCHEMISTRY
OF
SEDIMENTS
A Brief Survey

EGON T. DEGENS

Associate Scientist in Chemistry and Geology
Woods Hole Oceanographic Institution

PRENTICE-HALL, INC.

Englewood Cliffs, New Jersey

PRENTICE-HALL INTERNATIONAL, INC., *London*
PRENTICE-HALL OF AUSTRALIA, PTY., LTD., *Sydney*
PRENTICE-HALL OF CANADA, LTD., *Toronto*
PRENTICE-HALL OF INDIA (PRIVATE) LTD., *New Delhi*
PRENTICE-HALL OF JAPAN, INC., *Tokyo*

Library of Congress Catalog Card Number: 65– 22355
Printed in the United States of America
C35123

Preface

This book is an introduction for students of geology into the fundamentals of low-temperature geochemistry. Its principal objective is to demonstrate how geochemical data can supplement geological field work or assist in petrographic and paleontologic research. Since this book was not written for the geochemical specialist, lengthy discussions, mathematical derivations and excessive details have been omitted. Instead, attention has been focused on the way in which geochemistry can contribute to a better understanding of basic geologic problems such as weathering, provenance, source, origin of sedimentary minerals, environment, facies, or diagenesis.

Bowen's reaction principle of high-temperature petrogenesis, gives igneous petrologists a convenient system to present data on geochemistry in a physically-chemically organized and methodical form. No such simple scheme exists in the field of sediment petrogenesis. This is caused by the fact that the various coexisting components in a given sediment are frequently not formed under equilibrium conditions. Namely, their occurrence in one rock is more or less accidental as a geochemist sees it. This infers that composition of a single mineral or organic compound generally has more geologic meaning than the sum total geochemistry of the whole sediment. For this reason, I have discussed petrogenetically related classes of compounds rather constituents are part of shales, greywackes, sandstones, limestones, or any other sedimentary rock.

This book is divided into *inorganic* and *organic* sections, in view of the fact that sediments contain both types of materials. The arrangement of data within each section follows to some extent the classification system adopted in mineralogy and organic chemistry respectively. Basic aspects of sediment geochemistry have been treated as comprehensively as possible within the scope and the limits of this book. It should be noted, however, that the chapters on clay minerals and carbonates are far from being all-embracing. The wealth of published information on these two subjects requires more room than could possibly be spared in a treatise like this one. Forced to make a choice, I selected data which have an important bearing on classical geology and paleontology in preference to data having mainly crystallochemical or physical-chemical significance.

Each chapter includes a list of references. The bibliography comprises chiefly publications of recent vintage—if possible in English—written by people who pioneered in a particular field. The older literature on a special topic may easily be obtained by consulting some of the quoted review papers.

I have done my best to present illustrative picture material, realizing that a graph will often reveal more information than a few pages of text. And finally, I apologize in advance for my English that sometimes has an unmistakable Teutonic flavor.

ACKNOWLEDGEMENTS

This book was written while I was teaching at the California Institute of Technology and it is a pleasant task to thank my colleagues there—in particular Dr. S. Epstein, Dr. E. Hare, Dr. H. A. Lowenstam, and Dr. K. H. Towe, who kindly furnished some of their unpublished results on stable isotope geochemistry and biological mineralization systems.

To Dr. K. O. Emery and Dr. J. M. Hunt of the Woods Hole Oceanographic Institution I am greatly indebted for their interest and contribution in the course of our joint scientific endeavors.

I owe gratitude to Dr. G. V. Chilingar of the University of Southern California, who read the entire text, offered constructive criticism, and provided valuable suggestions for improving the manuscript.

I am grateful to Mrs. Ruth Talovich for her excellent artwork and to Mrs. Lucille Lozoya for her secretarial help in the final preparation of the manuscript.

EGON T. DEGENS

Woods Hole Oceanographic Institution
Woods Hole, Massachusetts

Contents

4

Mobile Phases   184

1

Introduction

There are a number of ways to study sediments. An investigation by means of geochemical techniques is just one of them. Actually, most geochemical work is basically dependent on preceding field studies and petrographic observations which are needed to interpret the data in a geologically meaningful fashion.

In our study of the geochemistry of sediments we shall draw upon a great deal of knowledge in the areas of geology and petrography. However, it is neither the purpose nor the intention of this survey to give a detailed discussion of the essentials of these subjects. The interested reader is referred to the many excellent textbooks which are available; some of these are listed below.

The sole concern of this abridged survey is (1) to focus the attention on geochemical aspects of sediments, (2) to present the data in a clear and constructive manner, and (3) to show the significance of geochemical studies for the evaluation and solution of classical geologic problems.

The organic and inorganic components of a sediment which were not necessarily formed under chemical equilibrium conditions present a complicated picture. This makes it difficult, for instance, to interpret coexisting mineral assemblages from a physical-chemical point of view. In the following it has, therefore, been decided to investigate the principal organic or inorganic constituents of sediments separately, rather than the total sedimentary rock as a whole.

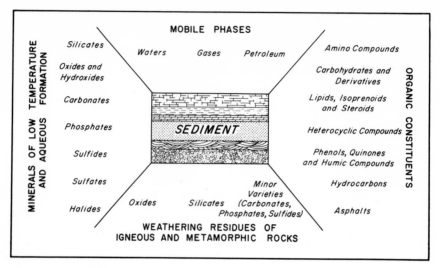

Fig. 1 Major inorganic and organic end-members of sediments. Materials are grouped according to mode of formation.

In order to illustrate what kind of components can be found in a sedimentary rock, the major mineral and organic end-members are listed in Figure 1. The data are arranged on the basis of the genetic type and the chemical or mineralogical nature of the individual compound. In principle, one can distinguish between four major types of end-members:

(1) Weathering residues of igneous and metamorphic rocks

(2) Minerals of low temperature and aqueous formation

(3) Mobile phases, and

(4) Organic constituents.

Single species of each of these four groups can occur alone or in combination with others. Monomineralic sediments such as pure limestones or quartz sandstones, however, are exceedingly rare. For the most part, sediments represent complex mixtures of a great number of petrogenetically unrelated compounds.

Textbooks and Manuals

Abelson, P. H., ed. *Researches in Geochemistry*. New York: John Wiley & Sons, Inc., 1959.

Braitsch, O. *Entstehung und Stoffbestand der Salzlagerstaetten: Mineralogie und Petrographie in Einzeldarstellungen*, III. Berlin-Goettingen-Heidelberg: Springer Verlag, 1962.

Breger, I. A., ed., *Organic Geochemistry*. New York: The Macmillan Company, 1963.

Carozzi, A. V., *Microscopic Sedimentary Petrography*. New York-London: John Wiley & Sons, Inc., 1960.

Clarke, F. W., *The Data of Geochemistry* (fourth edition): Washington, D. C. Government Printing Office, 1924.

Colombo, U. and G. D. Hobson, eds., *Advances in Organic Geochemistry*. New York: The Macmillan Company, 1964.

Craig, H., S. L. Miller, and G. J. Wasserburg, eds., *Isotopic and Cosmic Chemistry*. Amsterdam: North-Holland Publishing Company, 1964.

Deer, W. A., R. A. Howie and J. Zussman, *Rock-Forming Minerals*. London: Longmans, Green and Co., Ltd., 1962, 1963. Vol. 3 (Sheet Silicates, 1962), Vol. 4 (Framework Silicates, 1963), Vol. 5 (Non-silicates, 1963).

Emery, K. O., *The Sea Off Southern California: A Modern Habitat of Petroleum*. New York: John Wiley & Sons, Inc., 1960.

Engelhardt, W. von, *Der Porenraum der Sedimente: Mineralogie und Petrographie in Einzeldarstellungen*, II. Berlin-Goettingen-Heidelberg: Springer Verlag, 1960.

Garrels, R. M., *Mineral Equilibria at Low Temperature and Pressure*. New York: Harper and Row, Publishers, 1960.

Goldschmidt, V. M., *Geochemistry*. Oxford: Clarendon Press, Inc., 1954.

Grim, R. E., *Clay Mineralogy*. New York-Toronto-London: McGraw-Hill Book Company, 1953.

Grim, R. E., *Applied Clay Mineralogy*. New York-Toronto-London: McGraw-Hill Book Company, 1962.

Hutchinson, G. E., *A Treatise on Limnology*. I. New York: John Wiley & Sons, Inc., 1957.

Ingerson, E., ed., *Clays and Clay Minerals*. Proc. Eleventh Nat. Conf. Clays and Clay Minerals. New York: The Macmillan Company, 1963.

Krumbein, W. C. and L. L. Sloss, *Stratigraphy and Sedimentation* (second edition). San Francisco and London: W. H. Freeman and Company, 1963.

Larsen, G. and G. V. Chilingar, eds., *Diagenesis of Sediments*. Amsterdam-New York-London: Elsevier Publishing Co., 1965.

Mason, B., *Principles of Geochemistry* (second edition). New York: John Wiley & Sons, Inc., 1958.

Milligan, W. O., ed., *Clays and Clay Minerals*. Proc. Third Nat. Conf. Clays and Clay Minerals. Nat. Acad. Sci.-Nat. Res. Counc. Publ., **395** (1955).

Milner, H. B., *Sedimentary Petrography*. New York: The Macmillan Company, 1962.

Pask, J. A. and M. D. Turner, eds., *Clays and Clay Technology*. Proc. First Nat. Conf. Clays and Clay Technology. Cal. Div. Mines Bull., **169** (1955).

Pauling, L., *The Nature of the Chemical Bond* (third edition). Ithaca, N. Y.: Cornell University Press, 1960.

Pettijohn, F. J., *Sedimentary Rocks* (second edition). New York: Harper and Row, Publishers, 1957.

Rankama, K., *Isotope Geology*. New York: McGraw-Hill Book Company, 1954.

Rankama, K. and T. G. Sahama, *Geochemistry*. Chicago: University of Chicago Press, 1950.

Searle, A. and R. W. Grimshaw, *The Chemistry and Physics of Clays and Other Ceramic Materials* (third edition). New York: Interscience Publishers Inc., 1959.

Sears, M., ed., *Oceanography*. Washington, D. C.: Publication No. **67** of the American Association for the Advancement of Science, 1961.

Sognnaes, R. F., ed., *Calcification in Biological Systems*. Washington, D. C.: Publication No. **64** of the American Association for the Advancement of Science, 1960.

Sverdrup, H. U., M. W. Johnson and R. H. Fleming, *The Oceans*. Englewood Cliffs, N. J.: Prentice-Hall, Inc., 1942.

Swineford, A., ed., *Clays and Clay Minerals*. Proc. Fourth Nat. Conf. Clays and Clay Minerals. Nat. Acad. Sci.-Nat. Res. Counc. Publ. **456** (1956).

Swineford, A., ed., *Clays and Clay Minerals*. Proc. Fifth Nat. Conf. Clays and Clay Minerals. Nat. Acad. Sci.-Nat. Res. Counc. Publ., **566** (1958).

Swineford, A., ed., *Clays and Clay Minerals*. Proc. Sixth (1959), Seventh (1960), Eighth (1960), Ninth (1962), Tenth (1962) Nat. Conf. Clays and Clay Minerals. London-New York: Pergamon Press, Inc., 1959–1962.

Swineford, A. and N. Plummer, eds., *Clays and Clay Minerals*. Proc. Second Nat. Conf. Clays and Clay Minerals. Nat. Acad. Sci.-Nat. Res. Counc. Publ., **327** (1954).

Teodorovich, G. I., *Authigenic Minerals in Sedimentary Rocks*. New York: Consultants Bureau Enterprise, Inc., 1961. (The Russian text was published by the USSR Academy of Sciences Press, Moscow, 1958).

Termier, H. and G. Termier, *Erosion and Sedimentation*. London-Princeton-Toronto: D. Van Nostrand Co., Inc., 1963.

Twenhofel, W. H., *Principles of Sedimentation* (second edition). New York-Toronto-London: McGraw-Hill Book Company, 1950.

2

Weathering Residues of Igneous and Metamorphic Minerals

Introduction

During weathering and subsequent denudation the individual igneous and metamorphic minerals respond differently to chemical, biochemical and physical attacks. Thus, some mineral species will be destroyed rather radically and in short periods of time, while others are little affected, if at all.

The relative stability of the more common high temperature minerals under conditions of weathering has been determined by Goldich (1938). The results are summarized in Figure 2. Inasmuch as mafic minerals are generally less stable than the salic minerals, a distinction was made between the two series. Interestingly enough, the arrangement in Figure 2 is identical with the reaction series of high temperature petrogenesis as determined by Bowen (1922). However, this should not imply that, for instance, olivine weathers to

EXOGENIC STABILITY OF
HIGH-TEMPERATURE MINERALS

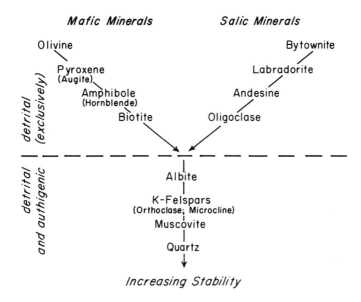

Fig. 2   Weathering stability series of primary rock-forming minerals (after Goldich, 1938)

pyroxene and the pyroxene to amphibole, etc.; but it may indicate that the equilibrium conditions for olivine formation deviate more severely from the environmental conditions established at or near the earth surface than they do for any other high temperature mineral. This suggestion receives support from the fact that the four most stable minerals of Goldich's stability series can also occur as authigenic sedimentary mineral species.

Freise (1931) and Thiel (1940) determined experimentally the abrasion or mechanical resistance of a number of rock-forming minerals. Freise (1931) constructed an abrasion series in which the mechanical abrasion of a single mineral is compared to that of crystalline hematite. The data indicate that aside from hardness, the cleavage and "tenacity" of a mineral influences its abrasion characteristics.

The chemical and mechanical overall stability will therefore determine the fate of crystalline materials in the exogenic cycle. It is evident that the mineral with the lowest abrasion effect and the highest chemical stability will survive weathering and denudation best. This will eventually result in the relative enrichment of the stable versus the metastable mineral fraction. Differential sorting during transportation due to the differences in size and specific gravity of the individual minerals may further enhance the fractionation effect (Rittenhouse, 1943). If all the chemical and physical phenomena continue long enough, only the chemically and physically most stable end-member will be left over. Pure sand and placer deposits are typical examples of the efficiency of this exogenic purification process.

The occurrence, the absence, or the ratio of primary rock-forming minerals in a sediment may be used for the interpretation of a variety of syngenetic and diagenetic phenomena such as, for instance, source aspects, provenance, weathering and transportation processes, paleogeography, or general diagenesis. Although morphological, paragenetic, and occasionally chemical relationships among the coexisting primary constituents can best be recognized and evaluated by classical petrographical tools (e.g., thin section studies), there are also geochemical techniques available which can supplement petrographic observation. So far, geochemists have given little attention to the weathering residues of igneous and metamorphic rocks present in sediments. The wealth of petrographic information accumulated over the last thirty to forty years, and the relative ease of thin section studies have conceivably discouraged efforts in this direction. Consequently, little can be said now on the geochemistry of primary rock-forming minerals in sediments that has not already been discussed extensively by Pettijohn (1957), Milner (1962), Carozzi (1960), and Krumbein and Sloss (1963). The following presentation, therefore, should only be considered as an attempt to point out a few ideas on geochemical research potentialities in the area of primary weathering residues.

Geochemistry

1. Absolute Age Determination

Radioactive methods are nowadays widely used to determine the absolute ages of rocks. However, in sedimentary rocks the use of isotope techniques for the determination of the time of deposition is limited by the fact that there are only a few syngenetic-authigenic minerals; e.g., glauconite or sylvite, that allow absolute age dating.

Krylov (1961) and Vistelius (1964) have pointed out that age dating of sediment constituents may also serve a different purpose, namely paleogeographic and paleotectonic reconstruction. In particular, the potassium-argon method is most suitable for reasons of (1) the wide distribution of potassium-bearing detrital minerals, and (2) the apparent retention of argon in the detrital rock constituents.

What Krylov (1961) suggests is to analyze K-containing mineral residues and rock fragments of sediments, and compare the obtained age with that of metamorphic and igneous complexes exposed in areas nearby. If the ages in the prospective crystalline source areas differ sufficiently from each other, the age of the detrital rock fragments may be used as a criterion for the ultimate source of the sedimentary residue, thus allowing paleogeographic and paleotectonic reconstructions.

In order to illustrate Krylov's basic concept, the age of fluvioglacial deposits of Northern and Central Europe, as well as the age of coastal sand deposits of the Black Sea are compared with the age of their prospective source rocks (Fig. 3). It becomes apparent that the

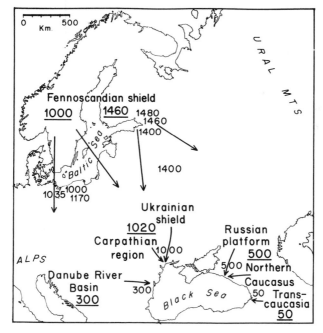

Fig. 3   Potassium-argon ages of detrital rock constituents in some sediments of Northern Europe and the Black Sea area in relation to the ages of their source rocks; age of source rock underlined (after Krylov, 1961)

fluvioglacial sediments which have been transported over hundreds of miles correspond in respect to age to their original crystalline source in southern Sweden and Finland. Similarly, the age of the Black Sea deposits is identical with the age of their crystalline sources in the Transcaucasus (50 m.y), the Northern Caucasus and Russian platform (500 m.y), the Ukranian Shield and (partially) the Carpathian region (1020 m.y.), and the Danube River Basin (300 m.y.). Total sediment analyses will only yield average ages because mixing from old and young rocks may occur. A study on cogenetic primary minerals, however, should give the true age.

The data indicate that there is no substantial loss in argon during weathering and transportation, even when the mineral particles are of subcolloidal size. Thus, the age of the primary detrital constituents in sediments reflects the age of the rock material. This is true also for clay minerals which apparently inherit the potassium-argon age of their crystalline precursor. Inasmuch as the formation of clay minerals, from feldspars e.g., generally involves a loss of potassium, one has to assume that argon is lost at about the same rate. Since, according to Krylov (1961), the potassium/argon age of the crystalline material is not modified during weathering so that the detrital clay minerals reflect the age of their "crystalline ancestors," a number of geological questions may eventually be answered. Studies of this type may well be extended to nonpotassium containing detrital minerals such as zircon, or may involve other methods of absolute age dating. A recent publication by Ledent et al. (1964) reveals interesting details on the ages of coexisting detrital zircon and feldspars in North American beach and river sands. A similar study on mineral concentrates from the Franconia Sandstone (Cambrian) was made by Tatsumoto and Patterson (1964).

2. CHEMISTRY

A study of the chemistry of detrital rock fragments generally requires a physical separation into the individual mineral grains, unless microscopic techniques (thin section studies) can be applied. But chemical data on concentrates of feldspars or of amphiboles can be geochemically misleading because the coexisting feldspars or amphiboles in such a mineral concentrate may be petrogenetically unrelated. It is largely only since the discovery and the development of electron probe microanalysis that individual mineral grains in sediments have been submitted to chemical analysis. The new technique is a powerful tool which has opened up new vistas in the study of detrital and authigenic rock components. A compilation of the use of electron probe microanalysis to problems of geology and mineralogy has been made by Heinrich (1963). Arrhenius (1963) presents electron probe data on various minerals from the bottom of the sea.

It is hoped that future developments in this area of research can make use of the undiscovered wealth of information contained in the primary rock-forming minerals commonly found in sedimentary rocks of all environments and ages.

3. STABLE ISOTOPES

Among the stable isotopes, those of oxygen, hydrogen, and sulfur appear to be the most promising ones for studies on weathering residues in sediments. As shown by Taylor and Epstein (1962) and by Silverman (1951), the distribution of oxygen isotopes in crystalline rocks is related to petrogenesis and chemical composition. The more mafic the rock, the lower the O^{18}/O^{16} ratio (Fig. 4). Similarly, the O^{18}/O^{16} ratio of a single mineral species changes systematically as one

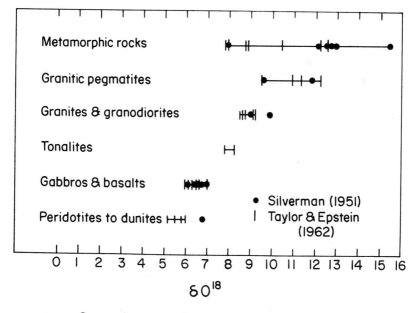

Fig. 4 Oxygen isotope analyses of total rock samples of igneous and metamorphic origin (after Taylor and Epstein, 1962)

goes from the most basic to the most acidic rock members in the reaction series of igneous petrogenesis; and the O^{18}/O^{16} ratios of metamorphic minerals are higher than in the corresponding minerals of igneous rocks Taylor and Epstein (1962).

An oxygen isotope study of coexisting detrital mineral pairs in sediments (e.g., hornblende/magnetite) would be extremely helpful for any interpretation regarding the source and provenance of the crystalline material.

4. SUMMARY

The weathering residues of igneous and metamorphic rock have not been studied sufficiently from a geochemical point of view. As mentioned before, these residues are potentially very valuable for the interpretation of geological phenomena such as paleogeography, paleotectonics, source, weathering, transportation, diagenesis and other problems. This list of topics is by no means exhaustive; it is mainly a sampling of the type of work that can be done in the area of geochemistry and geology.

Selected References

Arrhenius, G., "Pelagic Sediments" in *The Sea. Ideas and Observations on Progress on the Study of the Seas,* ed. M. N. Hill. New York: Interscience Publishers, 1963, pp. 655–727.

Bowen, N. L., "The Reaction Principle in Petrogenesis." *J. Geol.,* **30** (1922), 177–198.

Carozzi, A. V., *Microscopic Sedimentary Petrography.* New York and London: John Wiley & Sons, Inc., 1960.

Freise, F. W., "Untersuchung von Mineralen auf Abnutzbarkeit bei Verfrachtung im Wasser." Tschermaks Min. Petr. Mitt., **41** (1931), 1–7.

Goldich, S. S., "A Study in Rock-Weathering." J. Geol., **46** (1938), 17–58.

Heinrich, K. F. J., *Bibliography On Electron Probe Microanalysis and Related Subjects* (second revision). Wilmington, Del.: E. I. du Pont de Nemours & Co., Inc., Experimental Station, Delaware, 1963.

Krumbein, W. C. and L. L. Sloss, *Stratigraphy and Sedimentation* (second edition). San Francisco and London: W. H. Freeman and Company, 1963.

Krylov, A. Ya., "The Possibility of Utilizing the Absolute Age of Metamorphic and Fragmental Rocks in Paleogeography and Paleotectonics." Ann. New York Acad. Sci., **91** (1961), 324–340.

Ledent, D., C. Patterson, and G. R. Tilton, "Ages of Zircon and Feldspar Concentrates from North American Beach and River Sands." J. Geol., **72** (1964), 112–122.

Milner, H. B., *Sedimentary Petrography*. I. *Methods in Sedimentary Petrography*. II. *Principles and Applications*. New York: The Macmillan Company, 1962.

Pettijohn, F. J., *Sedimentary Rocks* (second edition). New York: Harper and Row, Publishers, 1957.

Rittenhouse, G., "Transportation and Deposition of Heavy Minerals." Bull. Geol. Soc. Amer., **54** (1943), 1725–1780.

Silverman, S. R., "The Isotope Geology of Oxygen." Geochim. et Cosmochim. Acta, **2** (1951), 26–42.

Taylor, H. P., Jr. and S. Epstein, "Relationship Between O^{18}/O^{16} Ratios in Coexisting Minerals of Igneous and Metamorphic Rocks." Bull. Geol. Soc. Amer., **73** (1962), 461–480, 675–693.

Thiel, G. A., "The Relative Resistance to Abrasion of Mineral Grains of Sand Size." J. Sed. Petrol., **10** (1940), 103–124.

Tatsumoto, M. and C. Patterson, "Age Studies of Zircon and Feldspar Concentrates from the Franconia Sandstone." J. Geol., **72** (1964), 232–242.

Vistelius, A. B., "Paleogeographic Reconstructions by Absolute Age Determinations of Sand Particles." J. Geol., **72** (1964), 483–486.

3

Minerals of

Low Temperature and

Aqueous Formation

Silicates

1. CLAY MINERALS

(a) *Classification and Nomenclature.* Clay minerals can be amorphous or crystalline. The basic properties of amorphous clays are difficult to ascertain, in particular if they are mixed with other materials. The crystalline varieties are far more interesting and significant from a geochemical point of view since they can be identified analytically with comparative ease.

Crystalline clay minerals are hydrated silicates with layer or chain lattices consisting of sheets of silica tetrahedra arranged in a hexagonal form and condensed with octahedral layers (Mackenzie, 1959). Each sheet consists of planes of cations (silica, aluminum, magnesium, iron) in which the individual cation is surrounded by either four (tetrahedral) or six (octahedral) oxygen and hydroxyl ions.

The greatest progress in the study of clay minerals was made over the last thirty years, beginning chiefly with the work of Bragg (1937) and Pauling (1930). Especially with the development of X-ray techniques, the structure of clay minerals was gradually deciphered (Brindley, 1951; Brown, 1955). In the past many classification systems had been proposed, the majority being constructed on the basis of crystallochemical and structural elements. As a function of the steadily growing output of fundamental data and information new systems were introduced and older ones were abandoned or had to be revised.

Previously, one of the great obstacles to establishing an unequivocal system with a good chance to become adopted by all earth scientists was the disagreement among clay experts as to what structural, crystallochemical or other features of clays are most significant and critical. At present, however, there is general agreement that the three most suitable characteristics for classification purposes are: (1) structural arrangement of layers, (2) population of the octahedral sheet, and (3) type of chemical bonding between the layers (ionic, intermolecular, hydrogen bonding) (Frank-Kamenetsky 1960).

The classification system of the pure end-member layer lattice type clays, as presented in Table 1, takes some of these characteristics into consideration. First of all, it is based on the way the various cation sheets are structurally arranged. The two sheet, or 1:1 clays, contain one silica sheet and one sheet of either aluminum, magnesium, or iron. The three sheet, or 2:1 clays, contain two silica sheets which enclose an aluminum, magnesium, or iron sheet ("sandwich" structure). It has to be emphasized that some clay minerals such as the montmorillonites and illites may have part of their tetrahedral sites occupied by aluminum. In addition, montmorillonites contain one or two water sheets. The three sheet plus one sheet, or 2:2 clays, have two silica sheets, which alternate with two magnesium or iron sheets.

The system takes further into consideration the character of the population of the octahedral sheet, which may be dioctahedral according to the gibbsite pattern $Al_2(OH)_6$, or trioctahedral according to the brucite pattern $Mg_3(OH)_6$.

The stability of the structure which is determined by the type of chemical bonding between the layers, is partly reflected in the swelling properties of a clay which has been treated with glycol or other polar media. Although the kind and amount of expansion is no indication of the type of bonding that exists between the individual layers (hydrogen bonding, etc.), it can be used as a characterizing feature. Additional structural and crystallochemical data relevant for the classification and characterization of pure end-member crys-

Table 1 Classification of Principal Clay Minerals in Sediments (Excluding Impure Minerals and Amorphous Phases)

LAYERS	POPULATION OF OCTAHEDRAL SHEET	EXPANSION	GROUP	SPECIES	CRYSTALLOCHEMICAL FORMULA	SPACE GROUP	STRUCTURE (SCHEMATIC)
Two-Sheet (1:1)	Dioctahedral	Non-Swelling	Kaolinite	Kaolinite / Dickite / Nacrite	$Al_4(OH)_8[Si_4O_{10}]$	Cc or $P\bar{1}$ / Cc / Cc or $R3c$	
Two-Sheet (1:1)	Dioctahedral	Non-Swelling and Swelling	Halloysite	Halloysite / Metahalloysite	$Al_4(OH)_8[Si_4O_{10}] \cdot (H_2O)_4$ / $Al_4(OH)_8[Si_4O_{10}]$	Cm	
Two-Sheet (1:1)	Trioctahedral	Non-Swelling	7Å-Chlorite (Septechlorite)	Berthierine ("Kaolin-Chamosite")	$(Fe'',Fe''',Al,Mg)_6(OH)_8[(Al,Si)_4O_{10}]$	Cm	
Three-Sheet (2:1)	Dioctahedral	Swelling	Montmorillo-nite (Smectite) *	Montmorillonite / Beidellite / Nontronite	$\{(Al_{2-x}\cdot Mg_x)(OH)_2[Si_4O_{10}]\}^{-x} Na_x\cdot nH_2O$ $Al_2(OH)_2[(Al,Si)_4O_{10}]\}^{-x} Na_x\cdot nH_2O$ $\{(Fe'''_{2-x}\cdot Mg_x)(OH)_2[Si_4O_{10}]\}^{-x} Na_x\cdot nH_2O$	Monoclinic	
Three-Sheet (2:1)	Dioctahedral	Non-Swelling	Illite (Hydromica) *	Illite-Varieties	$(K,H_3O)Al_2(H_2O,OH)_2[AlSi_3O_{10}]$	$C2/m$ or Cm	
Three-Sheet (2:1)	Trioctahedral	Swelling	Vermiculite **	Vermiculite	$(Mg,Fe)_3(OH)_2[AlSi_3O_{10}]Mg\cdot(H_2O)_4$	Cc	
Three-Sheet + One-Sheet (2:2)	Trioctahedral	Non- + Swelling	14Å-Chlorite (Normal Chlorite) **	Chlorite-Varieties	$(Al,Mg,Fe)_3(OH)_2[(Al,Si)_4O_{10}]Mg_3(OH)_6$	Monoclinic	

Structure legend: • Si ● Al, Mg, Fe exchangeable cations ○ K ○ O ○ OH ○ H_2O

Structures shown: Kaolinite (7.1 Å), Halloysite (10.0 Å), Illite (10.0 Å), Halloysite (14.2 Å), Montmorillonite Vermiculite (14.2 Å), 14Å-Chlorite (14.2 Å)

* also trioctahedral varieties } less common
** also dioctahedral varieties }
+ swelling chlorites are rare and intermediate forms between vermiculite and chlorite

talline clays include the standardized crystallochemical formula, the space group and a schematical presentation of the structure.

Inasmuch as geologists are extremely conservative in changing the already existing nomenclature on clay minerals and hesitate to drop familiar names such as illites in exchange against new and unpopular terms, only those mineral names which are well rooted in the geologic literature were adopted as group names.

(b) *Structure.* Clay minerals of the kaolinite group are made up of one octahedral and one tetrahedral layer. The individual sheets are firmly tied by the hydrogen bonding of the $(OH)^-$ ions on the bottom of one layer to the O^{-2} ions at the top of the neighboring layer (Hendricks, 1945). The only cations necessary to build up the kaolinite structure are Si^{+4} and Al^{+3}. The basal spacing amounts to 7.1Å. Depending on the superposition of layers having the ideal $Al_4 (OH)_8$ Si_4O_{10} composition, the three species kaolinite (1 layer), dickite (2 layers), and nacrite (4 layers) can be differentiated (Brindley and Robinson, 1946; Gruner, 1932; Hendricks, 1938).

Structurally and chemically, the halloysite group resembles the kaolinite group. The mineral species designated as halloysite* contains a layer of water between the original kaolinite layer units, causing a simultaneous increase in basal spacing from about 7.1 Å to 10.1 Å. This is the 4 H_2O form that is made up of curved sheets of kaolinite type species and which gives rise to a tube-like appearance (Bates, 1962). Upon dehydration the tubes may collapse or unroll, and metahalloysite, the second species of the halloysite group, will develop.

The montmorillonite unit is a combination of one octahedral and two tetrahedral layers. In order to balance the structure, $(OH)^-$ ions are replaced by O^{-2} ions wherever atoms belong to both the tetrahedral and the octahedral layer. Consequently, O^{-2} layers of each unit are faced by O^{-2} layers of the neighboring unit. Water and other polar molecules, such as organic substances, can slip between the unit layers thereby causing expansion. Exchangeable cations exist between the structural units where they are loosely held by excess negative charges within the units. The basal spacing fluctuates strongly with the type of exchangeable cations and the thickness of

---

* The name, endellite, had formerly been proposed. The "Nomenclature Subcommittee of Clay Minerals Group," Cambridge, 1956, however, has rejected the adoption of this term.

water layers, which in turn is dependent on the type of cation present at any given water-vapor pressure (Carroll, 1959). Since the montmorillonite structure favors ionic substitution in various structural positions, a great number of species are known in addition to montmorillonite, beidellite, or nontronite. As a function of the relative ease of ionic substitution, a clay mineral which has the ideal beidellite composition is rather uncommon in nature. In the British literature the term *smectite group* is used in preference to *montmorillonite group* (Mackenzie, 1959).

The mica structure is essentially the same as that of montmorillonite. The only significant difference is that the small excess of negative charge between the silicate layers is balanced by a weakly positive cation-water interlayer in the case of montmorillonite, and by neutralizing K^+ ions in the case of mica. The introduction of potassium stabilizes the structure to such an extent that the uptake of water molecules is prevented. Hydromica species of clay particle size are commonly referred to as illitic clays. They differ from muscovite in that there is less substitution of Al^{+3} for Si^{+4} and consequently less of an unbalanced charge deficiency (Grim, 1953). Even so, the amount of potassium ions is generally not sufficient to neutralize the small excess of negative charge between the silicate layers with the result that other cations can be introduced. A great number of illite varieties are known, for instance bravaisite, leverrierite, or cryptotile. There is evidence (Yoder and Eugster, 1955) that some clay minerals, denoted as illites on the basis of routine X-ray analysis, do actually have mixed layer structures.

The vermiculite structure consists of sheets of trioctahedral mica or talc separated by layers of water molecules occupying a definite space (4.98 Å) which is about the thickness of two water molecules. In its natural state, therefore, the mineral consists of an alternation of mica and double water layers (Gruner, 1934; Grim, 1953). The charge deficiency between the silicate layers is satisfied by cations, largely of an exchangeable nature.

Structural investigations reveal that most of the chlorites contain in their crystal structure alternating mica type layers such as $[Mg_3Al\ Si_3O_{10}\ (OH)_2]^-$ and charged brucite type layers of the general formula $[Mg_2Al\ (OH)_6]^+$ (Pauling, 1930; McMurchy, 1934). But other chlorites are represented by layer structures consisting of trioctahedral 7 Å units. The term septechlorite (7 Å chlorite) and normal chlorite (14 Å chlorite) was proposed by Nelson and Roy (1954) to differentiate between the two forms of chlorite.

Some of the pure end-member clays summarized in Table 1 may be interstratified. Interstratification refers to the manner in which layers of different clay minerals are piled up. Basically, one may distinguish between (1) regular and (2) random interstratified or mixed layer clays. A regular mixed-layer clay mineral has a crystal lattice composed of several regularly interstratified layer lattices showing a long spacing corresponding to the sum of the cell heights of the component layers. In more general terms, one is dealing with a superlattice of distinct spacing. Random mixed-layer clays are composed of different kinds of layer lattices piled up randomly and disposed in a c-crystallographic direction.

Mineral names are often assigned to these mixed-layer clays, regardless of whether they are regular or random in nature. But only in case of regularly interstratified clay minerals is it appropriate to adopt specific mineral names such as α-corrensite or rectorite. Information on interstratified clay minerals is summarized in Table 2. Principal components are listed along the vertical and minor components along the horizontal axis.

(c) *Chemistry*. The chemical spectrum of clay minerals is quite colorful. Rarely are there two clay specimens that are absolutely identical in chemical composition. That structurally different clay minerals exhibit a wide range in element distribution is not surprising. The reason for chemical fluctuations within one species is less obvious.

Table 2 CLASSIFICATION OF INTERSTRATIFIED CLAY MINERALS
(AFTER FRANK-KAMENETSKY, 1960).

Principal Component >50% \ Minor component <50%	Kaolinite	Montmorillo-nite	Vermiculite	Illite	Chlorite	Halloysite
Kaolinite		Regular Random	—	Random	Random	Random
Montmorillo-nite	Random		—	Regular Random	Random	—
Vermiculite	—	—		Regular (rectorite) Random	—	—
Illite	Random	Regular Random	Regular Random		Random	—
Chlorite	Random	Regular (α-Corrensite) Random	Regular (β-Corrensite) Random	—		—

Most of the observed chemical variations between clay end-members of one species are caused by (a) isomorphous substitution and (b) ion exchange phenomena. With regard to the first mechanism, there are three possible structural positions where isomorphous substitution can take place: (1) within the octahedral layers (six-fold coordination), (2) within the tetrahedral layers (four-fold coordination), and (3) between the silicate units (interlayer position). Ionic replacements in interlayer position may be referred to as ion exchange if one regards interlayer ions as a part of an extended surface. Factors such as charge, ionic radius, coordination number or solubility of the participating ions determine the isomorphous substitution efficiency of a clay mineral. Within reasonable range, some deviations in the outlined requirements exist as for instance, the isomorphous substitution of Si^{+4} by Al^{+3} in tetrahedral position. The extent of substitution is naturally also a function of the availability of the substitute during clay-forming processes, sedimentation, and diagenesis. For example, the size and charge of gallium makes it a suitable deputy for aluminum, particularly in six-fold coordination. Boron, on the other hand, is one of the elements which is an ideal substitute for aluminum in tetrahedral position. Rubidium which is only slightly larger in ionic radius than potassium can substitute for potassium, an essential cation of illitic materials, in interlayer position.

The second mechanism — that is, ion exchange — refers to exchange reactions taking place at the solid-liquid interface between anions and cations held in unbalanced charges at or near the surface of the solid material and with ions present in the surrounding mobile phase. Absorption phenomena caused by unsatisfied valences form an essential part of ion exchange processes. The exchange reactions always proceed in a stoichiometrical manner, but even so, there is no simple way to predict the ion exchange capacity of a given clay mineral. Too many factors, including pH and Eh, are involved which may stimulate or prevent ion exchange reactions.

Based on the work of Hendricks (1945), and Carroll (1959), we enumerate the following structural causes for the fixation of ions to the clay minerals, and the simultaneous elimination from the liquid phases:

(1) Unsatisfied valences produced by "broken bonds" at surfaces and edges of the clay particles

(2) Unbalanced charges caused by isomorphous substitution

(3) Dissociation of OH^- radicals, the H^+ of which may be exchanged

(4) Accessibility of atoms in structural positions when brought to the exchange site as a result of a change in environment.

Most significant among the environmental factors which influence ion exchange reactions are:

(1) Availability of exchangeable constituents in the mobile phase

(2) pH-Eh relationship

(3) General chemistry of the environment

(4) Pressure and temperature conditions.

The number of broken bonds around the edges of the silica-alumina units is a function of particle size. The smaller the particles, the larger the exchange capacity. Irregularities in the lattice structure (lattice distortions) have similar effects by providing a greater number of unsatisfied bonds at the edges. Thus a perfectly crystallized clay mineral has fewer exchange sites than a poorly crystallized one. It has been shown (Hendricks, 1945) that the exchange capacity of a given kaolinite is directly proportional to grain size, surface area, and stage of crystallinity.

Isomorphous substitution which makes a greater number of exchange sites available is responsible for a great many ion exchange phenomena. Due to more complex substitution characteristics, the chemically and structurally more complicated clays such as montmorillonites have generally a higher exchange capacity than the simpler species of the kaolinite-halloysite group. In the latter case broken bonds supply most of the ion exchange positions.

Cations as well as anions are exchangeable in clays. For structural reasons, 1:1 layer clays show preference in anion absorption over the 2:1 layer clays; the latter, however, have more cation exchange sites. In the case of cations, the alkalies, ammonia, and alkaline earths are the most common constituents taking part in exchange reactions. Noll (1931) suggested that, in general, multivalent ions should be more strongly absorbed than univalent ions, and small ions more strongly than large ions of the same valence. The main factors are the amount of electrostatic charge and the distance of closest approach between the metal ions and other atoms.

Many experiments and geological observations contradict the above statement that small ions are more strongly absorbed than larger ones. For instance, the three alkaline metals, potassium, rubidium, and cesium, are effectively removed from dilute aqueous solutions at moderate pH by clay minerals such as montmorillonites or illites, whereas sodium and lithium remain preferentially in solution. Jenny (1932, 1936) has demonstrated in clay exchange experiments with diluted alkaline and alkaline earths solutions that the following exchange affinity series are obeyed: $Li < Na < K < Rb < Cs$ and $Mg < Ca < Sr < Ba$. Jenny's data for the alkaline ions are given in Figure 5. This feature may partially account for the retention of potassium on the continents and the transportation of sodium to the sea.

Many attempts have been made to explain this affinity series. According to the ionic hydration theory, ions in aqueous solutions are assumed to be hydrated — the small ions more than the large ones — so that actually the affected radius decreases with atomic number. However, Hendricks et al. (1940) showed that Na^+ and K^+ ions are not hydrated at the moment they are picked up by clay minerals; and the hydration stage of other ions does not necessarily follow the outlined pattern. Bär and Tendeloo (1936) suggested that polarization of ions has a significant effect on ion exchange phenomena. Polarization of ions refers to the partial separation of electrical charges of opposite sign at the moment the ion enters an electrostatic field, whereby an ionic deformation is accomplished. Polarization effects increase from Li^+ toward Cs^+ and from Mg^{+2} toward Ba^{+2}. Because of their electron configuration, non-noble gas configurated elements are generally more polarizable than comparable elements of noble gas character, for example, Zn^{+2} vs. Ca^{+2}. Apparently, the loss of attraction with increase in ionic

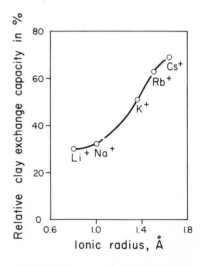

Fig. 5   Relative clay exchange capacity of the alkalies (after Jenny, 1932, 1936)

radius is less significant in the determination of ion exchange capacities than the gain of attraction caused by polarization phenomena in the same direction.

Anions known to become absorbed or exchanged on clay minerals include F^-, Cl^-, NO_3^-, SO_4^{-2}, PO_4^{-3}, and AsO_4^{-3}. Anion exchange can involve the replacement of OH^- ions exposed on the planar surfaces or around the edges of the clay mineral. It was further suggested (Schofield, 1949) that cation — as well as anion — exchange spots may develop on basal plane surfaces and result in the simultaneous fixation of both K^+ and Cl^- ions, which may later be replaced by other cations and anions in response to changes in environment.

It is noteworthy that not only inorganic constituents but organic compounds can participate in ion exchange reactions. A great variety of organic compounds is known to be associated with clay minerals. They are frequently rather tightly bound to the clay particles. Their mode of fixation, however, is not fully understood.

The base exchange capacity of clay minerals is commonly expressed in milliequivalents per 100 grams clay, determined at a pH of 7. Within a given species there is a spread in capacity depending on particle size, crystallinity, grinding technique and chemistry. The base exchange capacity values listed below (in m.eq./100 g) are therefore only approximate figures: kaolinite (3–15); halloysite (5–50); illite (20–40); montmorillonite (80–100), and vermiculite (100–150).

During diagenesis the chemical composition of clays can be modified as a result of chemical equilibration. Although the kinetics of the reactions are generally slow, significant chemical alterations can be achieved over geological periods of time. Increase in the weight of overburden (water or rock) and in temperature (geothermal gradient) will accelerate the reactions.

In Table 3, eight representative chemical analyses of the common amorphous and crystalline clay minerals are presented. Of particular interest for a study of clay mineral formation are the three following features which account for the differences in the chemical composition of the various clay minerals listed: (1) Al:Si ratio, (2) distribution of alkalies, alkaline earths and iron and, (3) total amount of water.

As for kaolinite and halloysite, the chemical compositions correspond closely with the theoretical formula (Table 1). Al^{+3} and Si^{+4} are practically the only cations used to build up the structure (Ross and Kerr (1930, 1934). In montmorillonite and vermiculite, the

Table 3 CHEMICAL ANALYSES OF CLAY MINERALS.

	(1) Allophane	(2) Kaolinite	(3) Halloysite	(4) Montmorillo- nite	(5) Vermiculite	(6) Illite	(7) Glauconite	(8) Chlorite
SiO_2	33.96	45.44	44.08	51.14	35.92	49.26	52.64	26.68
Al_2O_3	31.12	38.52	39.20	19.76	10.68	28.97	5.78	25.20
Fe_2O_3	Trace	0.80	0.10	0.83	10.94	2.27	17.88	
$Fe\ O$					0.82	0.57	3.85	8.70
$Mg\ O$		0.08	0.05	3.22	22.00	1.32	3.43	26.96
$Ca\ O$	2.26	0.08		1.62	0.44	0.67	0.12	0.28
Na_2O		0.66	} 0.20	0.04			0.13	0.18	
K_2O		0.14		0.11		7.47	7.42	
$H_2O^{-105°}$	12.84	0.60	1.44	14.81	} 19.84	3.22	2.83	
$H_2O^{+105°}$	20.28	13.60	14.74	7.99		6.03	5.86	11.70
Total:	100.46	99.92	99.81	99.52	100.64	99.91	99.99	99.52

(1) Liege, Belgium   (Ross and Kerr, 1936)   (5) Pilot, Maryland   (Ross et al, 1928)
(2) Roseland, Virginia   (Ross and Kerr, 1931)   (6) Ballater, Scotland   (Mackenzie et al, 1949)
(3) Hickory, North Carolina (Ross and Kerr, 1936)   (7) New Zealand   (Hutton and Seelye, 1941)
(4) Montmorillon, France (Ross and Hendricks, 1946)   (8) Ducktown, Tennessee (Mc Murchy, 1934)

Al:Si ratio is drastically reduced, partly as a result of the structural composition (2:1 layer), and partly because magnesium substitutes largely for aluminum in the octahedral position. Calcium and alkalies may assume exchange positions to match the deficit in electrical charge caused by substitution phenomena. The water content is the highest of all the clays under consideration (Ross and Hendricks, 1946).

The Al:Si ratio of the illite falls approximately between that of montmorillonite-vermiculite and that of kaolinite-halloysite. Substitutional effects in tetrahedral and octahedral sites account for the high concentration in magnesium and iron. Either one of the two elements is essential to balance the structure. Most striking in this respect is the substitution phenomenon in the case of glauconite, a variety of the 2:1 layer clay minerals. The Al:Si ratio is appreciably reduced in favor of iron. The excess of negative charge, developed between the silicate layers, is neutralized by large amounts of potassium in both illite and glauconite. The presence of potassium is, in fact, the most characteristic feature of illites and glauconites. Potassium acts as a structural stabilizer and prevents swelling along the c-axis of the clay. A low water concentration is the result.

The Al:Si ratio of chlorites may fluctuate over a wide range but generally it is of the same magnitude as in kaolinite. The high concentration of two-valent iron or magnesium, or sometimes of both elements, is typical for all chlorites. Since chlorite is with rare exception a nonswelling clay mineral, the low water concentration is in keeping with this characteristic. A classification of chlorites has been proposed by Foster (1962).

(d) *Origin of Clays.* The wide range in the chemical and structural composition of clay minerals indicates that there are several ways by which clays can be produced. According to Keller and his associates (1956, 1957, 1963) clay minerals may be considered fundamentally a product of the parent material and the energy impressed upon it.

One may distinguish between the so-called primary and secondary parent materials. The primary category includes all igneous rocks, e.g., granites and granodiorites (K-Na rocks), basalts and gabbros (Ca-Mg rocks), and various kinds of tuffs. It is of interest that granites and granodiorites are the principal intrusive rocks and basalts the major extrusive ones (Daly, 1933). This feature can be linked to the evolution of continents and oceans. For details one may consult Daly (1933) and Wickman (1954).

Parent materials of secondary nature are those that once in their history have gone through the exogenic cycle. All sediments and some of the low-grade metamorphic rocks derived from sediments fall into this category, whereas the overwhelming portion of the metamorphic rocks have to be considered as primary parent materials.

The average chemical composition of some of the parent materials is presented in Table 4. The data are largely taken from a review paper by Wickman (1954). The numbers in column 1 are calculated from the average granite and granodiorite analysis (Daly, 1933), assuming a distribution of 1:1 in nature. As is well known, basalts fall into two categories: (a) the olivine basalt magma type and (b) the tholiitic magma type. Column 4 (Table 4), contains the average chemical composition of basalts that are widespread on land areas (plateau basalt type) (Walker and Poldervaart, 1949). As estimated by Wickman (1954), the ratio of intrusive to extrusive rocks exposed on the continents is about 2:1 in favor of the granites and granodiorites (column 3) and by averaging the mean value of igneous rocks (column 5), a factor of 2.13 was assigned. For details and explanation on the overall calculation procedure one may refer to Wickman (1954). Because carbonates are included in the shale average of col-

Table 4   CHEMICAL COMPOSITION OF IGNEOUS ROCKS AND SEDIMENTS.

IGNEOUS ROCKS   SEDIMENTS

	(1) Granite	(2) Granodiorite	(3) Average 1+2	(4) Basalt	(5) Average 3+4 (3/4=2.13)	(6) Sandstone	(7) Limestone	(8) Shale	(9) Shale (CO$_2$ corrected)
SiO$_2$	70.77	65.69	68.23	51.55	62.90	79.63	5.24	61.16	65.08
TiO$_2$	0.39	0.57	0.48	1.48	0.80	0.25	0.06	0.68	0.72
Al$_2$O$_3$	14.59	16.11	15.35	14.95	15.22	4.85	0.82	16.21	17.25
Fe$_2$O$_3$	1.58	1.76	1.67	2.55	1.96	1.09	} 0.55	4.23	4.50
FeO	1.79	2.68	2.23	9.10	4.43	0.31		2.58	2.74
(Fe)	2.50	3.31	2.90	8.86	4.81	0.99	0.43	4.96	5.28
MnO	0.12	0.07	0.10	0.20	0.13	Trace	Trace	Trace	Trace
MgO	0.89	1.93	1.41	6.63	3.08	1.18	7.96	2.57	2.24
CaO	2.01	4.47	3.24	10.00	5.40	5.59	42.97	3.27	0.52
Na O$_2$	3.52	3.74	3.63	2.35	3.22	0.46	0.05	1.37	1.46
K$_2$O	4.15	2.78	3.47	0.89	2.65	1.33	0.33	3.41	3.63
P$_2$O$_5$	0.19	0.20	0.20	0.30	0.23	0.08	0.04	0.18	0.19
CO$_2$						5.11	41.93	2.77	
Misc.						0.12	0.05	1.57	1.67
Total:	100.00	100.00	—	100.00	—	100.00	100.00	100.00	100.00

(1) + (2) : Daly (1933)
(4)   : Walker and Poldervaart (1949)
(6),(7),(8): Clarke (1924)

umn 8, the data were recalculated on a carbonate-free basis (column 9), assuming a CaO/MgO ratio of the carbonates equal to 6.

In principle, there are two ways to calculate the relative proportions of the three major sediment types. Based on geochemical calculations, the ratio limestone : sandstone : shale is approximately 1:2:8 (Clarke and Washington 1924; Goldschmidt, 1933; von Engelhardt, 1936; Holmes, 1937; Borchert, 1951; Wickman, 1954). By estimating the total volume of limestones, sandstones, and shales from the areal distribution on continents the ratio is more on the order of about 1:2:3 (Leith and Mead, 1915; Schuchert, 1931; Krynine, 1948).

Some of the differences between the geochemical and geological estimates can be linked to the "evolution" of continents. It is common knowledge that deep-sea sediments are fine-grained materials which contain besides fossil remains (radiolaria, diatoms, foraminifera etc.) a considerable amount of clay minerals; in contrast the amount of sandstone-sized minerals is negligible. It is further established that the deposition sites of deep sea sediments fall generally outside the areas close to orogenetic belts which are the potential source areas of continents. As a result, deep sea sediments are not tectonically "activated" during orogenetic events that lead to the formation of continents. Ancient sediments presently exposed on continents are, therefore, almost entirely made up of sedimentary materials deposited in a continental, freshwater, or shallow marine (epicontinental shelf sea) environment. Future studies on "Mohole-type" drill cores of deep sea sediments are bound to add markedly to our understanding of the past history of the earth. For the present, our knowledge is based largely on the sediments exposed on the continents.

In addition to the parent material which furnishes the essential elements for the clay structure, the type and amount of energy supplied to the clay forming system determines the kind of clay mineral that finally will be formed.

First of all, water has to be present to start alteration processes. Water acts as the universal solvent and transportation medium; it is the most common agent initiating changes in matter. Chemically pure water is rare, because in its predestinated role on this planet water reacts with, takes up, holds, and discharges foreign materials.

Most dominant as a factor of energy in aqueous environments are the activities of protons and electrons; they will ultimately determine the direction of the alteration processes. Because the activity of hydrogen ions is involved in, or can with little effort become involved in reactions with dissolved species, it has been found convenient to use the a_{H+} as a characterizing variable to provide a common reference activity for a variety of reactions (Garrels, 1960); since activities are often expressed as logarithmic functions, the term $pH = (-\log a_{H+})$ has been introduced.

The other parameter is the reduction-oxidation potential, or simply redox potential, which may be defined as a quantitative measure of the energy of oxidation or the electron-escaping tendency of a reversible oxidation-reduction system. When referred to hydrogen, the redox potential is commonly expressed as Eh, in terms of volts — E being the potential difference between the standard hydrogen electrode and the system which is being measured. According to Baas Becking et al. (1960) four types of reactions are conceivable:

(1) Neither electrons nor protons are involved:
$$Fe_2O_3 + H_2O \longrightarrow 2\,FeO \cdot OH$$

(2) Protons only are involved:
$$H_2CO_3 \longrightarrow H^+ + HCO_3^-$$

(3) Electrons only are involved:
$$Fe^{+2} \longrightarrow Fe^{+3} + e^-$$

(4) Both protons and electrons are involved:

$$FeSO_4 + 2\ H_2O \longrightarrow SO_4^{-2} + FeO \cdot OH + 3\ H^+ + e^-$$

Most reactions in natural environments are of type 4 and therefore depend on both the pH and Eh of the system in which they take place.

Concerning the mechanism of clay mineral formation, three principal theories have been proposed.

According to the first one, clay minerals form by interaction of isolated species of monomeric silica and monomeric alumina with OH^- and H^+ ions, resulting in octahedra and tetrahedra units, the principal building blocks of clay minerals. The second theory proposes an intermediate colloidal phase from which crystallization subsequently proceeds. According to the third theory, clay minerals are assumed to form by selective leaching of parent materials, such as feldspars, followed by reconstitution of the remaining silica and alumina in some fashion. All three suggestions agree only insofar as ion exchange, isomorphous substitution, the pH and Eh characteristics of the environment and the type of parent material are responsible for the wide variation in chemical composition of clay minerals.

Under hydrothermal conditions, where silica and alumina are dissolved in greater quantities and furthermore where relatively high reaction rates prevail, clay minerals may perhaps crystallize from true ionic or colloidal solutions. The colloidal theory was favored and accepted for a long time largely because silica and alumina colloids have different charges. The concentration of silica and alumina in weathering solutions, however, is too small for the formation of the corresponding colloids. For kinetic reasons, the structural rearrangement theory seems to be the most acceptable process responsible for the formation of clays.

During the formation of clay minerals from a suitable parent material, the most pronounced chemical changes are the following: Hydration and hydrolysis of mineral matter such as feldspars is the first step toward altering parent materials in the direction of clay minerals. By substitution or ion exchange hydrogen ions will replace some of the ionic constituents present in the parent material thereby initiating a gradual breakdown of the original silicate structure. This process is accompanied by equilibrium reactions along the intergranular film which will preferentially remove some of the original ions present in the silicate structure but leave others unaffected. It all depends on the activity of the dissolved species which, in an ideal solution, would be proportional to its concentration in terms of a mole fraction.

Of particular interest is the preferential removal of silicon relative to alumina. The solubility of silica is little affected until a pH of 9 is reached; above this value it increases quite rapidly. Such alkaline conditions are rather uncommon in geological environments, but at the immediate interface of hydrolyzing feldspars and water, pH values can be as high as 10 (Stevens and Carron, 1948). This is the abrasion pH of a mineral (Fig. 6). Because of the high abrasion pH of feldspars, silica may be released to the water phase, whereas alumina, which is relatively insoluble in the pH range of about 5 to 10, is left behind.

The structural rearrangement of the remaining silica and alumina and the hydrous decomposition in the case of alkaline feldspars has been thoroughly discussed by DeVore (1959). It was tentatively concluded that, feldspars for instance, decompose into metastable chains, or fragments of chains, having the feldspar Al:Si ratio, which may

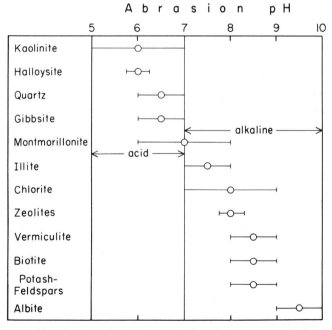

Fig. 6   Abrasion pH of various minerals (after Stevens and Carron, 1948)

eventually collapse to individual hydrated Al and Si tetrahedra. Since chains certainly have at least a temporary stability, those units removed from the $[100]$–$[010]$ surfaces of the feldspar could form an ordered Al-Si array of $(AlSi_3)O_{10}$ composition upon polymerization. These sheets, by combining with six and twelve coordinated cations, could lead to minerals such as chlorite, Al-montmorillonite, or muscovite. A simple transformation in these chains would even permit the kaolinite sheet structure to develop. The close spacial relationship between clays and parent material can be explained in part by the mica-like surface chemistry of the feldspar acting as nucleation sites for clay minerals. However, if individual Al and Si tetrahedra are produced from the original chain the mechanism of clay formation is less obvious because of differences in the mobility between Al-hydroxides and Si-hydroxides. In the case of the individual tetrahedra association, one can, however, find a simple mechanism for the formation of minerals such as boehmite $Al(OH)_3$. Alumina stays behind, whereas the more soluble silica is removed from the system in the form of monosilic acid (H_4SiO_4).

In conclusion, it can be said that the efficiency of the various chemical reactions leading to the hydrous decomposition of parent materials and the subsequent formation of clay minerals from the decomposition products is a function of: (1) parent material, (2) general environment in terms of chemical composition, pH, Eh, and temperature, and (3) water circulation, i.e., removal of soluble materials and supply of "fresh" rain water to the system activated by biogenic and atmospheric CO_2. Some of the parameters under (2) and (3), i.e., temperature, rainfall, and humidity, are more popularly known by the term climate.

(e) *Environment of formation.* Clay minerals of the kaolinite and halloysite group are relatively modestly constituted. All they require is unlimited access to Al and Si in a chemical-structural arrangement which permits crystallization to a simple hydrous aluminum silicate. However, to satisfy this "modest" desire, a series of chemical reactions is necessary to effectively remove the bases from the clay-forming system, since constituents other than Al, Si, and the active hydrogen ion interfere quite seriously in the structural framework of these clays.

Parent materials influence the reactions insofar as they contribute the essential clay-forming constituents. If Ca, Mg, and Fe are scanty or absent there is, of course, no problem involved in reducing the system to a hydrous aluminum silicate; the same holds true if the Al:Si ratio already fits the structural requirements. Parent materials are generally more complex in chemical composition than either kaolinite or halloysite. Thus the environment of formation has to be such as to remove constituents other than Al and Si almost entirely from the clay-forming system.

These requirements can largely be realized in a climate where rainfall exceeds evaporation and where the pH is on the acid side of the scale, which implies an excess of H^+ ions. The leaching activity of the water and its dissolved ingredients can be particularly effective if parent materials are highly permeable. The function of redox potential is to oxidize or reduce materials in such a way that they no longer interfere. For instance, iron can be removed by oxidation processes in the form of oxides or oxyhydroxides, or else it can be precipitated under reducing conditions in the presence of H_2S as pyrite or marcasite.

The differences between the individual members of the kaolinite and halloysite group are small; therefore, the differences in the conditions of origin are presumably subtle and difficult to evaluate. The step from kaolinite to halloysite involves the appearance of interlayer water with an accompanying increase in height of the unit cell, a change in morphology, and a marked increase in randomness. Bates (1952, 1962) suggested that the type of parent material determines whether kaolinite or halloysite will form. Kaolinite generally requires a mica-type intermediate obtained, for instance, from the decomposition of K-feldspar, whereas halloysite usually forms from plagioclase by direct alteration. A former suggestion that humidity is the main agent which determines the kaolinite-halloysite relationship does not seem to be valid. However, there is no way to proceed from halloysite to kaolinite simply by dehydration and an increase of order in the original particles after the original halloysite structure has been developed. A complete recrystallization is required.

The chemical composition of the clay minerals of the montmorillonite group is more complicated. In particular, magnesium, iron, and probably calcium are essential to build up the montmorillonite structure. The Al:Si ratio is appreciably lower than for kaolinite, and the amount of interlayer water is a direct function of the type and concentration of cations in exchangeable positions. It is inferred that the environment favorable for a montmorillonite formation is generally the opposite of that in which the kaolinite and halloysite formation takes place. Certain bases which have to be present can only be retained and kept active in the clay-forming system if intensive leaching is prevented. The water circulation must be comparatively small, the pH must be high (alkaline conditions), and the redox potential has to keep iron in an accessible form. In a semi-arid climate the above outlined requirements may be fulfilled.

Illite resembles montmorillonite in that it is also a high-silica 2:1 layer clay mineral; it differs in that it contains more Al in tetrahedral position. In addition, great amounts of potassium are essential to neutralize the small negative charge between the silicate layers. Slight alkaline conditions are favorable for the illite formation, but specific conditions cannot be formulated as precisely as in the case of montmorillonite and kaolinite. It has been suggested by various authors (Millot, 1949, 1952; Keller, 1956) that illite is one of the most stable clay minerals under marine conditions. Whether it actually forms under marine conditions is, however, doubtful.

Vermiculite has a structural formula which can be deduced as that of chlorite by the manner in which the brucite-like layer occupying the interlayer space of chlorite is replaced by exchangeable magnesium ions. These in turn are surrounded by water molecules some of which may be attached to the magnesium ions, whereas others may be in an unbound state (Walker, 1951). Both chlorite and vermiculite require magnesium and iron far in excess of the concentrations required to build up montmorillonite or illite. It is inferred that parent materials high in magnesium and iron ought to be present, or, as another alternative, that these elements are supplied by some other means (aqueous solutions) to the clayforming system. Alkaline conditions and a redox potential which leaves iron in an accessible form in the reacting system will support the crystallization of vermiculite and chlorite. From a structural and chemical point of view micas — in particular, biotite — are most suitable as source material for both types of clay minerals. This can be seen from the large crystals of vermiculite pseudomorphs after mica commonly found in soils (Jackson, 1959). This idea is further supported by the widespread occurrence of vermiculite-biotite structures, which can be looked upon as an intermediate stage in the alteration of biotite to vermiculite (Frysinger, 1960). By reacting biotite with $MgCl_2$ over a period of some months, vermiculite can be artificially produced (Barshad, 1950). Because montmorillonites and mixtures of aluminum and magnesium hydroxides interact so easily to form chlorite-like structures, Slaughter and Milne (1960) proposed a simple mechanism by which montmorillonite can be changed to chlorite under natural conditions.

One of the most powerful tools to evaluate the mode of clay mineral formation is the study of the mixed layer structures. The mode of interstratification, be it regular or random, and the type of clay structures involved will indicate the directions in which the alterations proceed. The common occurrence of chlorite-vermiculite (β-corrensite), vermiculite-illite (rectorite), illite-montmorillonite, and kaolinite-montmorillonite probably has something to do with the stability fields of the individual species involved. A discussion of the thermodynamic status of mixed-layer minerals in general has been made by Zen (1962). pH and Eh are undoubtedly two of the most critical factors in determining the fate of a parent material and the type of clay mineral that will ultimately develop. Other requirements and conditions that must be met to form a particular type of clay mineral are summarized in Figure 7. Time, as in all geological processes, will always operate toward the development of an end-member which is the most stable phase under the given environmental conditions.

Among the clay minerals of the 2:1 layer-type variety, the so-called glauconites are of particular geological interest for the following reasons:

(1) Glauconites are easily recognizable in outcrops by color, size, and shape, and

(2) They are formed in the marine environment more or less penecontemporaneously.

The term glauconite is currently used with a double connotation. Originally coined as a description for a blue-green monomineralic material with the structural properties of hydro micas, it is now widely used as a morphological term for small, spherical, greenish, and earthy-looking pellets. By X-ray techniques, these pellets fall into four general mineralogical groups; only one of these has the diffraction properties usually attributed to the mineral glauconite (Burst, 1958). The structural differences are usually not apparent in the size, shape, color, or other visible features of the pellets. They can be partly recognized in chemical variations, particularly as manifested in the dis-

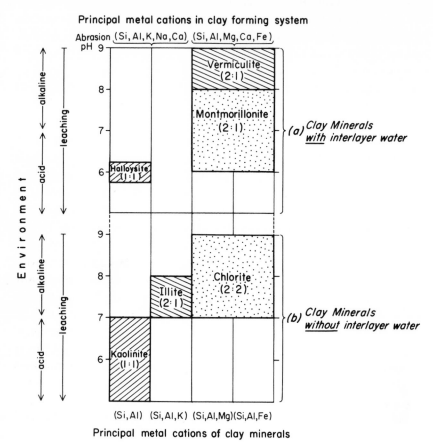

Principal metal cations in clay forming system

Fig. 7 Major requirements and conditions for clay mineral formation

tribution pattern of potassium and two- and three-valent iron. Such chemical fluctuations simultaneously affect the optical properties of a glauconite mineral.

Glauconite pellets are believed to result from a variety of origins — all of which require the three-layer lattice —, supplies of potassium and iron, and a suitable oxidation potential. Variations in these requirements are held to be responsible for the pellet variation. Glauconite pellets are considered to develop under restricted environmental conditions. They can be composed of illite, montmorillonite, chlorite, and certain mixed-layer type clay minerals such as illite-montmorillonite. It seems possible that source material may determine the type of glauconite that will eventually form. In a general way one can say that clay-like materials are altered to glauconite by picking up and exchanging a great number of ions. The fact that various mineral constituents are present in many pellets called glauconite does not change the concept that a mineral can result from adjustment to certain marine geochemical equilibria. There is probably no difference in the type of reaction which changes a feldspar into an illite under weathering conditions on the continents, or an illite to a glauconite during halmyrolysis (submarine weathering). It is noteworthy that despite major chemical alterations, glauconitization apparently does not change the basic structure of the detrital precursor.

Available records indicate that the formation of glauconite requires marine waters near normal salinity, reducing conditions, and an appropriate clay-type sources material (2:1 layered clay). It is favored by a high organic content of the sediments in which it forms and by a slow — or, even better — negative sedimentation, where submarine weathering (halmyrolysis) removes constituents not essential for the glauconite formation. This feature suggests that at least a certain time is necessary before the adjustment to the environment and the beneficiation of the source materials to glauconite pellets is accomplished. Other parameters which may operate as a rate controlling factor during the process of glauconitization are the type of source material in terms of lattice structure, chemistry, crystalline state (degraded or well-crystallized), grain size, and the general environmental conditions.

Since the size of the glauconite pellets generally falls within a definite range (20–40 micron), a deposition or collection of argillaceous materials in pelletal form has to take place before the process of glauconitization proceeds. Four processes have been listed (Burst, 1958) by which such an aggregation of materials can be accomplished:

(1) Conversion of remains in fecal pellets of sediment-infesting organisms

(2) Alteration of internal fillings of foraminifera

(3) Transformation of biotite booklets, and

(4) Agglomeration of clay minerals.

It is inferred that the presence of certain types of organic debris will directly or indirectly favor the formation of glauconite, most likely by establishing a reducing micro-environment within the general oxidizing macro-environment ocean. This in turn can mobilize iron and other ions which are essential to build up a glauconite from the surrounding sediment matrix, by making them easily accessible to the "proto" glauconite structure. Other ions may be supplied from the sea. It is surprising, however, that glauconites are rare or absent from beds that are rich in algae, corals, or bryozoans. If found in or near such beds, it can be assumed that they have been probably reworked or transported there.

The presence of synsedimentary glauconites in recent sediments which are being recorded from the Black Sea, may be used as indication that glauconites can form within short periods of time. It is of further interest that this mineral can originate at a fairly wide (but not unlimited) range of temperatures and depths.

This latitude in the limiting factors combined with the easy field recognition makes glauconite much more useful in paleogeographical studies than other contributing minerals which are known to provide clues to depositional environments (Ehlmann et al., 1963).

(f) *Geological applications of clay mineral data.* Clay mineral data can be used for the interpretation of numerous geological phenomena. They are extremely helpful in studies on weathering, source, transportation mechanisms, environment, facies, tectonics, or diagenesis.

It has previously been mentioned that most clay minerals present in the stratigraphical column are a result of the metastability of certain minerals when exposed to environmental conditions established at or near the earth surface (Correns, 1963). A variety of factors, such as the type of parent material and the extent of weathering, determine the type of clay mineral that will accumulate in weathering residues. Consequently, one may assume that fossil clay minerals can serve as a key for the evaluation of the source and of paleoclimates. However, first it has to be proved that the prospective clay has not been significantly altered chemically or structurally during transportation, deposition, and diagenesis. Inasmuch as two unknowns, i.e., parent rock and weathering determine the type of clay mineral, one has to find means to distinguish between these two processes.

In the following example, one of the unknowns can be eliminated by keeping the source material constant and by changing only the weathering conditions. Data collected by Sherman (1952) of Hawaiian soil samples indicate that variations in climate are responsible for the development of different types of clay minerals from a basalt of the same petrography and age (Fig. 8). For instance, in an alternating wet and dry climate, a certain correlation between annual rainfall and type and amount of clay is obtained. At moderate precipitation montmorillonite is the principal mineral. This observation agrees with the previous statements regarding the overall requirements for montmorillonite formation. An increase in annual rainfall causes the formation of kaolinite at the expense of both montmorillonite and basaltic rock fragments. In the final stage, montmorillonites disappear completely from the soil, kaolinites decrease sharply in abundance, and a progressive development of bauxites and laterites takes place. That is, basalt and clay minerals are gradually eliminated and replaced by Al, Fe, and Ti oxides or hydroxides.

Similar observations have been made in studies on various recent soil profiles from all over the world. However, only limited information is so far available concerning the application of these results to paleoclimatical investigations.

Although the alteration of montmorillonite to kaolinite under weathering conditions was observed at many locations, the actual transformation mechanism remained a puzzle. Recently, Altschuler et al. (1963) tried to explain the low-temperature conversion of mont-

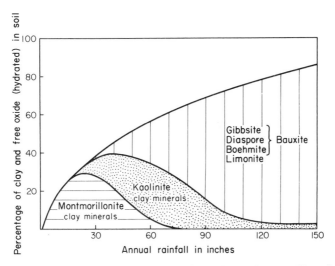

Fig. 8 Distribution of clay minerals and bauxites in Hawaiian soil samples; alternating wet and dry climate (after Sherman, 1952)

morillonite to kaolinite. It was suggested that the breakdown of montmorillonite was started by intracrystalline leaching of interlayer cations and simultaneous or subsequent stripping of tetrahedral silica layers, resulting in a regular mixed layer montmorillonite-kaolinite. The actual formation of authigenic kaolinite was subsequently accomplished by lateral epitaxy at the expense of montmorillonite. Both the formation of a superlattice (mixed layer) and the lateral outgrowth of kaolinite may be regarded as a structural transformation of a complex sheet silicate to a simpler 1:1 layer clay mineral. The mechanism outlined above may further account for geochemical differences that exist between montmorillonite and kaolinite with respect to crystallographical properties (dimension; layer orientation) and chemistry (substitutional effects in tetrahedral and octahedral sites).

In the following example we shall show the usefulness of clay petrology in the evaluation of source aspects, paleogeography, and regional tectonics at the time of sedimentation. According to Weaver (1958b), the clay mineral series of late Paleozoic sediments from the Oklahoma-Arkansas area may change gradually or abruptly in geological time or in space, by moving from one basin to the other (Fig. 9).

The possible application of clay mineral analysis for environmental evaluations, i.e., in terms of fresh-water versus marine, is a controversial subject. Whereas some investigators (Millot, 1949, 1952; Grim, 1958) favor the concept that clay minerals are more "at home"

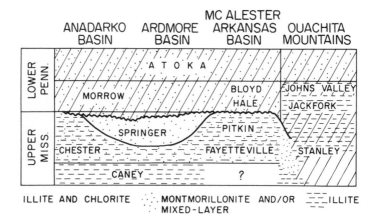

Fig. 9   Clay mineral suite of late Paleozoic sediments from the Oklahoma-Arkansas area (after Weaver, 1958b)

in certain environments than in others, Weaver (1958a) and other experts conclude that the great majority of clay minerals in sedimentary rocks are not significantly altered both structurally and chemically (bulk composition) by the environment of deposition; that is, the majority of the clay minerals are formed during continental weathering and consequently are largely detrital in origin.

Considering the distribution of clay minerals in geologic time and their abundance ratio in different environments, there appears indeed to be a greater probability that the second hypothesis is right. It maintains that environment, i.e., fresh-water versus marine, has only little to do with the mineralogical transformation of clay minerals. This deduction is also supported on geochemical grounds. For instance, illite which is found in recent and ancient sediments is predominantly the high temperature 2 M variety and not the 1 M or 1 M_d variety expected for authigenic illite of low-temperature origin. Actually, this type of illite is scarce and is restricted largely to glauconites (Weaver, 1958a).

This, however, does not necessarily mean that the average clay minerals cannot partially adjust geochemically to the environment of deposition by exchanging some of their "detrital" elements against those present in the surrounding aqueous environment. It should be emphasized that this adjustment is mainly on a small scale (ion exchange level), unaccompanied by marked structural and chemical changes in the detrital clay composition. In case trace elements are participating in ion exchange reactions during the exposure of clays to the environment of deposition, certain geochemical differences in the trace element pattern are expected to occur, if the potential elements are more abundant in one than in another type of environment. Among trace elements suitable as environmental criteria to distinguish, for example, between marine and fresh-water sediments, boron has been studied most intensively and successfully so far. The reason is first, that boron is highly abundant in the sea and virtually absent from most fresh-waters and, second, that boron can be fixed rather tightly and effectively to certain clay minerals. Even subsequent leachings with hot mineral acids will not remove the boron from the clays.

The mode of boron fixation in clay minerals has received great attention and has been studied in detail (Harder, 1961). Various theories have been advanced to account for the presence of boron in the clay fraction. It was suggested that among clays, only dioctahedral micas incorporate boron in significant quantities into their structure. On geochemical grounds it is believed that boron substitutes for aluminum in tetrahedral position (four-fold coordination). Calculating the total amount of boron that theoretically may substitute for aluminum in tetrahedral positions of micas, a value of 2.9 per cent in boron is obtained. Actually, the highest value in boron reported from clays amounts to only 0.2 per cent. This may indicate that perhaps only the outer aluminum positions can be occupied by boron, and that the uptake of boron is stopped as soon as the outer Al-positions are exchanged.

The usefulness of boron and other trace elements such as lithium, rubidium and gallium to distinguish between fresh-water and marine sediments has been shown in clay mineral studies of recent and ancient sediments (Ernst et al., 1958; Keith and Degens, 1959; Potter et al., 1963). Marine clays high in illites do contain about 100 to 200 ppm in boron, as against fresh-water clays with about 10 to 50 ppm. Inasmuch as this amount represents only a small fraction of what can theoretically be substituted for aluminum in the silicon tetrahedra, reworked clays may pick up additional amounts of boron under marine conditions. This suggests that the amount of boron in illites is a function of both the surface area and the frequency or the length of exposure of the clay to marine conditions. Uncertainty as to the reliability of boron as environmental criterion is introduced in areas where the continental bedrock is already enriched in boron or where terrestrial volcanic activities supply greater amounts of boric acid to the next environments.

An interesting application of clay minerals to geology is their use for the absolute age dating of rocks. Until recently, estimates of the duration of geologic events in the earth's development were made exclusively by determining the age of minerals of intrusive rocks that intersected sediments of known biostratigraphic age. In order to circumvent the uncertainties that necessarily are introduced by such a deductive approach, geochemists looked for authigenic sedimentary materials which contain radioactive isotopes and their stable daughter products in measurable quantities. The possibility of such an absolute age determination became feasible with the development of the potassium-argon method through the utilization of glauconites and other potassium bearing minerals such as authigenic feldspars and sylvite. In particular, the world-wide occurrence of glauconites in marine sediments of all ages and the apparent synchronism of their formation with that of marine sediments (penecontemporaneous), opened a real possibility for dating sedimentary formations throughout geologic time by the potassium-argon method. A graphical presentation of K^{40}/A^{40} age analyses on glauconites and a few authigenic feldspars and sylvites from the Cambrian and up is given in Figure 10. Pre-Cambrian glauconites also have been dated but, unfortunately, the apparent stratigraphic position is less accurately known. The information on K^{40}/A^{40} analyses was gathered from papers by Nier et al., (1941); Polevaya et al., (1960, 1961); Everden et al., (1961); Hurley (1961); Wasserburg et al., (1956); Lipson (1958); Amirkhanov et al., (1957); Vinogradov and Tugarinov (1962); and Gentner et al., (1953, 1954). The absolute time scale of Kulp (1961) was applied.

The problems inherent in the potassium-argon method in terms of radiogenic argon leakage with time, and the mode of fixation of argon and potassium in glauconites, have been extensively discussed

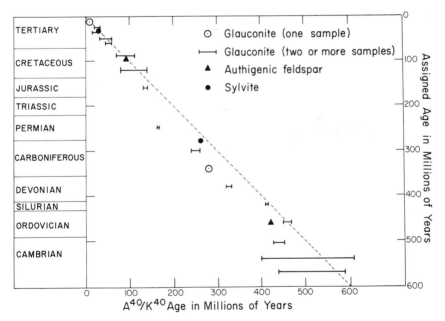

Fig. 10   Relation of potassium-argon age analyses of glauconites, authigenic feldspars, and sylvite to assigned age in millions of years (after Nier et al., 1941; Polevaya et al., 1960, 1961; Hurley, 1961; Wasserburg et al., 1956; Lipson, 1958; Amirkhanov et al., 1957; Vinogradov and Tugarinov, 1962; Gentner et al., 1953, 1954; and Kulp, 1961)

in various papers presented during the symposium of "Geochronology in Rock Systems" (Kulp, 1961). Despite some uncertainties that have been expressed concerning the reliability of glauconite dating, the K^{40}/A^{40} ages published so far agree surprisingly well with the ages obtained by other methods.

Recently, illites and certain mixed-layer clays have been dated by K^{40}/A^{40} measurements (Hurley et al., 1959, 1963ab). The dating of illitic clays, however, faces so many pitfalls that it is to be avoided unless the investigator is well aware of all the problems and uses the method as an analogy only and with limited objectives. Recent illites from the Atlantic, for example, yield ages ranging from about 170 to 470 million years, indicating a detrital origin of these clay minerals. Age dating of illites, however, may reveal interesting details on the mechanism of clay mineral formation, if ages of the parent materials (i.e., crystalline rock minerals) are available for comparison. It is conceivable, assuming the structural rearrangement theory on the origin of clay minerals is correct, that there is no preferential loss of argon over potassium during the transformation of high-temperature minerals to clays. Consequently, the age of the parent material may be incorporated in the newly-formed clay mineral, although the absolute amount of argon and potassium has changed during the transformation.

For comparison, a few rubidium-strontium analyses have been performed on glauconites. The ages generally agree well with those obtained from potassium-argon ratios (Hurley, 1961).

One of the most challenging areas for future clay mineral research lies in the field of "organo-clays." Organo-clays are reaction products of specific clay minerals with specific organic molecules involving the formation of chemical bonds. These may be ionic bonds resulting from acid-base neutralization or simple ion exchange, or they may be strong adsorption-type van der Waals' bonds. Lately, the great value and importance of organo-clays for various industrial purposes has been recognized, as can be judged by the increasing number of patents being granted in this field of applied chemistry. Inasmuch as a review and discussion of possible industrial applications is beyond the scope of this book, the interested reader is referred to an up-to-date summary on this subject by Nahin (1963).

Only limited data are so far available on organic-clay complexes as they occur in nature. This has largely to do with the difficulties of analytical identification. Most of our knowledge is based on controlled experiments, by treating or exposing "normal" clays to a variety of organic molecules and observing the alteration they undergo during this treatment. Clays of the montmorillonite group are the most thoroughly studied samples for their ability to retain organic constituents. The reason for this preference is obvious: montmorillonites offer a large internal surface (nearly 7×10^6 cm^2 g^{-1}), they can be saturated with any particular cation, and their interlamellar dimensions can be measured by X-ray diffraction with relative ease and accuracy. Finally, the restrictions imposed by steric consideration permit a simplified interpretation of the mode of packing of the adsorbed molecules.

From the knowledge of the lattice dimensions of the montmorillonite sheet the van der Waals' thickness of the absorbed molecule can be calculated. By comparing the theoretical van der Waals' thickness of the organic molecule with that of the observed spacing, the degree of contraction can be measured. This contraction can be attributed to H-bonding to the oxygen sheets on either side of the adsorbed molecule (Figs. 11 and 12).

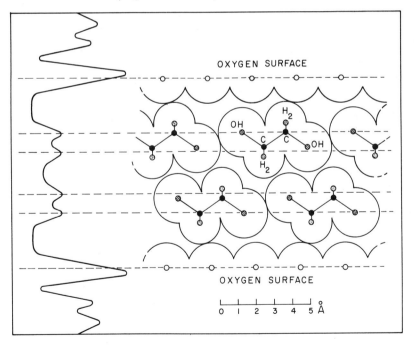

Fig. 11 Part of a one-dimensional Fourier synthesis of an ethylene glycol complex of allevardite. Upper part of the figure shows a possible arrangement of two layers of organic molecules, OH · CH$_2$ · CH$_2$ · OH, between the micalike layers (after Brindley, 1956, and Brindley and Hoffmann, 1962)

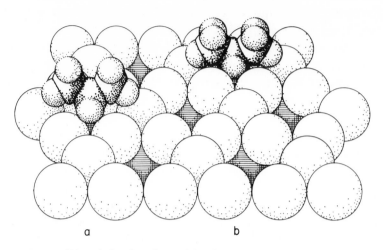

a   b

Fig. 12 Dimethylamine ion with the plane of a zigzag chain parallel to the oxygen surface; one hydrogen penetrates the hole; $d(001) = 12.6$ Å. After the charge is satisfied, an additional dimethylamine hydrochloride molecule may occupy one of the two remaining holes (after Rowland and Weiss, 1963)

In order to determine orientation, type of packing, or chemical nature of the interlayer organic molecules, a variety of analytical methods have been employed. These include first-order spacing measurements (difference $\triangle$ between the expanded and unexpanded spacings of montmorillonite), differential thermal analysis (desorption characteristics), electron microscopy, one-dimensional Fourier synthesis in case of clays with superior crystallinity, or electron spin resonance spectra (Friedlander, et al., 1963).

In Figure 12, a structural model of methylamine-clay type complexes is presented as an example of the structural relationship that may exist between the clay mineral and the incorporated organic molecule (Rowland and Weiss, 1963). The dimethylamine $(CH_3)_2$ $NH \cdot H^+$ cation resembles the beginning of a zigzag carbon chain, except that the central nitrogen is the site of the charge. Three positions are possible: (1) where the plane of the chain lies parallel to the oxygen surfaces; 2) where the plane is perpendicular to the oxygen surfaces; and (3) with the axes of the carbon and nitrogen chains almost perpendicular to each other.

Among organic constituents studied in detail are amines, amino acids, proteins, carbohydrates, phenols, hydrocarbons, humic acids, alcohols, and even antibiotics and enzymes MacEwan (1948, 1962); Talibudeen (1955); Greene-Kelly (1956); Ensminger and Gieseking (1939); Deuel (1957); Brindley and Hoffmann (1962); Weiss (1963); Pinck (1962); Cowan and Hartwell (1958); Cowan and White (1962); Greenland et al., (1955, 1956, 1962); Emerson (1960); Cowan (1963).

The results of these studies not only reveal interesting details as to the type of bonding established between organic molecules and clay minerals or the structural orientation or packing of the organic constituent in interlayer position; they also yield valuable information regarding the conservation of biochemical materials in the zone of microbiological activity (soil; sea floor), and the surprising stability of certain thermodynamically instable organic compounds such as serine or threonine in ancient rocks.

Although great progress has been made over the last decade in the area of organo-clays there is still much to be learned before one can hope to get a better understanding of the nature and complexity of interactions between clays and the surrounding organic molecules in a soil or a sediment.

In connection with petroleum exploration most of the major basins of the United States have been examined for type and proportions of clay minerals present in the rock strata. There appears to be an interesting relationship insofar as basins high in montmorillonites and other expandable clays also produce and contain more crude oil on average than basins where non-expandable clay minerals predominate. The explanation of this coincidence between montmorillonite content and amount of oil according to Weaver (1960) is that for structural reasons montmorillonites can hold more water down to greater depth of burial than the non-expanded clays (kaolinite, illite and chlorite); the latter lose most of their water already in the early stages of compaction. Water, however, is necessary to flush the hydrocarbons from the shales to the reservoir rocks. Assuming that hydrocarbon release starts at a greater depth, only expandable clays still hold the water essential to expel and transport the hydrocarbons in the direction of the reservoir rock. The relation of oil production to age and relative montmorillonite content is presented in Figure 13.

It is too early to judge whether Weaver's hypothesis on the water-hydrocarbon relationship is correct. But the correlation between oil production and montmorillonite content, which is based on more than 20,000 clay mineral analyses certainly holds true. Perhaps mont-

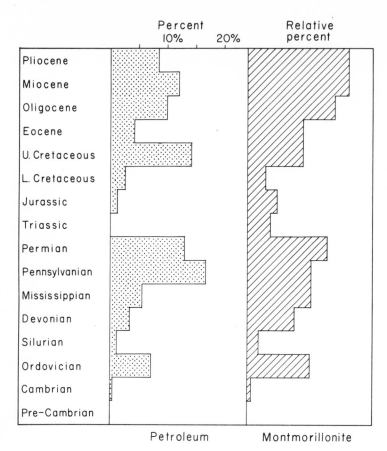

Fig. 13 Relation of petroleum production to age and relative montmorillonite content in most of the major basins of the United States (after Weaver, 1958b)

morillonites, due to their "organophilic" character, have a greater affinity for hydrocarbons or their organic precursors than the nonexpandable clay minerals. Water may be only a secondary requirement.

In summary, one can say that the distribution of clay minerals in the stratigraphic record is systematic and can always be related to some type of geologic phenomenon. Clay minerals may provide useful information on weathering, source aspects, transportation, environment, diagenesis, age dating, or even petroleum genesis and origin of life, just to list a few of the more important applications.

It must be emphasized that, as in all geochemical studies of this type, a well balanced integration with petrographical and geological field observations is essential for the intelligent interpretation of clay mineral data.

2. AUTHIGENIC FELDSPARS

The crystal structure of feldspar minerals is that of a framework silicate in which (Si, Al)O$_4$ tetrahedra are linked via oxygen in all directions. Potassium sodium and calcium ions are located in the interstices of this framework. Although chains of tetrahedra do not exist, the structural nature of feldspars can best be understood by considering the atomic arrangement as the linking and deformation of horizontal rings made up of four (Si,Al)O$_4$ tetrahedra. As a result, chains of (Si,Al)$_4$O$_{12}$ rings develop (Table 5).

Chemically, most feldspars are members of the ternary system: NaAlSi$_3$O$_8$ — KAlSi$_3$O$_8$ — CaAl$_2$Si$_2$O$_8$. The mineralogical classification of feldspars is based on the relative proportions of these three individual constituents. In broad terms, one generally distinguishes between alkaline feldspars (potassium-sodium) and plagioclases (sodium-calcium).

Feldspars are the most abundant group of minerals in the lithosphere and occur in almost any crystalline or sedimentary rock. They also come in all sizes, ranging from the submicroscopic to dimensions of several feet. Occasionally, as in some pegmatites, they may reach the height of a medium-sized monolith. Although sedimentary feldspars range second in abundance to quartz, the majority of them are of high-temperature origin (detrital) and as such merely survivors of weathering and diagenesis. However, apparently some feldspars may form at low pressures and temperatures at the earth surface or at moderate depth within the crust. Specimens of this type are called authigenic feldspars to distinguish them from their more common detrital counterparts. The actual time of formation is not important. Feldspars may form contemporaneously with deposition, or else at any one time during diagenesis or epigenesis. The only requirement for authigenic feldspars is their formation in situ.

What kind of criteria may be used to distinguish between feldspars formed authigenically and those of detrital origin? In many instances, crystalline outlines with straight edges and sharp corners are an indication of growth in place (idiomorphic character). Metaso-

Table 5 Classification of Authigenic Feldspars in Sediments.

CHEMICAL SERIES	SPECIES	CRYSTALLOCHEMICAL FORMULA	SPACE GROUP	STRUCTURE (SCHEMATIC)
Potassium feldspar	Orthoclase (Adularia habit)	$K[(Si, Al)_4 O_8]$	Monoclinic	
	Microcline	$K[Al Si_3 O_8]$	$P\bar{1}$	
Sodium feldspar	Albite	$Na[Al Si_3 O_8]$	$P\bar{1}$	

Feldspar "chain" of $(Si, Al)O_4$ tetrahedra

matic replacement of oolites and fossils (Straaten, 1948; Stringham, 1940), or feldspar metasomatism of dolomite and secondary calcite are further criteria of authigenic growth. The most comprehensive survey on identification, nature and origin of authigenic feldspars is that of Baskin (1956). He shows that besides idiomorphic outlines of crystals, the chemical composition and twinning pattern may serve as a useful tool in establishing an authigenic origin. In particular, the nonperthitic character, a result of the chemical "purity" of the individual member, is noteworthy. Also, the four-ling twinning (checker-board pattern) of authigenic microcline is unique. "Nonauthigenic" microcline crystals most commonly have crosshatch twinning, which indicates original crystallization in the monoclinic system followed by a transformation to the triclinic form. Another type of fourling twinning after the albite and carlsbad twin laws (Roc Tourne twinning) is characteristic only for low temperature albite. These criteria provide so far the most forceful diagnosis of authigenic feldspars in sediments.

Among these authigenic feldspars found in sedimentary beds from the Pre-Cambrian up to the Tertiary are (a) orthoclase (adularia habit), (b) microcline, and (c) albite. Calcium feldspars (plagioclase) and members of the potassium-sodium solid solution series are missing. This observation agrees with the experimental data collected by a number of investigators on the phase relationship in the system: $NaAlSi_3O_8 - KAlSi_3O_8 - CaAl_2Si_2O_8$.(See, for instance, Schairer, 1950; Schairer and Bowen, 1956; Bowen and Tuttle, 1950; Laves, 1952, 1960; Goldsmith and Laves, 1954, 1956; Yoder et al., 1957.)

The amount of authigenic feldspars rarely exceeds 1 to 2 per cent of the total rock. Only a few exceptions are known from the literature (Daly, 1917; Weiss, 1954), where authigenic feldspars constitute almost 40 to 70 percent of the sediment. Sodium feldspars are restricted to carbonates, whereas potassium feldspars can occur in limestones as well as in sandstones and shales. It is interesting to note that authigenic feldspar is commonly found as rims around detrital microcline or orthoclase, and in some instances around albite. The growth on microcline can be either orthoclase (adularia-type) or microcline, whereas the rims on orthoclase and albite are of the same variety of feldspar as the core (Heald, 1950).

In general, albites are consistently larger than potassium feldspar crystals, but the individual crystals rarely exceed 1 mm in diameter. This difference in size between potassium and sodium feldspars has also been observed in a cross-section of the German Triassic, and has been explained on the grounds (Füchtbauer, 1950) that the formation of albite was an early diagenetic process: the host sediment was still unconsolidated and intercommunication with the original environment of deposition was still possible. The source for sodium ions might have been the sea. The formation of potassium feldspar came at a later stage, at a time when the country rock was partly or completely consolidated. The essential potassium was probably supplied from micaceous materials.

There is still much speculation as to the origin of low temperature feldspars. All attempts to synthesize feldspars at moderate temperatures have failed. The lowest temperature at which feldspars (orthoclase) have been experimentally produced is 250° C (Gruner, 1936). The mode of authigenic feldspar formation has to be discovered from field investigations. Rather important in this connection seems to be the almost universal association of carbonate minerals — both dolomites and secondary calcites — with authigenic feldspars. Even pyroclastic materials that generated albite and analcite in the course of diagenesis (Gulbrandsen and Cressman, 1960) contain appreciable amounts of carbonates. Moreover, the only authigenic feldspars of recent age are known from carbonate caliche deposits which were formed under severe arid to semi-arid conditions.

It is tentatively suggested that the authigenic feldspar formation results from the fact that a carbonate-water solution, free of carbon dioxide, is one of the most common geologically occurring solutions with an alkalinity high enough to stabilize feldspars at low temperatures. That authigenic feldspars are generally only trace constituents of sediments is just a matter of lack of supply of the essential cations, in particular alumina, to the feldspar-forming system. Silica and sodium are generally available in sufficient quantities due on the one hand to the instability of amorphous silica supplied by diatoms or radiolaria and, on the other, to the high abundance of sodium in most connate waters. In certain instances (Coombs et al., 1959; Gulbrandsen and Cressman, 1960), zeolites may be "beneficiated" to authigenic albite in a silica-rich hydrous system at somewhat elevated temperatures. However, we have no information on the precise temperature of transition of analcite to albite. From a geological point of view, there are reasons to assume that the transition takes place at a temperature below 200° C. Also, high saline environments seem to favor the authigenesis of feldspars, as can be inferred from the frequent occurrence of albite and potassium feldspar in Permian and Tertiary evaporite deposits of Germany (Füchtbauer and Goldschmidt, 1959; Braitsch, 1960).

One authigenic feldspar of Cretaceous (Cenoman) and another of Ordovician age have been dated by the potassium-argon method (Wasserburg et al., 1956; Lipson, 1958). Ages of about 95 and 400 million years, respectively, were obtained (Fig. 7). Although the dates agree reasonably well with the ages of those periods, there is still doubt as to the general applicability of feldspar dating. The actual time of feldspar formation within a sediment is beset by too many uncertainties.

3. ZEOLITES

The structure of zeolites is made up of $(Si,Al)O_4$ tetrahedra in which each oxygen is shared between two tetrahedra. The net negative charge is balanced by cations, most commonly Ca, Na or K, located in cavities within the aluminosilicate framework. These cavities are intercommunicating and give rise to a channel-type system; water molecules are present in structural openings. A schematic diagram, representing the structure of a common fibrous zeolite (natrolite) is given in Table 6. As can be seen, two types of channel systems –(a) parallel to the c-axis, and (b) between neighboring chains – are developed. Dehydration and cation exchange phenomena, characteristic for all zeolites, must be attributed to the latter type of channels (Meier, 1960).

A survey of the literature on zeolites in sedimentary rocks reveals that analcite and the members of the heulandite-clinoptilolite group are by far the most common species recognized; but other zeolites such as phillipsite, natrolite, erionite, laumontite and chabazite are also known from sediments. However, most of the latter are found where field evidence indicates that the bed rock has been exposed to higher pressures (i.e., deep sea sediments) or elevated temperatures (hydrothermal activity; low-rank metamorphism).

The presence of zeolites in sediments, even in insignificant amounts, can be geochemically rather rewarding since some zeolites may serve as thermal indicator minerals. Encouraged by the close agreement between field criteria and experimental data regarding the mode of zeolite formation (Fenner, 1936; Coombs, 1954; Coombs et al., 1959; Fyfe et al., 1958; Saha, 1961) the concept of a zeolite "facies" was developed to bridge the wide gap between low tem-

Table 6 CLASSIFICATION OF PRINCIPAL ZEOLITES IN SEDIMENTS.

TYPE OF TETRAHEDRA LINKAGE	SPECIES	CRYSTALLOCHEMICAL FORMULA	SPACE GROUP	STRUCTURE (SCHEMATIC)
Chain (fibrous)	**Natrolite**	$Na_2 Al_2 Si_3 O_{10} \cdot 2 H_2O$	Fdd	
	Laumontite	$CaAl_2 Si_4 O_{12} \cdot 4 H_2O$	$C2$ or Cm	
Plane (platy cleavage)	**Heulandite** * **Clinoptilolite** *	$(Ca,Na_2) Al_2 Si_7 O_{18} \cdot 6 H_2O$	$I2/m$	
Framework (random)	**Analcite** ** **Phillipsite** **Chabazite** **Erionite** +	$NaAlSi_2 O_6 \cdot H_2O$ $(\tfrac{1}{2}Ca,Na,K)_3 Al_3 Si_5 O_{16} \cdot 6 H_2O$ $CaAl_2 Si_4 O_{12} \cdot 6 H_2O$ $(Na_2,K_2,Ca,Mg)_{4\cdot5}[Al_9 Si_{27} O_{72}] 27 H_2O$	$Ia3d$ $P2_1/m$ or $P2_1$ $R\bar{3}m$ $P6_3/mmc$ (?)	

(a)

(b)

(c)

Natrolite
cell dimensions:
$a = 18.3$ Å
$b = 18.6$ Å
$c = 6.6$ Å

● Na
○ H_2O

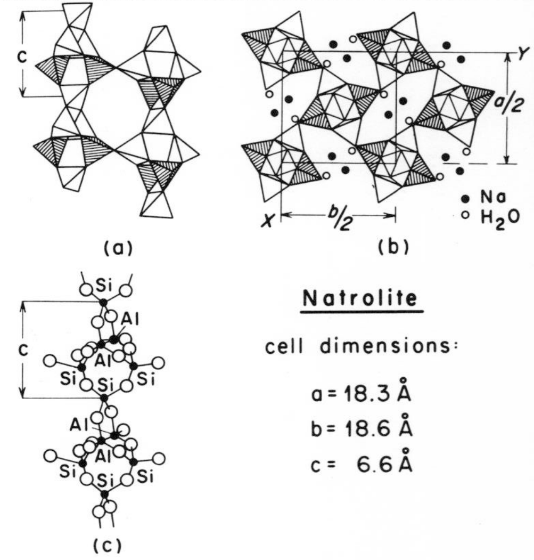

* High silica member of the heulandite structure group, containing more monovalent than divalent cations

** Close affinities with felspathoids

+ Structure similar to framework–type, but the mineral is fibrous

perature diagenesis and the well-established metamorphic "facies." Laumontite, in particular, is regarded as a potential indicator mineral.

In order to provide some information on the temperature-pressure relationship of zeolites, we present the results of a study by Coombs et al. (1959) on a rock sequence of about 30,000 feet from the marine Triassic of New Zealand. The following data were obtained:

(1) Fresh analcite is common in the upper 20,000 feet; only pseudomorphs of albite and, less commonly, of adularia and laumontite after analcite are present in the lower 10,000 foot section.

(2) Members of the heulandite-clinoptilolite group are frequent in the upper 20,000 feet but sharply decrease with depth from there on.

(3) Laumontite is common only in the lower 10,000 feet of sediment.

(4) Detrital lime-bearing plagioclase, rich in the upper 20,000 feet, is albitized in the lower 10,000 feet of the rock sequence.

The formation of analcite and heulandite at shallow depths is a result of the interaction of volcanic glass and saline waters. With increasing depths, the analcite-quartz assemblage is replaced by albite-quartz; heulandite is replaced by laumontite, and calcic plagioclase gives rise to albite and laumontite.

The occurrence of authigenic zeolites, especially analcite in sediments which are for the most part deposited in a lacustrine environment, has frequently been reported. These zeolite-bearing sediments are often of pyroclastic origin (tuff beds), but zeolites are also found in sedimentary basins free of pyroclastic debris. Interesting and well studied examples of the latter type are found in the Eocene Green River Formation (Bradley, 1928, 1929; Milton and Eugster, 1959), in the Popo Agie Member of the Chugwater Formation (Keller, 1952), and in the Hector, California, Bentonite deposits (Ames et al., 1957). An interesting feature of these deposits, as well as of others mentioned in the literature, is that analcite and montmorillonite apparently exclude each other. In the Green River Formation clay minerals are frequent in the units without analcite; in the Chugwater Formation clays underlie the analcite horizon, and in the Hector bentonite deposits, clay and analcite layers alternate.

The occurrence of zeolites in these lacustrine beds indicates that apparently restricted environmental conditions are required for their formation. Such conditions are, for instance, established in closed basins where water is steadily removed by evaporation (arid environment), thus increasing the activity of certain ions essential for the origin of zeolites. It has been suggested that montmorillonite represents a stable phase at the initial stages of evaporation, whereas analcite crystallizes at the exclusion of montmorillonite at a later stage, when the activity of sodium has reached a critical value. Alternating layers of montmorillonite and analcite may have been caused by periodic changes in the environment.

It must be emphasized that the formation of analcite or heulandite from volcanic precursor materials, clay minerals and other potential silicates, not only proceeds at the time of deposition (contemporaneous), but very often takes place during diagenesis in the presence of high saline waters (e.g., sodium-rich carbonate-sulfate solutions).

Rather remarkable is the almost constant association of analcite with free silica (microcrystalline quartz) and the virtual absence of authigenic albite as observed in many rock formations such as the Green River (Milton and Eugster, 1959). The relationship is given by the following reaction:

$$NaAlSi_2O_6 \cdot H_2O + SiO_2 \rightleftharpoons NaAlSi_3O_8 + H_2O$$

Considering the above reaction and calculating the free energy of formation of analcite, it is found that the assemblage analcite and quartz is stable at lower pressures and temperatures than that of albite and water. However, laboratory studies aiming at establishing precise equilibration phase relations in the analcite + quartz → albite + water system at low temperatures have been rather unsuccessful so far. No definite phase boundaries could be constructed (Saha, 1959, 1961; Mackenzie, 1957; Coombs, 1959; Noll, 1936; Greenwood, 1961).

Zeolites are also known from coal beds, where they are associated with pyrite concretions (Foster and Feicht, 1946). Phillipsite has been reported by Arrhenius and Goldberg (1955) derived from pelagic red clays in areas of slow marine sedimentation. In this case volcanic debris served as precursor material. For further details on the distribution of zeolites in sedimentary rocks see Deffeyes (1959).

4. MINOR VARIETIES

As data on authigenic "trace" silicates of low temperature origin accumulated, it became evident that former well established concepts on the thermal stability of certain silicates had to be revised. Minerals such as hornblende or pyroxene, for long times known only as high temperature species, suddenly were found in sediments as authigenic overgrowths or new idiomorphic crystals.

It is not intended to discuss at length all minor varieties that are known from sedimentary rocks. The accompanying Table 7 listing authigenic "trace" silicates should be regarded as a demonstration of the wide spectrum of geochemically different minerals that may occur in a sediment rather than as a complete inventory.

Table 7 SELECTION OF AUTHIGENIC "TRACE" SILICATES

Labuntsovite	$(K, Ba, Na, Ca, Mn) (Ti, Nb) (Si, Al)_2$ $(O, OH)_7 \cdot H_2O$	(Milton et al., 1958)
Searlesite	$NaBSi_2O_6 \cdot H_2O$	(Fahey, 1950)
Reedmergnerite	$NaBSi_3O_8$	(Milton et al., 1954)
Garrelsite	$(Ba, Ca, Mg) B_3SiO_6 (OH)_3$	(Milton et al., 1955)
Acmite	$NaFe^{+3} Si_2O_6$	(Milton and Eugster, 1959)
Riebeckite-magnesiorie-beckite	$Na_2(Mg, Fe^{+2})_3(Fe^{+3},Al)_2Si_8O_{22}(OH)_2$	(Milton and Eugster, 1959)
Sepiolite	$Mg_2Si_3O_6 (OH)_4$	(Bradley, 1929) (Teodorovich, 1961)
Loughlinite	$(Na_2, Mg)_2Si_3O_6 (OH)_4$	(Fahey, 1949)
Elpidite	$Na_2ZrSi_6O_{15} \cdot 3 H_2O$	(Milton and Eugster, 1959)
Leucosphenite	$CaBaNa_3B Ti_3Si_9O_{29}$	(Milton et al., 1954)
Penninite	$Mg_{5.2}Fe^{+2}_{0.3}Al_{0.1}Fe^{+3}_{0.4}Al_{0.5}$ $Si_{3.5}O_{10}(OH)_8$	(Braitsch, 1962)
Talc	$Mg_3 (OH)_2Si_4O_{10}$	(Steward, 1949) (Braitsch, 1958) (Dreizler, 1962) (Griffin, 1963) (Teodorovich, 1961)
Zircon	$ZrSiO_4$	(Awasthi, 1961) (Smithson, 1937) (Butterfield, 1936)
Tourmaline	$Na(Li, Mg, Fe^{+2}, Al)_3Al_6B_3Si_6(OH)_4$	(Krynine, 1946) (Gokhale et al., 1959) (Awasthi, 1961)

Three of the more comprehensive studies in the field of authigenic "trace" silicates are those by Krynine (1946), Milton and Eugster (1959), and Teodorovich (1961). Whereas Krynine threw appreciable light on the mode of tourmaline formation in sedimentary rocks, Milton and Eugster investigated the complex mineral assemblages of the saline beds of the Green River Formation in Wyoming, Utah and Colorado. Teodorovich's contribution, a summary of all authigenic minerals in sedimentary rocks, further adds to our understanding of the often puzzling occurrence of "high temperature" minerals in low temperature environments.

On a geological basis, one can differentiate between trace silicates which are known to occur in sediments of all ages and types (i.e. sandstones, shales, limestones) and others that are only found in sediments deposited under restricted environmental conditions. Only two minerals of our selection (Table 7), i.e., tourmaline and zircon, belong to the first category; the others require an environmental set-up which is only met in certain evaporite basins.

It has previously been shown that the physical-chemical conditions established in a syngenetic evaporite or in a diagenetic high saline environment stimulate the growth of silicates such as feldspars and zeolites. In all instances these silicates were associated with carbonates. The same characteristics, namely the presence of carbonates and saturated alkaline brines, were observed when the sodium-bearing silicates of the Green River Formation were formed which suggests a cause-effect relationship. Details on the phase relationships in the various systems have been presented by Milton and Eugster (1959).

Selected References

1. *Clay Minerals*

   Altschuler, Z. S., E. J. Dwornik, and H. Kramer, "Transformation of Montmorillonite to Kaolinite during Weathering." Science, **141** (1963), 148–152.

   Amirkhanov, Kh. I., K. S. Magataev, and S. B. Brandt, "The Determination of Absolute Age of Sedimentary Minerals by Radioactive Methods." Proc. Acad. Sci. USSR, Geol. Sci. Sect., **117** (1957), 675–677.

   Baas Becking, L. G. M., I. R. Kaplan, and D. Moore, "Limits of the Natural Environment in Terms of pH and Oxidation-Reduction Potentials." J. Geol., **68** (1960), 243–284.

Bär, A. L. S. and H. J. C. Tendeloo, "Über die Doppelschicht der Tonkolloide." Kolloid-Beihefte, **44** (1936), 97–124.

Barshad, I., "The Effect of the Interlayer Cations on the Expansion of the Mica Type of Crystal Lattice." Amer. Mineralogist, **35** (1950), 225–238.

Bates, T. F., "Interrelationships of Structure and Genesis in the Kaolinite Group." Amer. Inst. Min. Metal. Eng., Problems of Clay and Laterite Genesis, (1952), 144–153.

Bates, T. F. "Halloysite and Gibbsite Formation in Hawaii." Clays and Clay Minerals, **9** (1962), 315–328.

Borchert, H., "Zur Geochemie des Kohlenstoffs." Geochim. et Cosmochim. Acta, **2** (1951), 62–75.

Bragg, W. L., *Atomic Structure of Minerals*. Ithaca, N. Y.: Cornell University Press, 1937.

Brindley, G. W., *X-ray Identification and Crystal Structures of Clay Minerals*. London: Mineralogical Society, 1951.

Brindley, G. W., "Allevardite, a Swelling Double-Layer Mica Mineral." Amer. Mineralogist, **41** (1956), 91–103.

Brindley, G. W. and R. W. Hoffmann, "Orientation and Packing of Aliphatic Chain Molecules on Montmorillonite." Clays and Clay Minerals, **9**th Conf. (1962), 546–556.

Brindley, G. W. and K. Robinson, "The Structure of Kaolinite." Mineralog. Mag., **27** (1946), 242–253.

Brown, G., "Report of the Clay Minerals Group Sub-committee on Nomenclature of Clay Minerals." Clay Min. Bull., **2** (1955), 294–302.

Burst, J. F., "Glauconite" pellets: Their Mineral Nature and Applications to Stratigraphic Interpretations." Bull. Amer. Assoc. Petrol. Geol., **42** (1958), 310–327.

Carroll, D., "Ion Exchange in Clays and Other Minerals." Bull. Geol. Soc. Amer., **70** (1959), 749–780.

Clarke, F. W. and H. S. Washington, "The Composition of the Earth's Crust." U. S. Geol. Survey Prof. Paper **127** (1924), 117 pp.

Correns, C. W., "Experiments on the Decomposition of Silicates and Discussion of Chemical Weathering." Clays and Clay Minerals, **10**th Conf. (1963), 443–459.

Cowan, C. T. and J. M. Hartwell, "The Mechanism of Exchange Reactions occurring between Sodium Montmorillonite and Various *n*-primary Aliphatic Amine Salts." Trans. Faraday Soc., **54** (1958), 691–697.

Cowan, C. T. and D. White, "Adsorption by Organo-clay Complexes." Clays and Clay Minerals, **9**th Conf. (1962), 459–467.

Cowan, C. T., "Adsorption by Organo-clay Complexes Part 2." Clays and Clay Minerals, 10th Conf. (1963), 226–234.

Daly, R. A., *Igneous Rocks and the Depth of the Earth;* containing some revised chapters of *Igneous Rocks and their Origin* (1914). New York and London: McGraw-Hill Book Company, 1933.

Deuel, H., "Organic Derivatives of Clay Minerals." Agrochemica, 1 (1957), 248–267.

DeVore, G. W., "The Surface Chemistry of Feldspars as an Influence on their Decomposition Products." Clays and Clay Minerals, 6th Conf. (1959), 26–41.

Ehlmann, A. J., N. C. Hulings, and E. D. Glover, "Stages of Glauconite Formation in Modern Foraminiferal Sediments." J. Sed. Petrol., 33 (1963), 87–96.

Emerson, W. W., "Complexes of Calcium-Montmorillonite with Polymers." Nature, 186 (1960), 573–574.

Engelhardt, W. von, "Die Geochemie des Bariums." Chem. Erde, 10 (1936), 187–246.

Ensminger, L. E. and J. E. Gieseking, "The Adsorption of Proteins by Montmorillonitic Clays." Soil Science, 48 (1939), 467–473.

Ernst, W., K. Krejci-Graf, and H. Werner, "Parallelisierung von Leithorizonten im Ruhrkarbon mit Hilfe des Bor-Gehaltes." Geochim. et Cosmochim. Acta, 14 (1958), 211–222.

Everden, J. F., G. H. Curtis, J. Obradovich, and R. Kistler, "On the Evaluation of Glauconite and Illite for Dating Sedimentary Rocks by the Potassium Argon Method." Geochim. et Cosmochim. Acta, 23 (1961), 78–99.

Foster, M. D., "Interpretation of the Composition and a Classification of the Chlorites." U. S. Geol. Survey Prof. Paper 414-A (1962), 1–33.

Frank-Kamenetsky, V. A., "A Crystallochemical Classification of Simple and Interstratified Clay Minerals." Clay Min. Bull., 4 (1960), 161–172.

Friedlander, H. Z., J. Saldick, and C. R. Frink, "Electron Spin Resonance Spectra in Various Clay Minerals." Nature, 199 (1963), 61–62.

Frysinger, G. R., "Cation Exchange Behavior of Vermiculite-biotite Mixtures." Clays and Clay Minerals, 8th Conf. (1960), 116–121.

Garrels, R. M., *Mineral Equilibria at Low Temperature and Pressure.* New York: Harper and Row, Publishers, 1960.

Gentner, W., R. Präg and F. Smits, "Argonbestimmungen an Kalium-Mineralien. II. Das Alter eines Kalilagers im Unteren Oligozän." Geochim. et Cosmochim. Acta, 4 (1953), 11–20.

Gentner, W., K. Goebel, and R. Präg, "Argonbestimmungen an Kalium-Mineralien. III. Vergleichende Messungen nach der Kalium-Argon-und Uran-Helium-Methode." Geochim. et Cosmochim. Acta, 5 (1954), 124–133.

Goldschmidt, V. M., "Grundlagen der quantitativen Geochemie." Fortschr. Min. Krist. Petr., **17** (1933), 112–156.

Greene-Kelly, R., "The Sorption of Saturated Organic Compounds by Montmorillonite." Trans. Faraday Soc., **52** (1956), 1281–1286.

Greenland, D. J., "The Adsorption of Sugars by Montmorillonite. I. X-ray Studies. II. Chemical Studies." J. Soil Sci., **7** (1956), 319–334.

Greenland, D. J. and E. W. Russell, "Organo-clay Derivatives and the Origin of the Negative Charge on Clay Particles." Trans. Faraday Soc., **51** (1955), 1300–1307.

Greenland, D. J., R. M. Laby, and J. P. Quirk, "Adsorption of Glycine and its Di-, Tri-, and Tetra-peptides by Montmorillonite." Trans. Faraday Soc., **58** (1962), 829–841.

Grim, R. E., "Concept of Diagenesis in Argillaceous Sediments." Bull. Amer. Assoc. Petrol. Geol., **42** (1958), 246–253.

Grim, R. E., *Clay Mineralogy*. New York-Toronto-London: McGraw-Hill Book Company, 1953.

Gruner, J. W., "The Crystal Structure of Kaolinite." Ztschr. Krist., **83** (1932), 75–88.

Gruner, J. W., "The Structures of Vermiculites and their Collapse by Dehydration." Amer. Mineralogist, **19** (1934), 557–575.

Harder, H., "Einbau von Bor in detritische Tonminerale. Experimente zur Erklärung des Borgehaltes toniger Sedimente." Geochim. et Cosmochim. Acta, **21** (1961), 284–294.

Hendricks, S. B., "Base-exchange of Crystalline Silicates." Ind. Eng. Chem., **37** (1945), 625–630.

Hendricks, S. B., "On the Crystal Structure of the Clay Minerals: Dickite, Halloysite and Hydrated Halloysite." Amer. Mineralogist, **23** (1938), 295–301.

Hendricks, S. B., R. A. Nelson, and L. T. Alexander, "Hydration Mechanism of the Clay Mineral Montmorillonite Saturated with Various Cations." J. Amer. Chem. Soc., **62** (1940), 1457–1464.

Holmes, A., *The Age of the Earth*. New York: Thomas Nelson and Sons, 1937.

Hurley, P. M., "Authigenic Versus Detrital Illite in Sediments." Bull. Geol. Soc. Amer., **70** (1959), 1622.

Hurley, P. M., "Glauconite as a Possible Means of Measuring the Age of Sediments." Ann. New York Acad. Sci., **91** (1961), 294–297.

Hurley, P. M., J. M. Hunt, W. H. Pinson, and H. W. Fairbairn, "K-Ar Values on the Clay Fractions in Dated Shales." Geochim. et Cosmochim. Acta, **27** (1963a), 279–284.

Hurley, P. M., B. C. Heezen, W. H. Pinson, and H. W. Fairbairn, "K-Ar Age Values in Pelagic Sediments of the North Atlantic." Geochim. et Cosmochim. Acta, **27** (1963b), 393–400.

Jackson, M. L., "Frequency Distribution of Clay Minerals in Major Great Soil Groups as Related to the Factors of Soil Formation." Clays and Clay Minerals, **6**th Conf. (1959), 133–142.

Jenny, H., "Studies of the Mechanism of Ionic Exchange in Colloidal Aluminum Silicates." J. Phys. Chem., **36** (1932), 2217–2258.

Jenny, H., "Simple Kinetic Theory of Ionic Exchange: Ions of Equal Valency." J. Phys. Chem., **40** (1936), 501–517.

Keith, M. L. and E. T. Degens, "Geochemical Indicators of Marine and Fresh-Water Sediments" in *Researches in Geochemistry;* Editor: P. H. Abelson. New York: John Wiley & Sons, Inc., (1959), 38–61.

Keller, W. D., "Clay Minerals as Influenced by Environments of their Formation." Bull. Amer. Assoc. Petrol Geol., **40** (1956), 2689–2710.

Keller, W. D., *Principles of Chemical Weathering.* Columbia, Mo.: Lucas Bros., Publishers, 1957.

Keller, W. D., W. D. Balgord, and A. L. Reesman, "Dissolved Products of Artificially Pulverized Silicate Minerals and Rocks, I." J. Sed. Petr., **33** (1963), 191–204.

Krynine, P. D., "The Megascopic Study and Field Classification of Sedimentary Rocks." J. Geol., **56** (1948), 130–165.

Kulp, J. L., "Geological Time Scale." Bull. Geol. Soc. Amer., **70** (1959), 1634.

Kulp, J. L., "Geochronology of Rock Systems." Ann. New York Acad. Sci., **91** (1961), 159–594.

Leith, C. K. and W. J. Mead, *Metamorphic Geology.* New York: Holt, Rinehart & Winston, Inc., 1915.

Lipson, J., "Potassium Argon Dating of Sedimentary Rocks." Bull. Geol. Soc. Amer., **69** (1958); 137–150.

MacEwan, D. M. C., "Complexes of Clays with Organic Compounds." Trans. Faraday Soc., **44** (1948), 349–367.

MacEwan, D. M. C., "Interlamellar Reactions of Clay and Other Substances." Clays and Clay Minerals, **9**th Conf. (1962), 431–443.

Mackenzie, R. C., "The Classification and Nomenclature of Clay Minerals." Clay Min. Bull., **4** (1959), 52–66.

Mackenzie, R. C., G. F. Walker, and R. Hart, "Illite in Decomposed Granite at Ballater, Aberdeenshire." Mineralog. Mag., **28** (1949), 704–714.

McMurchy, R. C., "Structure of Chlorites." Ztschr. Krist., **88** (1934), 420–432.

Millot, G., *Relations entre la constitution et la genese des roches sedimentaires argileuses.* Geol. Appl. Prosp. Min., Univ. Nancy, vol. II. (1949).

Millot, G., "Prospecting of Useful Clays in Relation with their Condition of Genesis." Amer. Inst. Min. Met. Eng., Problems of Clay and Laterite Genesis (1952), 107–114.

Nahin, P. G., "Perspectives in Applied Organo-clay Chemistry." Clays and Clay Minerals, **10**th Conf. (1963), 257–271.

Nelson, B. W. and R. Roy, "New Data on the Composition and Identification of Chlorites." Clays and Clay Minerals, **2**nd Conf. (1954), 335–348.

Nier, A. O., R. W. Thompson, and B. F. Murphy, "The Isotopic Constitution of Lead and the Measurement of Geologic Time, III." Phys. Rev., **60** (1941), 112–116.

Noll, W., "Über die geochemische Rolle der Sorption." Chem. Erde, **6** (1931), 552.

Pauling, L., "Structure of Chlorites." Proc. Natl. Acad. Sci. U.S., **16** (1930), 578–582.

Pinck, L. A., "Adsorption of Proteins, Enzymes and Antibiotics by Montmorillonite." Clays and Clay Minerals, **9**th Conf. (1962), 520–529.

Polevaya, N. I., G. A. Kazakov, and G. A. Murina, "Glauconites as Indicators of Geologic Time." Geokhimiya, No. **1** (1960), 1–11.

Polevaya, N. I., G. A. Murina, and G. A. Kazakov, "Utilization of Glauconite in Absolute Dating." Ann. New York Acad. Sci., **91** (1961), 298–310.

Potter, P. E., N. F. Shimp, and J. Witters, "Trace Elements in Marine and Fresh-water Argillaceous Sediments." Geochim. et Cosmochim. Acta, **27** (1963), 669–694.

Ross, C. S. and P. F. Kerr, "The Kaolin Minerals." U. S. Geol. Survey Prof. Paper **165-E** (1930), 151–176.

Ross, C. S. and P. F. Kerr, "Halloysite and Allophane." U. S. Geol. Survey Prof. Paper **185-G** (1934), 135–148.

Ross, C. S. and S. B. Hendricks, "Minerals of the Montmorillonite Group; their Origin and Relation to Soils and Clays." U. S. Geol. Survey Prof. Paper, **205-B** (1946), 23–77.

Rowland, R. A. and E. J. Weiss, "Bentonite-methylamine Complexes." Clays and Clay Minerals, **10th** Conf. (1963), 460–468.

Schuchert, C., "The Age of the Earth, on the Basis of Sediments and Life." Bull. Nat. Res. Council, **80** (1931), 10–64.

Sherman, G. D., "The Genesis and Morphology of the Alumina-rich Laterite Clays." Amer. Inst. Min. Metal. Eng., Problems of Clay and Laterite Genesis (1952), 154–161.

Slaughter, M. and I. M. Milne, "The Formation of Chlorite-like Structures from Montmorillonite." Clays and Clay Minerals, 7th Conf. (1959), 114–124.

Stevens, R. E. and M. K. Carron, "Simple Field Test for Distinguishing Minerals by Abrasion pH." Amer. Mineralogist, **33** (1948), 31–49.

Strunz, H., *Mineralogische Tabellen* (third edition). Leipzig: Akademische Verlagsgesellschaft, Geest and Portig, 1957.

Talibudeen, O., "Complex Formation between Montmorillonoid Clays and Amino-acids and Proteins." Trans. Faraday Soc., **51** (1955), 582–590.

Vinogradov, A. P. and A. I. Tugarinov, "Problems of Geochronology of the Pre-Cambrian in Eastern Asia." Geochim. et Cosmochim. Acta, **26** (1962), 1283–1300.

Walker, F. and A. Poldervaart, "Karoo Dolerites of the Union of South Africa." Bull. Geol. Soc. Amer., **60** (1949), 591–706.

Walker, G. F., "Vermiculite and some Related Mixed-layer Minerals" in "X-ray Identification and Structure of the Clay Minerals," Min. Soc. Great Britain (1951), 199–223.

Wasserburg, G. J., R. J. Hayden, and K. J. Jensen, "Ar^{40} -K^{40} Dating of Igneous Rocks and Sediments." Geochim. et Cosmochim. Acta, **10** (1956), 153–165.

Weaver, C. E., "Geologic Interpretation of Argillaceous Sediments. Part II: Clay Petrology of Upper Mississippi-Lower-Pennsylvanian Sediments of Central United States." Bull. Amer. Assoc. Petrol. Geol., **42** (1958a), 272–309.

Weaver, C. E., "Geologic Interpretation of Argillaceous Sediments. Part I: Origin and Significance of Clay Minerals in Sedimentary Rocks." Bull. Amer. Assoc. Petrol. Geol., **42** (1958b), 254–271.

Weaver, C. E., "Possible Uses of Clay Minerals in the Search for Oil." Clays and Clay Minerals, **8th** Conf. (1960), 214–227.

Weiss, A., "Mica-type Layer Silicates with Alkylammonium Ions." Clays and Clay Minerals, **10th** Conf. (1963), 191–224.

Whitehouse, U. G., L. M. Jeffrey, and J. D. Debbrecht, "Differential Settling Tendencies of Clay Minerals in Saline Waters." Clays and Clay Minerals, 7th Conf. (1959), 1–79

Wickman, F. E., "The 'Total' Amount of Sediments and the Composition of the 'Average Igneous Rock'." Geochim. et Cosmochim. Acta, **5** (1954,) 97–110.

Yoder, H. S. and H. P. Eugster, "Synthetic and Natural Muscovites." Geochim. et Cosmochim. Acta, **8** (1955), 225–280.

Zen, E., "Problem of the Thermodynamic Status of the Mixed-layer Minerals." Geochim. et Cosmochim. Acta, **26** (1962), 1055–1068.

2. *Authigenic Feldspars*

Baskin, Y., "A Study of Authigenic Feldspars." J. Geol., **64** (1956), 132–155.

Bowen, N. L. and O. F. Tuttle, "The System $NaAlSi_3O_8$-$KAlSi_3O_8$-H_2O." J. Geol., **58** (1950), 489–517.

Braitsch, O., "Mineralparagenesis und Petrologie der Stassfurtsalze in Reyershausen." Kali und Steinsalz, **3** (1960), 1–14.

Coombs, D. S., A. J. Ellis, W. S. Fyfe, and A. M. Taylor, "The Zeolite Facies; with Comments on the Interpretation of Hydrothermal Syntheses." Geochim. et Cosmochim. Acta, **17** (1959), 53–107.

Daly, R. A., "Low-temperature Formation of Alkaline Feldspars in Limestones." Nat. Acad. Sci. Proc., **3** (1917), 659–665.

Füchtbauer, H., "Die nichtkarbonatischen Bestandteile des Göttinger Muschelkalkes mit besonderer Berücksichtigung der Mineralneubildungen." Heidelb. Beitr. Min. Petr., **2** (1950), 235–254.

Füchtbauer, H. and H. Goldschmidt, "Die Tonminerale der Zechsteinformation." Beitr. Mineral. Petrogr., **6** (1959), 320–345.

Goldsmith, J. R. and F. Laves, "The Microcline-sanidine Stability Relations." Geochim. et Cosmochim. Acta, **5** (1954), 1–19.

Goldsmith, J. R. and F. Laves, "Crystallisation of Metastable Disordered Anorthite at Low Temperatures." Ztschr. Krist., **107** (1956), 396–405.

Gruner, J. W., "Hydrothermal Alteration of Montmorillonite to Feldspar at Temperatures from 245° C to 300° C." Amer. Mineralogist, **21** (1936), 511–515.

Gulbrandsen, R. A. and E. R. Cressman, "Analcime and Albite in Altered Jurassic Tuff in Idaho and Wyoming." J. Geol., **68** (1960), 458–464.

Heald, M. T., "Authigenesis in West Virginia Sandstones." J. Geol., **58** (1950), 624–633.

Laves, F., "Phase Relations of the Alkali Feldspars." J. Geol., **60** (1952), 436–450, 549–574.

Laves, F., "Al/Si-Verteilungen, Phasen-Transformationen und Namen der Alkalifeldspäte." Ztschr. Krist., **113** (1960), 265–296.

Lipson, J., "Potassium Argon Dating of Sedimentary Rocks." Bull. Geol. Soc. Amer., **69** (1958), 137–150.

Schairer, J. E., "The Alkali-feldspar Join in the System $NaAlSiO_4$-$KAlSiO_4$-SiO_2." J. Geol., **58** (1950), 512–517.

Schairer, J. F. and N. L. Bowen, "The system $Na_2O-Al_2O_3-Al_2O_3-SiO_4$." Amer. J. Sci., **254** (1956), 129–195.

Straaten, L. M. J. U., van, "Note on the Occurrence of Authigenic Feldspar in Non-metamorphic Sediments." Amer. J. Sci., **246** (1948), 569–572.

Stringham, B., "Occurrence of Feldspar Replacing Fossils." Amer. Mineralogist, **25** (1940), 139–144.

Wasserburg, G. J., R. J. Hayden, and K. J. Jensen, "A^{40}-K^{40} Dating of Igneous Rocks and Sediments." Geochim. et Cosmochim. Acta, **10** (1956), 153–165.

Weiss, M. P., "Feldspathized Shales from Minnesota." J. Sed. Petrol., **24** (1954), 270–274.

Yoder, H. S., Jr., D. B. Steward, and J. R. Smith, "Ternary Feldspars." Ann. Rep. Director Geophys. Lab., Carnegie Inst. Washington, Year Book, **55-56** (1956-57), 190–194 and 206.

3. Zeolites

Ames, L. L., Jr., L. B. Sand, and S. S. Goldich, "A Contribution on the Hector, California Bentonite Deposit." Econ. Geol., **53** (1957), 22–37.

Arrhenius, G. and E. D. Goldberg, "Distribution of Radioactivity in Pelagic Clays." Tellus, **7** (1955), 226–231.

Bradley, W. H., "Zeolite Beds in the Green River Formation." Science, **67** (1928), 73–74.

Bradley, W. H., "The Occurrence and Origin of Analcite and Meerschaum Beds in the Green River Formation of Utah, Colorado and Wyoming." U. S. Geol. Survey Prof. Paper, **158-A** (1929), 1–7.

Coombs, D. S., "The Nature and Alteration of Some Triassic Sediments from Southland New Zealand." Trans. Roy. Soc., N. Z., **82** (1954), Part 1, 65–109.

Coombs, D. S., A. J. Ellis, W. S. Fyfe, and A. M. Taylor, "The Zeolite Facies; with Comments on the Interpretation of Hydrothermal Syntheses." Geochim. et Cosmochim. Acta, **17** (1959), 53–107.

Deffeyes, K. S., "Zeolites in Sedimentary Rocks." J. Sed. Petr., **29** (1959), 602–609.

Fenner, C. N., "Bore-hole Investigations in Yellowstone Park." J. Geol., **44** (1936), 225–315.

Foster, W. D. and F. L. Feicht, "Mineralogy of Concretions from Pittsburgh Coal Seam, with Special Reference to Analcite." Amer. Mineralogist, **31** (1946), 357–364.

Fyfe, W. S., F. J. Turner, and J. Verhoogen, "Metamorphic Reactions and Metamorphic Facies." Geol. Soc. Amer. Mem., **73** (1958), 166–179.

Greenwood, H. J., "The System $NaAlSi_2O_6$-H_2O-Argon; Total Pressure and Water Pressure in Metamorphism." J. Geophys. Res., **66** (1961), 3923–3946.

Keller, W. D., "Analcine in the Popo Agie Member of the Chugwater Formation." J. Sed. Petr., **22** (1952), 70–82.

Mackenzie, W. S., "The Crystalline Modifications of $NaAlSi_3O_8$." Amer. J. Sci., **255** (1957), 481–516.

Meier, W. M., "The Crystal Structure of Natrolite." Ztschr. Krist., **113** (1960), 430–444.

Milton, C. and H. P. Eugster, "Mineral Assemblages of the Green River Formation" in *Researches in Geochemistry*, Editor: P. H. Abelson. New York: John Wiley & Sons, Inc., (1959), 118–150.

Noll, W., "Über die Bildungsbedingungen von Kaolin, Montmorillonit, Serizit, Pyrophyllit und Analcime." Min. Petr. Mitt., **48** (1936), 210–247.

Saha, P., "Geochemical and X-ray Investigation of Natural and Synthetic Analcites." Amer. Mineralogist, **44** (1959), 300–313.

Saha, P., "The System $NaAlSiO_4$-(nepheline)-$NaAlSi_3O_8$-(albite)-H_2O." Amer. Mineralogist, **46** (1961), 859–884.

4. *Minor Varieties*

Awasthi, N., "Authigenic Tourmaline and Zircon in the Vindhyan Formations of Sone Valley, Mirzapur district, Uttar Pradesh, India." J. Sed. Petrol., **31** (1961), 482–484.

Bradley, W. H., "The Occurrence and Origin of Analcite and Meerschaum Beds in the Green River Formation of Utah, Colorado, and Wyoming." U. S. Geol. Survey Prof. Paper, **158-A** (1929), 1–8.

Braitsch, O., "Über den Mineralbestand der wasserunlöslichen Rückstände von Salzen der Stassfurtserie im südlichen Leinetal." Frieberger Forschung-shefte, **A-123** (1958) 160–163.

Braitsch, O., *Entstehung und Stoffbestand der Salzlagerstätten.* "Mineralogie und Petrographie in Eizeldarstellungen, Band III." Berlin-Göttingen-Heidelberg: Springer-Verlag, 1962.

Butterfield, J. A., "Outgrowth on Zircon." Geol. Mag., **73** (1936), 511–516.

Dreizler, I., "Mineralogische Untersuchungen zweier Gipsvorkommen aus der Umgebung von Göttingen." Beitr. Min. Petrogr., **8** (1962), 323–338.

Fahey, J. J., "Loughlinite, a New Hydrous Magnesium Silicate (with X-ray analysis by J. M. Axelrod)." Geol. Soc. Amer. Bull., **58** (1947), 1178–1179.

Fahey, J. J., "Searlesite from the Green River Formation of Wyoming (with X-ray notes by J. M. Axelrod)." Amer. Mineralogist, **35** (1950), 1014–1020.

Gokhale, K. V. G. K. and T. C. Bagchi, "Authigenic Tourmaline in the Baganapally Stage (Kurnool System), India." J. Sed. Petrol., **29** (1959), 468–469.

Griffin, G. M., "Occurrence of Talc in Clay Fractions from Beach Sands of the Gulf of Mexico." J. Sed. Petrol., **33** (1963), 231–233.

Krynine, P. D., "The Tourmaline Group in Sediments." J. Geol., **54** (1946), 65–87.

Milton, C., J. M. Axelrod and F. S. Grimaldi, "New Minerals Reedmergnerite ($Na_2OB_2O_3$ 6 SiO_2) and Eitelite ($Na_2O \cdot MgO \cdot 2 CO_2$) Associated with Leucosphenite, Shortite, Searlesite and Crocidolite in the Green River Formation, Utah." Geol. Soc. Amer. Bull., 1954, 1286–1287.

Milton, C., J. M. Axelrod, and F. S. Grimaldi, "New Mineral Garrelsite (Ba, Ca, Mg)$_4$H$_4$Si$_{26}$BO$_{20}$ from the Green River Formation, Utah." Geol. Soc. Amer. Bull., **66** (1955), 1597.

Milton, C. and H. P. Eugster, "Mineral Assemblages of the Green River Formation." In *Researches in Geochemistry*. Editor: P. H. Abelson. New York: John Wiley & Sons, Inc., (1959), 118–151.

Milton, C., M. Mrose, J. J. Fahey, and E. C. T. Chao, "Labuntsovite from the Trona Mine, Sweetwater County, Wyoming." Geol. Soc. Amer. Bull., **69** (1958), 1614–1615.

Smithson, F., "Outgrowths on Zircon in the Middle Jurassic of Yorkshire." Geol. Mag., **74** (1937), 281–283.

Steward, F. H., "The Petrology of the Evaporites of the Eksdale No. 2-boring, East Yorkshire. Part I.: the Lower Evaporite Bed." Min. Mag., **28** (1949), 621–675.

Teodorovich, G. I., *Authigenic Minerals in Sedimentary Rocks*. New York: Consultants Bureau Enterprises, Inc., 1961. (The Russian text was published by the USSR Academy of Sciences Press, Moscow, 1958).

Oxides and Hydroxides

1. ALUMINUM HYDROXIDES

(a) *Classification, Structure, and Chemistry*. At least four aluminum hydroxides are known to occur as authigenic minerals in sediments; these are (1) bayerite, (2) gibbsite, (3) boehmite, and (4) diaspore. The fact that very slight heating or aging transforms bayerite into gibbsite may account for its rare occurrence in nature

(Frederickson, 1952). The bulk of the sedimentary aluminum hydroxides consists therefore of the three species gibbsite, boehmite, and diaspore.

In Table 8 a few data on the chemical composition and structure of the various aluminum hydroxides are presented. The basic structure of gibbsite may be described as consisting of a layer of aluminum ions embedded between two sheets of closely packed hydroxyl ions; two out of three octahedrally coordinated sites between the oxygen layers are occupied by aluminum. Boehmite is structurally composed of double sheets of oxygen octahedra with aluminum ions at their centers. Only half of the oxygen atoms are hydrogen-bonded to oxygens in the opposite sheet. The other oxygen ions, located in the middle of the sheets, are shared by four octahedra. In contrast, all the oxygen in diaspore is hydrogen-bonded to one other oxygen; and

Table 8 CLASSIFICATION OF PRINCIPAL OXIDES AND HYDROXIDES IN SEDIMENTS.

CLASS	GROUP	SPECIES	CRYSTALLOCHEMICAL FORMULA	SPACE GROUP	STRUCTURE (SCHEMATIC)
OXIDES	R_3O_4	Magnetite	Fe_3O_4	$Fd3m$	
		Hausmannite	$Mn\,Mn_2O_4$	$I4_1/amd$	
	R_2O_3	Hematite	$\alpha-Fe_2O_3$	$R\bar{3}c$	
		Maghemite	$\gamma-Fe_2O_3$	$P2_13$	
		Perovskite	$Ca\,Ti\,O_3$	Monoclinic	
	RO_2	α-Quartz	SiO_2	$P3_121$ or $P3_221$	
		Opal-Varieties	$SiO_2 \cdot nH_2O$	Amorphous	
		Rutile	TiO_2	$P4_2/mnm$	
		Anatase		$I4_1/amd$	
		Brookite		$Pcab$	
		Pyrolusite	$\beta-MnO_2$	$P4_2/mnm$	
		Cryptomelane	$K_{\leq2}Mn_8O_{16}$	$I4/m$ or $I/2m$	
		Psilomelane	$(Ba,H_2O)Mn_5O_{10}$	$A2/m$	
HYDROXIDES	$R(OH)_3$	Bayerite	$\alpha-Al(OH)_3$	Hexagonal	
		Gibbsite (Hydrargillite)	$\gamma-Al(OH)_3$	$P2_1/n$	
	$RO\cdot OH$	Diaspore	$\alpha-AlO\cdot OH$	$Pbnm$	
		Goethite	$\alpha-FeO\cdot OH$		
		Boehmite	$\gamma-AlO\cdot OH$	$Amam$	
		Lepidocrocite	$\gamma-FeO\cdot OH$		

the way in which the aluminum ions are positioned between the layers results in strips of octahedra. Diagrams of the structure of both boehmite and diaspore can be seen in Ewing (1935ab) and Deer et al. (1962).

The phase relationship in the system Al_2O_3-H_2O has been determined by Kennedy (1959). Prior to his investigation it had been assumed that the dimorphs boehmite and diaspore were formed at elevated pressures and temperatures. This theory could not account for the fact that all three of the aluminum hydrates can coexist in sediments in a textural relation.

According to Kennedy (1959), the phase boundaries outlined in Figure 14 are not to be considered as equilibrium but rather as rate boundaries because boehmite is metastable at all temperatures and pressures encountered in natural environments. Thermodynamic measurements indicate that the stability field of boehmite must lie at higher temperatures and lower pressures than that of diaspore. But inasmuch as corundum is the stable phase under these predicted higher temperature and lower pressure conditions, it appears that there is no stability field for boehmite.

Thermodynamic and experimental data suggest that diaspore is the stable phase in equilibrium with gibbsite. Slow rates of conversion from one phase to another exist and do account for the persistence of metastable phases over long periods of time (Allen 1952, Kennedy 1959).

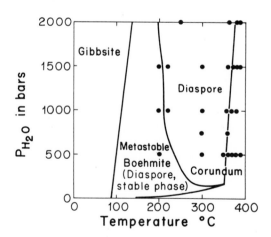

Fig. 14 Phase relationships in the system Al_2O_3—H_2O (after Kennedy, 1959)

(b) *Geochemistry of Bauxites.* Rocks which contain aluminum hydroxides as their major constituents are generally called bauxites. Coexisting minerals are frequently kaolinite, various iron and titanium oxides and hydroxides, and quartz. If the oxyhydrates of iron are more abundant than the associated aluminum hydroxides the sediments are no longer referred to as bauxites, but as laterites. Bauxite is economically of great importance since it is the major aluminum ore.

Since the disagreement between lab experiments and petrographical studies has been satisfactorily solved by Kennedy (1959), the main geochemical problem in the field of aluminum hydroxides now concerns the sequence of their formation. Are the various bauxite minerals to be regarded as (1) regular precipitates, (2) direct alteration products, or (3) end-members formed by desilication of clay minerals? For all three alternatives there are a number of convincing facts, and in all probability, all of these processes are operative in nature. It is interesting to note that the direct alteration of parent material, i.e., without passing through an intermediate kaolinite or halloysite stage, generally produces gibbsite. The front of strong leaching is exceedingly sharply defined; silica, calcium, and magnesium are removed rapidly as the front advances. However, in the final stage, even aluminum may migrate and become redeposited in fractures and cavities. Parent minerals with high abrasion pH (10 to 11), such as nepheline or amphiboles, seem to favor direct bauxitisation.

In the majority of the cases reported in the literature, desilication of feldspars and other potential primary minerals appears to be a two-step process: clay minerals such as kaolinite, halloysite, or nontronite are formed first and then the silica is removed from these to form gibbsite, boehmite, and diaspore. That the desilication of clay minerals is probably the usual mechanism to produce bauxites can be attributed to the fact that parent materials certainly respond to weathering and leaching by forming clay minerals before the extreme requirements are met which are necessary for a bauxite formation. From the plentiful literature on bauxites a few representative articles are by the following authors: Allen (1948, 1952), Bardossy (1958), Beneslavsky (1958), Carroll and Starkey (1959), Bushinskij (1958), Butterlin (1958), Gordon et al. (1958), Harder (1949), Frederickson (1952), Sherman (1952), Keller (1956, 1958), Konta (1958), McLaughlin (1955), Owen (1954), Schüller (1957), Bates (1962) and Coleman

(1962). General reviews of the bauxite literature have been presented by Fischer (1955) and Valeton (1962a, 1962b, 1964).

According to Keller (1956, 1958), the aluminum minerals in bauxite may come from any aluminum containing source rock of igneous, metamorphic, or sedimentary origin. Whereas the formation of clay minerals is frequently determined by the type of parent material, the energy factor is more important in the case of the bauxites. A warm-humid or tropical climate with alternative wet and dry seasons has to be maintained over long periods of time. The energy factors involved in such a climate have been presented in the chapter on clay minerals.

Whereas the effect of H^+ ion activity as a rate-controlling step in the system: parent material-bauxite-water is well understood, the effect of the redox potential is less well comprehended. It has been observed that bauxite deposits in which carbonaceous materials and sulfides are present, are composed only of diaspore and boehmite; gibbsite, on the other hand, occurs predominantly in bauxites where, according to geologic field criteria, strong oxidizing conditions were established at the time of formation. Following the suggestion of Valeton (1962), it may be said that in gibbsite/boehmite deposits, the gibbsite is formed at higher Eh than the associated boehmite.

About half of the world's bauxite ores have been mined from deposits associated with limestones and dolomites. It is well established (p. 56 and 99) that saturated bicarbonate solutions are the most common and aggressive solutions involved in the low temperature alteration of silicates. Inasmuch as diaspore tends to form from the metastable boehmite most readily in a limestone environment (Kennedy, 1959), it can be assumed that bicarbonate solutions accelerate the kinetics of the boehmite-diaspore transformation much more than any other type of bauxite-producing solution. The abundance of biogenic CO_2 in tropical calcareous soils is the best guarantee for a continuous supply of saturated bicarbonate solutions.

In order to assist in the geochemical evaluation of bauxites the mineral association in a typical bauxite deposit with depth of formation is illustrated in Figure 15. The information was obtained from a study by Loughnan and Bayliss (1961) on the mineralogy of the bauxite deposits near Weipa, Queensland.

The parent material, a loosely consolidated light colored kaolinitic sandstone, is exposed at a depth of about 35 feet from the present surface. Boehmite and gibbsite appear at about 30 feet of depth in

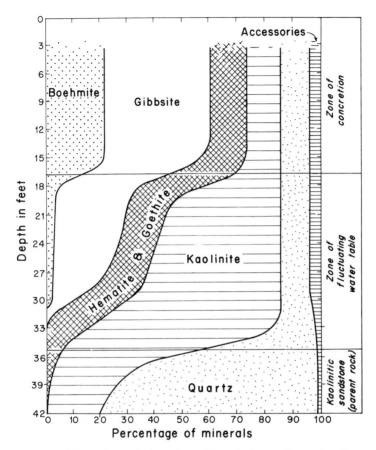

Fig. 15 Mineralogy of a bauxite soil in relation to depth. Locality: Pera Head, Queensland (after Loughnan and Bayliss, 1961)

the zone of a fluctuating water table. Going upward, the mineralogy changes gradually; gibbsite forms at the expense of kaolinite, and quartz decreases sharply in abundance. Etched and pitted surfaces indicative of chemical attack can be noted on some of the quartz grains. In the zone of concretion, gibbsite and the associated iron minerals form spherical pisolites from one to twenty mm in diameter. Also, concretion bands are developed. Boehmite has its maximum yield in the zone of concretion; its development is explained by the partial dehydroxylation of gibbsite. This example demonstrates that even a rock low in aluminum can produce bauxites if the environment is favorable and if there is a long time span.

Another example of bauxite and laterite formation given by Sherman (1952) deals with the genesis and morphology of the aluminum-rich laterite clays of Hawaii. In Figure 8, some of his data are presented. In a recent study on Hawaiian bauxites, Bates (1962) concludes that gibbsite in these deposits may form by (1) desilication of halloysite, (2) dehydration of Al and Al-Fe gels, and (3) precipitation from Al-rich solutions. All three genetic types may occur within the area of a single thin section.

Recently an interesting idea on the formation mechanism of aluminum hydroxides from pre-existing clay minerals has been put forward by Coleman (1962). He assumes that Al-ions move from clay lattice positions to ion-exchange sites under conditions of severe acid weathering. This results in the formation of Al-clays at the expense of the "metastable" hydrogen-saturated clay minerals. Temperature will accelerate the alteration; each 10 degree rise in temperature between $30°$ and $80°C$ will about double the rate of reaction: The Al-ions, either in exchange position or solution, will subsequently hydrolyze and thus make possible the deposition of $Al(OH)_3$, or the sorption of hydroxy-aluminum ions. This reaction yields H^+ ions which may encourage structurally fixed aluminum to move to exchange sites. In other words, this outlined clay mineral alteration may be considered as an "autocatalytic" reaction cycle. When silica is leached from the system the final product will be bauxite.

Acid conditions of the type necessary to initiate bauxitisation exist in source rocks with a high sulfur content. It is also noteworthy that clays overlaid by pyriteferous coal beds, as, for instance, in the Pennsylvania coal mining district, have been altered during weathering of the coals in the direction of high aluminum minerals.

Aluminum hydroxides, like iron and manganese oxides and hydroxides, show enrichment in certain trace elements (Adams and Richardson, 1960; Gordon et al., 1958; Gordon and Murata, 1952; and others). In order to evaluate enrichment processes quantitatively, one has to know the element composition of the present material. Elements which are most strongly enriched relative to their source rock include the following: chromium, gallium, niobium, molybdenum, zirconium, scandium, titanium, vanadium, arsenic, uranium, thorium, beryllium, and perhaps copper. The enrichment factor can be as high as 100-fold (e.g., in the case of chromium), but generally is 3-to 5-fold.

In summary, bauxites may develop on any Al-containing source rock. A warm, tropical and alternating wet and dry climate is essential to reduce the prospective parent material to the final Al-hydroxides. A peneplain-type morphology and flat relief, accompanied by high seasonal ground-water fluctuations, favor the development of extensive bauxite deposits. The presence of lignites or high organic matter stimulates the formation of CO_2, and results in the generation of aggressive bicarbonate solutions. Sulfide deposits have the same effect by producing strong acid conditions during weathering, which stimulate bauxitisation. A high redox potential favors the gibbsite formation, whereas boehmite and diaspore may also be found in coexistence with sulfides and carbonaceous materials. Half of the world's aluminum production depends on bauxite deposits associated with carbonate rocks.

Resilication of aluminum hydroxides, resulting in the formation of clay minerals, is a common process which takes place in diagenetic environments. Kaolinite and halloysite will be the principal end-members of this reaction. The rare occurrence of aluminum hydroxides as detrital constituents in ancient sediments can perhaps be attributed to this phenomenon.

2. SILICA

(a) *Classification.* The only crystalline modification of SiO_2 that can form in low temperature and pressure environments is α-quartz. Both α-quartz and the high temperature β-quartz are the most common individual minerals in sediments. Crystalline modifications of SiO_2 other than α- and β-quartz, i.e., tridymite, cristobalite, or coesite are of interest in high pressure and temperature petrology, or in connection with volcanic explosion or meteoritic impact craters; but they have practically no significance in the area of sedimentology.

Aside from detrital quartz, crystalline silica often appears as authigenic microcrystalline quartz known as chalcedony. Subvarieties of chalcedony include, agate, jasper, and carnelian. Chert, one of the most common siliceous sediments, is principally composed of microcrystalline quartz; small to moderate amounts of amorphous silica, however, may coexist with the quartz. The amorphous and crystalline modifications are mixed in a way which suggests that the latter have been derived from an amorphous silica substrate.

Amorphous silica refers to substances that are relatively pure SiO_2 but of extremely small size, and arranged in a crystallographic disordered state, as evidenced by the lack of a characteristic X-ray diffraction pattern. In the literature a number of different names have been adopted for the various hydrated forms of silica. One of the more commonly used terms is opal. It is of great interest that amorphous silica constitutes the skeletal framework of organisms such as diatoms, radiolaria, and siliceous sponges. Some plants (e.g., grasses) also contain amorphous silica, probably for reasons of structural stabilization. The water content of opal varies within certain limits, but rarely exceeds 12 per cent.

(b) *Dissolution and Precipitation of Silica.* Most of the information used in the forthcoming discussion has been obtained from the following sources: Hitchen (1945), Roy (1945), Kennedy (1950), Eitel (1954), Alexander et al. (1954), Iler (1955), Krauskopf (1956, 1959), Siever (1957, 1959), Okamoto et al. (1957), Bien et al. (1958), Ireland (1959), Dapples (1959), Thomson (1959), and Lewin (1961).

The present consensus is that silica in natural waters can be of two possible forms: (1) molecularly dispersed — that is, as a true solution — and (2) in a polymerized or colloidal state. Silica dissolves in water and forms a true solution (H_4SiO_4) of concentrations up to 120 to 140 ppm at room temperatures. Thus, silica in true solution never polymerizes as long as its concentration is lower than the solubility of amorphous silica. The temperature/solubility relationship of amorphous silica is plotted in Figure 16.

Surface waters, ground waters, and interstitial or formation waters which are the aqueous solutions of interest to the sedimentologist have in general silica values below 100 ppm. The silica in these waters,

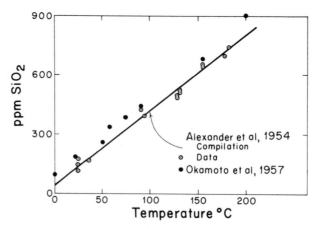

Fig. 16   Solubility of amorphous silica (after Alexander et al. 1954; and Okamoto et al., 1957)

therefore, is in the molecularly dispersed state. Occasionally thermal spring waters are greatly enriched in silica. As they cool off, they may release silica in the amorphous form. The only other way to produce silica values exceeding $\sim$ 120 ppm at room temperature is by evaporation. But because of the low silica content of most surface waters this process will only be of minor importance.

In contrast to amorphous silica, quartz at ordinary temperatures is soluble in near neutral solutions to the extent of about 6-10 ppm. This solubility characteristic in the SiO_2 system is in accordance with the general physical-chemical principle that the metastable form (amorphous silica) is more soluble than the stable form (quartz). A similar relationship exists in the case of the metastable aragonite and its more stable dimorph, calcite; but it may be pointed out that the solubility differences are here less pronounced than between quartz and amorphous silica.

Theoretically, one might expect that quartz crystallizes from any solution supersaturated with regard to its solubility product. This, however, is not the case, as evidenced by the lack of syngenetic quartz precipitates in recent and ancient environments. That quartz fails to form from supersaturated solutions in nature or the laboratory is probably due to kinetic reasons (extreme slowness of reaction). Temperatures in the neighborhood of at least $150°C$ are necessary to produce quartz experimentally within reasonable time. Consequently, in surface and diagenetic environments, silica can be carried in solution at concentrations far in excess of the solubility of the crystalline SiO_2 varieties.

Silica is known to dissolve readily in alkaline solutions. It was therefore assumed until recently that the solubility of SiO_2 is a function of pH. Figure 17 shows the solubility characteristics of SiO_2 in the pH range from 0 to 11. In some approximation the pH between 0 and 9 has no effect on the solubility, but the solubility increases sharply as the pH rises above 9 because of the ionization of H_4SiO_4. Thus, in alkaline solutions up to a pH of about 9 silica is no more soluble than in strong acids.

Strong alkaline environments, where the pH rises above 9, are rarely found in nature. The pH of the sea water usually stays in the range of 8.0 to 8.5; fresh waters are generally slightly acidic (pH 5.0 to 7.0), and pH values greater than 8.5 in formation and interstitial waters are exceptional. But, as pointed out by Stevens and Carron (1948) and Keller et al. (1963), in the case of some feldspars, amphi-

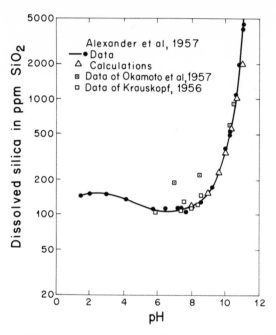

Fig. 17   Effect of *p*H on the solubility of monomeric silica (after Krauskopf 1956; Alexander et al., 1954; and Okamoto et al., 1957)

boles, and clay minerals, the *p*H at the solid-liquid interface of minerals, resulting from hydrolysis, may be as high as 9 to 11. Other factors aside from *p*H that may affect the solubility of silica in natural systems have been discussed by Siever (1957), Krauskopf (1957, 1959), DeVore (1959), Waddams (1957), and Keller et al. (1963). Geometry and type of ionic bonding on and near the surface of crystals, the size of the individual mineral, the chemical character of the participating solution, and, of course, pressure and temperature relationships, are a few of the dominant parameters controlling the solubility of silica.

In view of the reluctance of crystalline silica to precipitate in surface environments the undersaturation of natural waters with respect to amorphous silica is surprising. Most sea waters are even undersaturated with respect to quartz (~4 ppm). This immediately raises the question as to the mechanism that keeps the silica level so low. It has been pointed out that the process of dissolution of quartz and silicates is a very slow one. Thus, only small concentrations of silica are released at any one time to weathering solutions. Some of the monomeric silica in fresh and ocean waters can subsequently become deposited inorganically by coprecipitation and adsorption in the presence of particulate matter and high electrolyte concentration (Bien et al., 1958). In addition, silica secreting organisms can extract amorphous silica from solutions that are undersaturated even with respect to crystalline silica. The capacity of diatoms and other organisms for removing silica from natural waters has been impressively demonstrated by numerous experiments (Lewin, 1961; and others). Whether inorganic precipitation or biological uptake is the more dominant process responsible for keeping a sort of "pseudo-equilibrium" (Krauskopf, 1959) between dissolution and deposition of silica in surface environments is not known for sure. It appears, however, that biochemical extraction is the more significant process in holding the silica level of the ocean at about 4 ppm.

It has been stated before that for kinetic reasons quartz does not precipitate in surface environments. However quartz deposition, indicated by overgrowths on detrital grains or occurrence of interstitial cement, can be observed in many ancient rocks (Dapples, 1959; Siever, 1959; Pittman, 1959; Goldstein, 1959; and Bissel, 1959). Apparently, diagenetic environments are more favorable towards quartz deposition than syngenetic environments. After burial, the connate waters containing silica in solution will gradually equilibrate with quartz, and the excess of silica may crystallize as small quartz euhedra, microcrystalline aggregates, or overgrowths on detrital quartz. Interstitial solutions often contain silica in amounts between 10 and 50 ppm (Emery and Rittenberg, 1952).

In this connection, the carbonate-silica relationship in sediments may throw some light on the phenomenon of quartz deposition in diagenetic environments. It is generally established that a more or less reciprocal relationship exists between the solubilities of calcite and quartz in near-surface diagenetic environments (Siever, 1959). An increase in temperature will steadily increase the solubility of silica; if the partial pressure of CO_2 remains constant, the calcite solubility decreases with a rise in temperature, at least in the temperature range up to about $120°C$ (Miller, 1952). On the other hand, an increase in pH decreases the solubility of calcite; in contrast, silica solubility is not affected in the pH range of 0 to 9 (Figure 17), and increases sharply beyond this value. With an increase in overburden pressure, calcite and quartz solubilities are increased at about the same rate.

The following generalized picture is offered to account for the metasomatic replacement of quartz by carbonates or vice versa: at shallow depth of burial quartz will first equilibrate with the silica in interstitial solutions, causing either deposition of authigenic quartz or dissolution of detrital quartz, depending on the initial saturation stage. Assuming that the rock formation in which the interstitial water is now just about saturated with respect to both calcite and quartz gets more and more deeply buried, the rise in temperature (geothermal gradient) will bring more silica into solution; but it will also result in an instantaneous deposition of calcite if the partial pressure of CO_2 is not affected. A decrease in temperature due to uplift or transport of deeply buried waters to the earth surface will have the opposite effect. Carbonate may become dissolved and quartz deposited instead. Depending on the geological history of the rock strata, many generations of quartz and carbonates can be developed within the same sediment. It is at present not fully understood in what way the dissolved carbonates may affect the kinetics of quartz deposition and solution. The wide abundance and close association of carbonates and authigenic quartz in natural deposits suggests, however, that this relationship is not just fortuitous.

(c) *Origin of Chert.* The previous discussion on the carbonate-quartz relationship has obvious applications to the problem of chert genesis. There are several hypotheses about the origin of cherts. The most likely one assumes that amorphous silica which is extracted from the water system by silica secreting organisms eventually becomes deposited upon the death of the organisms. Although sea waters are undersaturated with regard to amorphous silica, dissolution of amorphous silica structures in diatoms, radiolarians, sponges, and silicoflagellates during the lifetime of the organisms have nowhere been observed. This characteristic has been attributed to the coating action of organic complexes, or, alternatively, to the deposition of polyvalent cations resulting in protective silicate shields (Cooper, 1952; Iler, 1955; Lewin, 1961).

Upon the death of the organisms the amorphous silica seems to be no longer protected, and may already start to dissolve when the silica skeletons sink down to the ocean floor. The rates of dissolution of amorphous silica are controlled by a number of parameters, all of which have been thoroughly discussed by Lewin (1961). Of critical importance appears to be the removal of the protective shield formed by certain metal ions and the size of the specific surface area exposed to the equilibrating fluids.

With respect to the chert problem, the bulk of the silica in cherts is supposed to have come from former amorphous silica skeletons. According to Bramlette (1946), diagenetically mobilized amorphous silica will migrate in true ionic solution in the direction of a concentration gradient to reprecipitate as quartz and accumulate at points of least solubility. This reorganization may occur shortly after deposition; but epigenetic chert formation is also known. It is also possible that deposits of amorphous silica, originally supplied from volcanic sources or thermal springs, will furnish the essential silica for the chert formation. These contributions, however, are only of local importance. Silica secreting organisms represent the major source for cherts found in ancient sediments, at least in rocks as old as the Cambrian.

The absence of large populations of silica secreting organisms during Pre-Cambrian time, which could have extracted silica from the water and maintained low concentrations of silica in the oceans, suggests that the silica content of the ancient sea was probably much higher than that of the modern ocean. Consequently, inorganic precipitations of amorphous silica might have been possible. Particularly in areas of upwelling waters, the conditions for the deposition of amorphous silica must have been favorable. Subsequent reorganization of the amorphous precipitate during diagenesis may have resulted in the formation of chert beds, and may account for their wide occurrence in shallow marine deposits of the Pre-Cambrian.

Cherts and other siliceous sediments are poor in trace elements. The reason for this deficiency is the small ionic radius of silicon which allows only a small number of elements to substitute for silicon. Boron, beryllium, and germanium may eventually enter the structure.

(d) *Stable Isotopes.* Silicon has three stable isotopes, Si^{28}, Si^{29}, and Si^{30}, in a ratio of about 92 to 5 to 3. The variations in the isotopic composition of silicon have been studied by Allenby (1954) and Reynolds and Verhoogen (1953). According to the latter, the observed variations in the Si^{30}/Si^{28} ratio are considerably smaller (~ 3 per mil) than those of carbon (~ 80 per mil), although the mass ratios of C^{13}/C^{12} and Si^{30}/Si^{28} are not significantly different from one another. A number of cherts and diatomites are enriched in Si^{30} over silicate minerals of igneous and metamorphic origin. Other cherts, however, do not differ from some of the high-temperature crystalline materials. In the light of the study by Hirt and Epstein (1964) on calcium isotope ratios, some of the unexplained differences and the small variations in the Si^{30}/Si^{28} ratios between low and high temperature rocks, may find their explanation.

More information is available on the oxygen isotope ratios in cherts and diatomites. In general, one can say that factors which will influence the O^{18}/O^{16} ratio in carbonates will similarly affect the O^{18}/O^{16} ratio in cherts and diatomites. Silica formed under marine conditions is highly enriched in O^{18} relative to igneous rocks; silica deposited under fresh water conditions may also be significantly enriched in O^{16} relative to silica of marine origin. Analogous to marine carbonates, time and diagenesis generally change the O^{18}/O^{16} of marine cherts to make the O^{18}/O^{16} ratio approach the ratio of fresh water cherts. This is a result of equilibration with meteoric waters present in the rock formation at somewhat elevated temperatures. It seems likely, therefore, that the original O^{18}/O^{16} ratios of marine cherts were controlled by marine environments. The analytical data are given in Figure 18. The application of oxygen isotope studies to the formation mechanism of chert deposition, paleotemperature evaluations, and diagenesis has been presented by Degens and Epstein (1962).

3. Iron and Manganese Oxides and Hydroxides

The close chemical similarity between iron and manganese is reflected geologically in their common association in rocks of all kinds. The association is especially marked in igneous rocks, where the ratio Mn/Fe rarely exceeds the limits of 1/10 and 1/100, except in rare pegmatites. It is for this reason that the oxides and hydroxides of both elements will be discussed together.

(a) *Classification, Structure, and Chemistry.* The iron oxides and hydroxides have been recently investigated by Bernal et al. (1959) in a study on the nature of their transformations. Their paper summarizes the data on the crystal structures of iron oxides and hydroxides. Other general sources of information on the iron and manganese minerals include Deer et al. (1962) and Strunz (1957).

Iron oxides and hydroxides have one structural feature in common, i.e., they are composed of different stackings of closely packed oxygen or hydroxyl sheets with various arrangements of the iron ions

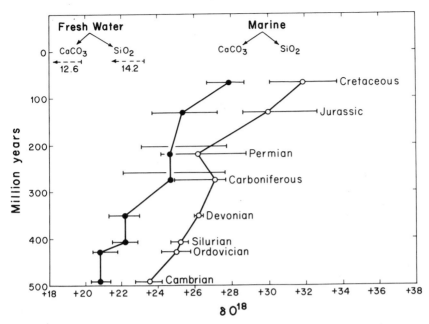

Fig. 18   Variation in O^{18}/O^{16} ratio of carbonates and cherts with geologic age (after Degens and Epstein, 1962)

in the tetrahedral or octahedral interstices. Magnetite ($Fe^{+2}Fe_2^{+3}O_4$) is the only member of the spinel group that has been identified in sediments as authigenic mineral. All other spinels are so far only known as detrital constituents. The unit cell of the spinel structure is composed of 16 six-fold and 8 four-fold coordinated cations besides the 32 oxygen ions (Table 8).

Hematite (α-Fe_2O_3) is one of the more common iron minerals in sediments. The oxygens are arranged in a slightly distorted hexagonal packing, and all the irons are six-fold coordinated.

According to Strunz (1957) at least four MnO_2 modifications occur in nature. The bulk of the manganese oxides, however, is composed of only two, namely pyrolusite and cryptomelane. The two other manganese oxides, i.e., psilomelane and δ-MnO_2 are less common. Pyrolusite (β-MnO_2) is isostructural with rutile. Each oxygen ion is surrounded by three manganese ions lying in a plane at the corners of an approximately equilateral triangle (see Table 8), whereas six oxygen ions surround each manganese ion at the corners of a slightly distorted regular octahedron. Cryptomelane is a dimorph of which one species is tetragonal and the other monoclinic. Cryptomelane, normally potassium bearing, can alternatively incorporate divalent and trivalent cations with resultant changes in structure and cell dimensions. Ions of a wide range of ionic size can be accommodated, from Ni^{+2} to Ba^{+2} and from Cr^{+3} to La^{+3} (Sreenivas, personal communication; Keith and Degens, 1959). Manganite (γ-MnO · OH) is a principal constituent of ocean-floor manganese nodules.

Goethite (α-FeO · OH) is structurally similar to diaspore, and lepidocrocite (γ-FeO · OH) is isostructural with boehmite. More comprehensive accounts of the structure of the iron hydroxides can be found in Glemser (1959), Hoppe (1940), and Bernal et al. (1959).

The term limonite is frequently used in the geologic literature for accumulations of hydrated oxides of iron. Actually, limonite is not a definite mineral but generally represents a mixture of cryptocrystalline goethite, lepidocrocite, adsorbed water, and traces of hematite.

(b) *Eh-pH Relationships.* The mobilization of iron and manganese from rocks proceeds during weathering. It has been stated before that most crystalline rocks have Mn/Fe ratios of about 1 to 25 or 1 to 50. The size of the ions of Mn^{+2} and Fe^{+2} is about the same; they occupy similar positions in the structure of Fe and Mn compounds containing silicates. Therefore, there is little reason to expect that manganese is preferentially leached away, while iron stays behind. Similar solution characteristics are expected to hold for both elements and this has recently been confirmed experimentally in leaching studies on Hawaiian andesites in the temperature range from 25° to 300° C (Krauskopf, 1957).

The existence of sedimentary manganese deposits and of sediments with extremely high or low Mn/Fe ratios, however, suggests that processes are operating that allow a fractionation of these two elements in the exogenic cycle. It is well known that iron and manganese ions respond differently to changes in pH and redox potential. The relationship may be quantitatively summarized by means of diagrams showing stability fields of possible compounds at room temperature and at different values of pH and Eh. Since Krumbein and Garrels (1952) first plotted the stability fields of chemical end-members in the form of convenient pH-Eh diagrams a number of investigators have adopted these graphs, not only to present the equilibrium stability relations in common mineral systems (Garrels, 1960), but also to outline the Eh/pH conditions that can be generated in the natural environment by the action of certain bacteria (Baas Becking et al., 1960).

Eh-pH diagrams have been constructed for the various oxides, hydroxides, carbonates, and sulfides of manganese and iron which describe the stability fields of the individual mineral end-members (Garrels, 1960; Krauskopf, 1957; Krumbein and Garrels, 1952; Marchandise, 1956). A representative Eh-pH diagram showing the stability relations of iron oxides, sulfides, carbonates, and silicates at 25° C and 1 atmosphere total pressure in the presence of water, is presented in Figure 19. The diagram was selected because it has great significance for studies of sedimentary iron ores. Many more graphs have been constructed for a great variety of mineral systems (Garrels, 1960). The Eh-pH graphs of Krauskopf (1957) on the iron and manganese equi-

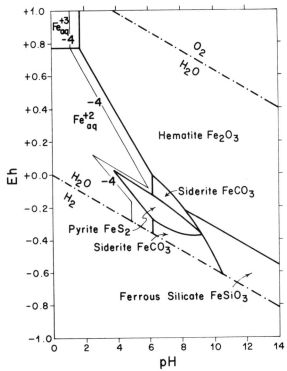

Fig. 19 Eh-pH stability relations among iron oxides, carbonates, sulfides and silicates at 25° C, and 1 atmosphere total pressure in the presence of water. Other conditions: Total $CO_2 = 10°$; total sulfur $= 10^{-6}$ m; amorphous silica is present. At slight undersaturation with respect to amorphous silica, magnetite enters the ferrous silicate stability field (after Garrels, 1960)

librium stability relations differ from those of Garrels (1960) insofar as in the former equations relating mineral pairs are plotted.

Calculations and experiments by Krauskopf (1957), Huber (1958, 1959), Garrels (1960), and Marchandise (1956) indicate that at any given pH iron oxides and hydroxides precipitate at lower oxidation potentials than manganese oxides. Similarly, under fixed Eh, iron starts precipitating as an oxide at a considerably lower pH than manganese. In case environmental conditions are such that carbonates can be deposited, both elements will precipitate together because the solubility rates of manganese and iron carbonates are not very different. Thus, one may conclude that both elements would be separated in most exogenic environments by virtue of the lower solubilities of the iron oxygen compounds, unless they are deposited as carbonates in the area of the carbonate stability field.

Concerning the stability relations in the iron mineral stability diagram, Huber (1958) contours the stability fields for hematite, magnetite, siderite, pyrite, and pyrrhotite in a normal sea water system. He states that, with the exception of the magnetite-siderite relationship, Eh is much more critical than pH in determining the final end-member that is to be formed. In general terms, hematite is the stable phase under oxidizing conditions, while siderite and magnetite will form under intermediate to moderately reducing conditions; it should be noted that under alkaline conditions magnetite will form in preference to siderite. Moderate to strong reducing conditions will favor the deposition of pyrite, while pyrrhotite requires still stronger reducing conditions. Little is known concerning the stability field for maghemite (γ-Fe_2O_3). It is conceivable that maghemite arises via oxidation of a poorly crystallized magnetite, whereas hematite may form by oxidation of a number of different precursor materials.

The boundaries of the stability fields in the manganese mineral stability diagram and their pH-Eh relations to the corresponding iron oxygen compounds can be seen in Krauskopf's graphs (1957) where both the anhydrous and hydrous mineral phases of iron and manganese are considered.

(c) *Geochemistry of Iron and Manganese Minerals.* The geochemistry and petrology of iron and manganese oxides and hydroxides have been studied rather thoroughly over the last 50 years. The special geological attention given to these two elements can partly be attributed to their economic importance as major iron and manganese ores. But aside from this, iron and manganese oxides and hydroxides have great scientific significance in the area of sedimentology, because the different minerals of the iron and manganese family were deposited in sediments according to specific environmental conditions. Thus, their presence may be used as an environmental criterion. Although various parameters such as salinity, temperature, microbial activity, pressure, and so on, determine the development of the prospective end-members, the Eh-pH relationship is the most decisive factor in low temperature and pressure environments at or near the surface of the earth. This concerns not only the oxides and hydroxides but, as was shown before, also the iron and manganese carbonates and sulfides.

Pertinent information and additional literature on this subject may be obtained by reference to Castaño and Garrels (1950), Krumbein and Garrels (1952), Huber and Garrels (1953), Sakamoto (1950), James (1954), White (1954), Huber (1958, 1959), Krauskopf (1955, 1957), Goldberg (1954, 1961), Ronov (1959), Turekian and Wedepohl (1961), Dietz (1955), Mero (1962), Garrels (1960), Hewett and Fleischer (1960), Menard and Shipek (1958), Kelley (1951), and Lepp (1963).

Although iron minerals are ubiquitous in sediments of all geologic environments and periods, the most impressive relationship among the various end-members is found in sediments of Pre-Cambrian age. Syngenetic iron oxides, carbonates, silicates, and sulfides of the same geologic formation are in some areas not only highly concentrated, but also spatially separated to such a degree that one may speak of an oxide, carbonate, silicate, or sulfide facies, respectively. The environmental characteristics and the observed facies relationships in so-called "iron-formations" are well correlated. Among the numerous regions throughout the world where Pre-Cambrian iron formations are known, those of the Lake Superior districts, e.g., the Gunflint, Mesabi, and Gogebic Range, have been studied most thoroughly from a geological and geochemical points of view (James, 1954; White, 1954; Huber, 1959; and others). Some of the highlights of these investigations are herewith presented.

Different opinions have been expressed with regard to the environment that existed at the time the iron formations were deposited. It is now generally accepted that an epicontinental shelf sea (marine environment) represented the environment of deposition, and that most of the iron minerals now present in the rock strata are syngenetic, or at most early diagenetic and not of a high-temperature origin. For a summary and different opinions concerning the origin of the iron formation one may consult James (1954), White (1954), Goodwin

(1956), Hough (1958) and Huber (1958, 1959). Figure 10 gives a plot of the generalized relations between the environments of deposition that existed during the first regression of the Animikie sea (White, 1954). A somewhat different picture is obtained if one compares the simultaneous deposits of a transgressing marine environment. With increasing distance from the shore line, the following sediment sequence is developed (1) clean sand, (2) silt and clay (occasionally), (3) lean chert with algal structures, (4) hematitic sediments, (5) chert-siderite rocks (minor abundance), (6) chert-magnetite, and finally furthest away from the shore, (7) iron silicates. Three of the more common iron silicates are greenalite, stilpnomelane, and minnesotaite, which are structurally related to antigorite (serpentine), vermiculite, and talc, respectively.

The solubility relations of the Eh-pH diagram (Fig. 19) supplement the geologic field observations. In an alkaline environment where the supply of oxygen is limited, hydrous Fe_3O_4 rather than hydrous Fe_2O_3 will be obtained by oxidation of ferrous hydroxide (Huber, 1958). The similar positions of the iron silicates and magnetite in the Eh-pH diagram (Garrels, 1960) may mean that aqueous solutions, somewhat undersaturated with respect to the solubility of amorphous silica, will deposit magnetite rather than ferrous silicates. But there may also be a rate factor involved as evidenced by the coexistence of chert and magnetite in deposits closer to the shore line (Fig. 20). Analogous to the dolomite-calcite relationship (p. 121), it is conceivable that despite favorable Eh-pH conditions magnetite in chert was not precipitated in a syngenetic environment but formed from a thermodynamical unstable phase, e.g., hydrous Fe_2O_3, during the early stages of diagenesis; or alternatively, the environment may have changed slightly after deposition, producing the required conditions for magnetite to form. A slight decrease in pH may have permitted siderite to form instead of magnetite, and in case H_2S became abundant pyrite developed. The abundance of pyrite in concentrations up to 40 per cent and that of organic carbon (usually between 5 and 15 per cent) in some of the black shales suggests that ultra-stagnant conditions did prevail at the time of their formation (James, 1954). The well oxygenated inshore environments favored the chemical deposition of hematite (White, 1954).

One must realize that nature is generally more complex than the relatively "pure" mineral systems for which Eh-pH diagrams have been constructed. Therefore, Eh-pH diagrams alone are not sufficient

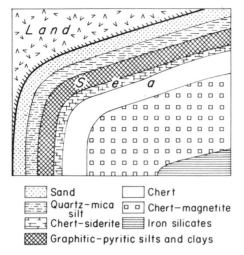

Sand
Quartz-mica silt
Chert-siderite
Graphitic-pyritic silts and clays
Chert
Chert-magnetite
Iron silicates

Fig. 20 Generalized relations between contemporaneous environments of deposition existing during the first regression of the Animikie sea (after White, 1954)

for geological interpretations; they should be used only as a supplement to geological field observations.

The term "iron formation" is restricted to Pre-Cambrian iron deposits, while iron-rich sediments of a more recent age are commonly referred to as ironstones. Sporadically, throughout the last 600 million years, ironstones developed here and there. A series of papers on this topic has been presented during special symposia held at the 19th International Geological Congress, Algiers (1952), and the 6th Sedimentological Congress, Amsterdam/Antwerp (1963). During these meetings the fact became clear that no geologic period produced so many complex contemporaneous iron mineral associations as the Pre-Cambrian. A major difference between Pre-Cambrian and later iron deposits is that in the Pre-Cambrian the iron minerals and silica were intimately mixed together. In younger deposits geochemical processes have effectively separated these two elements, and the resulting ironstones are frequently in coexistence with carbonates. Lepp (1963) suggests that an environment with a little free oxygen may favor the deposition of silica along with iron. Although during Pre-Cambrian time the free oxygen level in the atmosphere and hydrosphere was probably significantly smaller than it is today, the presence of cogenetic silica and iron oxides need not necessarily be connected with the free oxygen deficiency in the Pre-Cambrian atmosphere and ocean. The absence of silica-secreting organisms in the ancient sea may have allowed the concentration of silica to build up in excess of the solubility of amorphous silica so that inorganic silica precipitated. It should be emphasized that one does not have to postulate volcanic activity to account for the high silica content in the Pre-Cambrian sea; weathering processes continuing over long periods of time may have produced the silica quantities essential for amorphous silica to be precipitated.

Another significant difference between the Pre-Cambrian iron formations and their geologically younger counterparts is that magnetite is virtually absent from the later deposits; hematite, goethite, and lepidocrocite are virtually the only iron oxides and hydroxides that occur. As far as ferrous silicates are concerned some deposits are known from the Paleozoic in Germany and a few other sediments of younger age, but compared with the Pre-Cambrian their total concentration in deposits of the last 600 million years is small.

Iron minerals such as magnetite, goethite, and possibly maghemite, may also be formed by a biologic agent in sea water (Lowenstam, 1962a, 1962b; Towe et al., 1963; Towe and Lowenstam, personal communication). In Figure 54 electronmicrographs are presented which show various steps involved in the mineralization of lateral radular teeth of *Cryptochiton stelleri*. The fact that certain organic tissues cause the deposition of a number of iron minerals raises the question whether iron mineralization was not a more common feature among marine invertebrates during the Pre-Cambrian than later on.

Factors causing the separation of manganese and iron in the exogenic cycle have been discussed previously. One of the most famous manganese deposits of sedimentary origin is that of Tschiatura Kutais, in South Russia (Macco, 1898). The Eocene marine deposit, often oolithic in nature, is characterized by its high purity manganese oxides. It is not yet fully understood how such enormous concentrations of manganese ore could have accumulated.

Another puzzling form of manganese oxides is that of the ocean-floor manganese nodules. It is estimated that a total of 10^{12} metric tons of manganese nodules lie at the surface of the Pacific Ocean sediments (Mero, 1962). Mineralogically speaking, they contain a complex array of authigenic minerals aside from the manganese and iron oxides and hydroxides that represent the bulk of the material. The appearance of manganite (γ-MnO $\cdot$ OH) and δ-MnO$_2$ is noteworthy, particularly in connection with the origin of the nodules (Buser and Grütter, 1956).

Many hypotheses both organic and inorganic have been presented concerning the probable formation mechanism of the manganese nodules; and these have been reviewed by Dietz (1955), Goldberg (1961), Mero (1962), and Buser and Grütter (1956). According to Goldberg (1961), the most likely origin of the nodules involves the catalytic oxidation of manganese in the sea water on iron-oxide surfaces, leading directly to the formation of ferromanganese minerals, most of which are in a structurally disordered state. When iron is available in amounts greater than can be accommodated conveniently in the disordered layers, the mineral goethite will appear. Within a local area the chemical composition of manganese nodules is quite uniform, while the chemical composition of nodules from different places may vary widely.

Inasmuch as the rate of formation (accretion) is a relatively slow process, i. e., ~ 0.001 mm per thousand years, as was ascertained by the ionium-thorium method (Goldberg and Picciotto, 1955), it becomes evident that manganese nodules can only form at spots where the rate of sedimentation is small and where iron-oxide surfaces are available as nucleation sites for the manganese dissolved in the sea. Because the ferromanganese minerals possess rather high specific surface areas (Buser and Grütter, 1956), the organic matter dissolved in the sea may also become adsorbed. Thomas and Blumer (1964) reported the presence of biogenic hydrocarbons in manganese nodules, i.e., pyrene and fluoranthene. The relationship between trace elements and manganese and iron oxide and hydroxides in terms of exchange or adsorption capacities has been investigated by Goldberg (1954, 1961), Landergren (1948), Krauskopf (1955, 1957), Mero (1962), Chow and Patterson (1959), and Keith and Degens (1959). Pictures of manganese nodules on the floor of the Atlantic and Pacific can be seen in Mero (1962) and Shipek (1960).

(d) *Oxygen Isotope Data.* Concerning the O^{18}/O^{16} ratio magnetite has been observed to have the lowest O^{18} content of all minerals with which it coexists. Quartz, on the other hand, is the highest in O^{18}, and the resultant large fractionations between the two mineral species makes them suitable as a sensitive mineral pair for isotopic thermometry (James and Clayton, 1962; O'Neill, 1963; O'Neill and Clayton, 1964). Assuming both are formed under isotopic equilibrium conditions, the isotopic composition of the associated water phase at the time of mineral formation can also be calculated.

In applying the experimentally determined quartz-magnetite thermometer to coexisting quartz-magnetite pairs of the iron formation, temperatures in the neighborhood of 150° to 500° C are obtained (James and Clayton, 1962; O'Neill, 1963). Consequently, the crystals have to be regarded as metamorphic minerals. But in view of the cryptocrystalline character of the quartz material and the small size of the magnetite crystals (White, 1954), one may speculate that isotope exchange with the light meteoric water and stimulated by the geothermal gradient has caused some of the observed enrichment in O^{16} in the two sedimentary mineral phases. It has been demonstrated (Fig. 18) that coexisting sedimentary carbonates and cryptocrystalline quartz become progressively lighter with increasing geologic age and at about the same rate due to equilibration with the meteoric waters. Inasmuch as considerably more time was available in the case of the iron formation, there is no reason to assume that the original minerals (at least the cryptocrystalline quartz) have not exchanged parts of their isotopes against those of the surrounding fluids. It is interesting to note that the Pre-Cambrian magnetites have on an average a δO^{18} of about $+2$ to $+3$, a value which would be expected if magnetite had formed in isotopic equilibrium with mean ocean water at temperatures between 20° and 30° C. The quartz might have equilibrated with interstitial meteoric waters ($\delta O^{18} \sim -7$) at temperatures between 60° and 80° C to yield the observed δO^{18} values of about $+15$. Perhaps future isotope work, combined with geologic field data, may show more conclusive results.

4. TITANIUM OXIDES

Titanium may be incorporated in sediments in minerals such as ilmenite, rutile, anatase, brookite, sphene, biotite, amphiboles, and pyroxenes. Leucoxene, a secondary titanium mineral, is quite common and probably derived from sphene consisting now of partly "hydrated" TiO_2 minerals. The actual composition is still unknown. All of the listed minerals occur as heavy minerals in sediments, and as such they are quantitatively only of minor importance, unless concentrated in placer deposits.

The bulk of the titanium in sediments is incorporated in the clay fraction. Its presence there is explained by the interaction of clay minerals with amorphous or finely dispersed crystalline titanium oxide or titanium dioxide hydrate released during weathering. However, it has to be emphasized that titanium is not just adsorbed to the clay particles but occurs in the form of finely disseminated crypto-crystalline TiO_2 needles of one of the polymorphs of TiO_2 (rutile, anatase, and brookite). Rutile is reported from many shale deposits, anatase from carboniferous fire-clays in Great Britain, Triassic sandstones in Germany and laterites in Hawaii, and brookite has been found in bauxites of Arkansas. There is no reliable information as to the environmental conditions of low temperature and pressure formation of a particular polymorph of TiO_2. The low temperature phase relationship and the stability fields in the TiO_2-H_2O system have also not been determined so far. Data on the applications of titanium oxides to various problems of geochemistry are limited. (Arrhenius, 1959; Correns, 1954).

Selected References

1. Aluminium Oxides and Hydroxides

Adams, J. A. S. and K. A. Richardson, "Thorium, Uranium and Zirconium Concentrations in Bauxite." Econ. Geol., **55** (1960), 1653–1675.

Allen, V. T., "Formation of Bauxite from Basaltic Rocks of Oregon." Econ. Geol., **43** (1948), 619–626.

Allen, V. T., "Petrographic Relations in Some Typical Bauxite and Diaspore Deposits." Bull. Geol. Soc. Amer., **63** (1952), 649–688.

Bardossy, G., "The Geochemistry of Hungarian Bauxites. Part I and II." Acta Geol. Acad. Sci. Hung., **5** (1958), 103–155, 255–285.

Bates, T. F., "Halloysite and Gibbsite Formation in Hawaii." Clays and Clay Minerals, **9**th Conf. (1962), 315–328.

Beneslavsky, S. J., "Mineralogie des bauxites sédimentairé." In *Les Bauxites, leur mineralogie et leur genese*, Symp. Moscow, 1958, 1–50.

Bushinskij, G. J., "Types genetiques des bauxites." In *Les Bauxites, leur mineralogie et leur genese*, Symp. Moscow, 1958, 176–263.

Butterlin, J., "A propos de l'origine des bauxites des regions tropicales calcaires." Compt. Rend. Soc. Geol. France, **8** (1958), 121–123.

Carroll, D. and H. C. Starkey, "Leaching of Clay Minerals in a Limestone Environment." Geochim. et Cosmochim. Acta, **16** (1959), 83–87.

Coleman, N. T., "II. Decomposition of Clays and the Fate of Aluminum." Econ. Geol., **57** (1962), 1207–1218.

Deer, W. A., R. A. Howie, and J. Zussmann, *Rock-forming Minerals.* Vol. 5, London: Longmans, Green and Co., Ltd., 1962.

Ervin, G. Jr. and E. F. Osborn, "The System Al_2O_3–H_2O." J. Geol., **59** (1951), 381–394.

Ewing, F. J., "The Crystal Structure of Diaspore." J. Chem. Phys., **3** (1935a), 420.

Ewing, F. J., "The Crystal Structure of Lepidocrocite." J. Chem. Phys. **3** (1935b), 420.

Fischer, E. F., *Annotated Bibliography of the Bauxite Deposits of the World:* Bull. U.S. Geol. Surv. (1955), 999.

Frederickson, A. F., "The Genetic Significance of Mineralogy." Amer. Inst. Min. Metal. Eng., Problems of Clay and Laterite Genesis (1952), 1–11.

Gordon, M., J. I. Tracey Jr., and M. W. Ellis, *Geology of the Arkansas Bauxite Regions.* U. S. Geol. Surv. Prof. Paper, **299** (1958).

Gordon, M. and K. J. Murata, "Minor Elements in Arkansas Bauxite." Econ. Geol., **47** (1952), 169–179.

Harder, E. C., "Stratigraphy and Origin of Bauxite Deposits." Bull. Geol. Soc. Amer., **60** (1949), 887–908.

Keller, W. D., "Argillation and Direct Bauxitization in Terms of Concentrations of Hydrogen and Metal Cations at Surface of Hydrolyzing Aluminium Silicates." Bull. Amer. Assoc. Petrol. Geol., **42** (1958), 233–45.

Keller, W. D., "Clay Minerals as Influenced by Environments of their Formation." Bull. Amer. Assoc. Petrol. Geol., **40** (1956), 2689–2710.

Kennedy, G. C., "Phase Relations in the System Al_2O_3–H_2O at High Temperatures and Pressures." Amer. Jour. Sci., **257** (1959), 563–573.

Konta, J., "Proposed Classification and Terminology of Rocks in the Series Bauxite-Clay-Iron Oxide Ore." J. Sed. Petr., **28** (1958), 83–86.

McLaughlin, R. J. W., "Geochemical Changes due to Weathering under Varying Climatic Conditions." Geochim. et Cosmochim. Acta, **8** (1955), 109–130.

Loughnan, F. C. and P. Bayliss, "The Mineralogy of the Bauxite Deposits near Weipa, Queensland." Am. Mineralogist, **46** (1961), 209–217.

Owen, H. B., "Bauxite in Australia." Bureau of Mineral Resources, Geol. Geophys., Bull., **24** (1954), 234 pp.

Schüller, A., "Mineralogie und Petrographie neuartiger Bauxite aus dem Gun-Distrikt, Honan-Provinz (China)." Geologie, **6** (1957), 379–399.

Sherman, G. D., "The Genesis and Morphology of the Alumina-rich Laterite Clays." Amer. Inst. Min. Met. Eng., Problems of Clay and Laterite Genesis, (1952), 154–161.

Valeton, I., "Petrographie und Genese von Bauxitlagerstätten: (Ein Überblick über die Bauxitliteratur)." Geol. Rdsch., **52** (1962a), 448–474.

Valeton, I., "Petrographie der Bauxite von Mazaugues Südfrankreich." Geol. Rdsch., **52** (1962b), 475–492.

Valeton, I., "Bauxitische Bodenbildungen, ihr Wert als Klima-und Relief-Faktor." **54**th Jahrestagung der Geologischen Vereinigung, 5–7 März 1964, Köln.

2. *Silica*

Alexander, G. B., W. M. Heston, and H. K. Iler, "The Solubility of Amorphous Silica in Water." J. Phys. Chem., **58** (1954), 453–455.

Allenby, R. J., "Determination of the Isotopic Ratios of Silicon in Rocks." Geochim. et Cosmochim. Acta, **5** (1954), 40–48.

Bien, G. S., D. E. Contois, and W. H. Thomas, "The Removal of Soluble Silica from Fresh Water Entering the Sea." Geochim. et Cosmochim. Acta, **14** (1958), 35–54.

Bissell, H. J., "Silica in Sediments of the Upper Paleozoic of the Cordilleran Area." Soc. Econ. Paleo. Min., Special Publication No. **7,** (1959), Tulsa, Oklahoma, 150–185.

Bramlette, M. N., "The Monterey Formation of California and the Origin of its Siliceous Rocks." U. S. Geol. Sur. Prof. Paper, **212** (1946), 1–55.

Cooper, L. H. N., "Factors Affecting the Distribution of Silicate in the North Atlantic Ocean and the Formation of the North Atlantic Deep Water." J. Mar. Biol. Ass. U. K., **30** (1952), 511–526.

Dapples, E. C., "The Behavior of Silica in Diagenesis." Soc. Econ. Paleo Min., Special Publication No. **7,** Tulsa, Oklahoma, (1959), 36–54.

Degens, E. T. and S. Epstein, "Relationship between O^{18}/O^{16} Ratios in Coexisting Carbonates, Cherts, and Diatomites." Bull. Amer. Assoc. Petrol. Geol., **46** (1962), 534–542.

DeVore, G. W., "The Surface Chemistry of Feldspars as an Influence on their Decomposition Products." Clays and Clay Minerals, **6**th Conf., (1959), 26–41.

Eitel, W., *Physical Chemistry of the Silicates*. Chicago: The University of Chicago Press, 1954.

Emery, K. O., and S. C. Rittenberg, "Early Diagenesis of California Basin Sediments in Relation to Origin of Oil." Bull. Amer. Assoc. Petrol. Geol., **36** (1952), 735–806.

Goldstein, A., Jr., "Cherts and Novaculites of Ouachita Facies." Soc. Econ. Paleo. Min., Special Publication No. 7, Tulsa, Oklahoma, (1959) 135–149.

Hirt, B. and S. Epstein, *A Search for Isotopic Variations in Some Terrestrial and Meteorite Calcium.* (in press).

Hitchen, C. S., "A Method for Experimental Investigation of Hydro-thermal Solutions with Notes on its Application to the Solubility of Silica." Trans. Inst. Min. Met., **44** (1945), 255–280.

Iler, R. K., *Colloid Chemistry of Silica and Silicates*. Ithaca, N. Y.: Cornell University Press, 1955.

Ireland, H. A., "Introduction to Silica in Sediments." Soc. Econ. Paleo. Min., Special Publication No. **7**, (1959) Tulsa, Oklahoma, 1–3.

Keller, W. D., W. D. Balgord, and A. L. Reesman, "Dissolved Products of Artificially Pulverized Silicate Minerals and Rocks. Part I." J. Sed. Petr., **33** (1963), 191–204.

Kennedy, G. C., "A Portion of the System Silica-Water." Econ. Geol., **45** (1950), 629–653.

Krauskopf, K. B., "Dissolution and Precipitation of Silica at Low Temperatures." Geochim. et Cosmochim. Acta, **10** (1956), 1–26.

Krauskopf, K. B., "The Geochemistry of Silica in Sedimentary Environments." Soc. Econ. Paleo. Min., Special Publication No. **7**, (1959) Tulsa, Oklahoma, 4–19.

Lewin, J. C. "The Dissolution of Silica from Diatom Walls." Geochim. et Cosmochim. Acta, **21** (1961), 182–198.

Miller, J. P., "A Portion of the System Calcium Carbonate-Carbon Dioxide-Water, with Geological Implications." Am. J. Sci., **250** (1952), 161–203.

Okamoto, G., T. Okura, and K. Goto, "Properties of Silica in Water." Geochim. et Cosmochim. Acta, **12** (1957), 123–132.

Pittman, J. S., Jr., "Silica in Edwards Limestone, Travis County, Texas." Soc. Econ. Paleo. Min., Special Publication No. **7,** Tulsa, Oklahoma, (1959) 121–134.

Reynolds, J. H. and J. Verhoogen, "Natural Variations in the Isotopic Constitution of Silicon." Geochim. et Cosmochim. Acta, **3** (1953), 224–234.

Roy, C. J., "Silica in Natural Waters." Amer. J. Sci., **243** (1945), 393–403.

Siever, R., "The Silica Budget in the Sedimentary Cycle." Amer. Mineralogist, **42** (1957), 821–841.

Siever, R., "Petrology and Geochemistry of Silica Cementation in Some Pennsylvanian Sandstones." Soc. Econ. Paleo. Min., Special Publication No. **7**, (1959) Tulsa, Oklahoma, 55–79.

Stevens, R. E., and M. K. Carron, "Simple Field Test for Distinguishing Minerals by Abrasion pH." Amer. Mineralogist, **33** (1948), 31–50.

Thomson, A., "Pressure Solution and Porosity." Soc. Econ. Paleo. Min., Special Publication No. **7**, (1959) Tulsa, Oklahoma, 92–110.

Waddams, J. A., "Further Observations on the Interaction between Quartz and Water." Research (London), **10** (1957), 410–411.

3. Iron and Manganese Oxides and Hydroxides

Baas Becking, L. G. M., I. R. Kaplan, and D. Moore, "Limits of the Natural Environment in Terms of pH and Oxidation-reduction Potentials." J. Geol. **68** (1960), 243–284.

Bernal, J. D., D. R. Dasgupta, and A. L. Mackay, "The Oxides and Hydroxides of Iron and their Structural Inter-relationships." Clay Minerals Bull., **4** (1959), 15–30.

Buser, W. and A. Grütter, "Über die Natur der Mangan-Knollen." Schweiz. mineral petrogr. Mitt., **36** (1956), 49–62.

Castaño, J. R. and R. M. Garrels, "Experiments on the Decomposition of Iron with Special Reference to the Clinton Iron Ore Deposits." Econ. Geol., **45** (1950), 755–770.

Chow, T. J. and C. C. Patterson, "Lead Isotopes in Manganese Nodules." Geochim. et Cosmochim. Acta, **17** (1959), 21–23.

Deer, W. A., R. A. Howie, and J. Zussmann, Rock-forming Minerals. Vol. 5. London: Longmans, Green and Co., Ltd., 1962.

Dietz, R. S., "Manganese Deposits on the Northeast Pacific Sea Floor." Calif. Journ. Mines and Geology, **51** (1955), 209–220.

Garrels, R. M., Mineral Equilibria at Low Temperature and Pressure. New York: Harper and Brothers, Publishers, 1960.

Glemser, O., "Binding of Water in Some Hydroxides and Hydrous Oxides." Nature, **183** (1959), 943–944.

Goldberg, E. D., "Marine Geochemistry 1. Chemical Scavengers of the Sea." J. Geol., **62** (1954), 249–265.

Goldberg, E. D., "Chemistry in the Oceans." In Oceanography, ed. M. Sears. Washington, D. C., Amer. Assoc. Advancement Sci., Publ. No. **67,** (1961) 583–597.

Goldberg, E. D. and E. Picciotto, "Thorium Determinations in Manganese Nodules." Science, **121** (1955), 613–614.

Goodwin, A. M., "Facies Relations in the Gunflint Iron Formation." Econ. Geol., **51** (1956), 564–595.

Hewett, D. F. and M. Fleischer, "Deposits of the Manganese Oxides." Econ. Geol., **55** (1960), 1–55.

Hoppe, W., "Über die Kristallstruktur von α-AlOOH (Diaspor) und α-FeOOH (Nadeleisenerz)." Ztschr. Krist., **103** (1940), 73.

Hough, J. L., "Fresh-water Environment of Deposition of Pre-cambrian Banded Iron Formations." J. Sed. Petr., **28** (1958), 414–430.

Huber, N. K., "The Environmental Control of Sedimentary Iron Minerals." Econ. Geol., **53** (1958), 123–140.

Huber, N. K., "Some Aspects of the Origin of the Ironwood Iron Formation of Michigan and Wisconsin." Econ. Geol., **54** (1959), 82–118.

Huber, N. K. and R. M. Garrels, "Relation of pH and Oxidation Potential to Sedimentary Iron Formation." Econ. Geol., **48** (1953), 337–357.

James, H. L., "Sedimentary Facies of Iron Formation." Econ. Geol., **49** (1954), 235–293.

James, H. L. and R. N. Clayton, "Oxygen Isotope Fractionation in Metamorphosed Iron Formations of the Lake Superior Region and in Other Iron-Rich Rocks." Petrologic Studies: A volume to honor A. F. Buddington, Geol. Soc. America, (1962), 217–239.

Keith, M. L. and E. T. Degens, "Geochemical Indicators of Marine and Fresh-Water Sediments." In *Researches in Geochemistry,* ed. P. H. Abelson. New York: John Wiley & Sons, Inc., (1959), 38–61.

Kelley, V. C., "Oolithic Iron Deposits of New Mexico." Bull. Amer. Assoc., Petrol. Geol., **35** (1951), 2199–2228.

Krauskopf, K. B., "Separation of Manganese from Iron in Sedimentary Processes." Geochim. et Cosmochim. Acta, **12** (1957), 61–84.

Krauskopf, K. B., "Sedimentary Deposits of Rare Metals." Econ. Geol., **50**th Anniversary Volume, (1955) 411–463.

Krumbein, W. C. and R. M. Garrels, "Origin and Classification of Chemical Sediments in Terms of pH and Oxidation-reduction Potentials." J. Geol. **60** (1952), 1–33.

Landergren, S., "On the Geochemistry of Swedish Iron Ores and Associated Rocks. A Study of Iron Ore Formation." Sveriges Geol. Undersokn., Arsbok 42, No. **5,** ser. C, (1948) No. 496, 182 pp.

Lepp, H. "The Relation of Iron and Manganese in Sedimentary Iron Formations." Econ. Geol., **58** (1963), 515–526.

Lowenstam, H. A., "Magnetite in Denticle Capping in Recent Chitons (*Polyplacophora*)." Bull. Geol. Soc. Amer., **73** (1962a), 435–438.

Lowenstam, H. A., "Goethite in Radular Teeth of Recent Marine Gastropods." Science, **137** (1962b), 279–280.

Macco, E., "Die Excursion des VII internationalen Geologen-Congresses nach dem Kaukasus und der Krim." Ztschr. prakt. Geol., **1889** (1898), 196–206.

Marchandise, H., "Contribution à l'Étude des Gisements de Manganèse Sédimentaire." Intern. Geol. Congr., Manganese Symposium, **1** (1956), 107–118.

Menard, H. W. and C. J. Shipek, "Surface Concentrations of Manganese Nodules." Nature, **182** (1958), 1156–1158.

Mero, J. L., "Ocean-floor Manganese Nodules." Econ. Geol., **57** (1962), 747–767.

O'Neill, J. R., *Oxygen Isotope Fractionation Studies in Mineral Systems.* Ph. D. Thesis, The University of Chicago, June 1963.

O'Neill, J. R. and R. N. Clayton, "Oxygen Isotope Geothermometry." In *Isotopic and Cosmic Chemistry.* Editors: H. Craig, S. L. Miller, and G. J. Wasserburg, Amsterdam: North-Holland Publishing Company (1964), 157–168.

Ronov, A. B. and A. I. Ermishkina, "Distribution of Manganese in Sedimentary Rocks." Geochemistry (Russian), (1959), 206–225.

Sakamoto, T., "The Origin of the Precambrian Banded Iron Ores." Amer. J. Sci., **248** (1950), 449–474.

Shipek, C., "Photographic Study of Some Deep-sea Floor Environments in the Eastern Pacific." Bull. Geol. Soc. Amer., **71** (1960), 1067–1074.

Strunz, H., *Mineralogische Tabellen.* Leipzig: Akademische Verlagsgesellschaft Geest & Portig K.-G., 1957.

Thomas, D. V. and M. Blumer, "Pyrene and Fluoranthene in Manganese Nodules." Science, **143** (1964), 39.

Towe, K. H., H. A. Lowenstam, and M. H. Nesson, "Invertebrate Ferritin: Occurrence in Mollusca." Science, **142** (1963), 63–64.

Turekian, K. K. and K. H. Wedepohl, "Distribution of the Elements in Some Major Units of the Earth's Crust." Bull. Geol. Soc. Amer., **72** (1961), 175–192.

White, D. A., "The Stratigraphy and Structure of the Mesabi Range, Minnesota." Minnesota Geological Survey, Bull., **38** (1954). Minneapolis: The University of Minnesota Press.

4. *Titanium Oxides*

Arrhenius, G. O. S., "Sedimentation on the Ocean Floor." In *Researches in Geochemistry,* ed. P. H. Abelson. New York: John Wiley & Sons, Inc., 1–24.

Correns, C. W., "Titan in Tiefseesedimenten." Deep-Sea Research, **1** (1954), 78–85.

Carbonates

1. Introduction and Classification

Carbonate rocks represent about 20 per cent of all sedimentary matter. For the most part they are authigenic in nature, and thus differ from the bulk of the shales and sandstones which are detrital in origin.

The processes causing deposition and solution of carbonate minerals in common syngenetic and post-depositional environments are reasonably well understood. This knowledge, on the other hand, is extremely helpful to reconstruct the general environmental conditions that have led to deposition, solution, or metasomatic replacement of certain carbonates throughout geologic history. Studies in the area of carbonate geochemistry are further helped by the relative ease of carbonate analysis.

The early recognition of carbonates as reliable sources of geochemical information has resulted in a vast number of excellent studies. The solution kinetics of carbonates for instance have been investigated by Shternina and Frolova (1952), Graf and Lamar (1955), Garrels and Dreyer (1952), Chave et al. (1962), Weyl (1958) and Garrels (1960); the phase relationships were studied by Jamieson (1953), MacDonald (1956), Clark (1957) and Goldsmith (1959). The wide application of radioactive and stable isotope research to various aspects of carbonate geochemistry and geology have been presented in the works of Craig (1953, 1954ab, 1957ab, 1963), Revelle and Suess (1957), Epstein (1959), Münnich (1963), Bien et al. (1960), Turner (1958), and Broecker et al. (1961); and general reviews of other topics of carbonate geochemistry have been given by Graf and Lamar (1955), Revelle and Fairbridge (1957), Ingerson (1962), Cloud (1962) and Fairbridge (1957).

The minerals of the carbonate group have the CO_3^{-2} ion in common as the fundamental structural unit. Carbonates, however, can be conveniently classified on the basis of presence or absence of water and foreign anions such as OH^-, Cl^-, F^-, SO_4^{-2} and others (Strunz, 1957). Among the about 60 different carbonates known in nature only a few are important rock forming minerals. It is remarkable that some carbonates are equally at home in magmatic and metamorphic rocks, e.g., in carbonatites, nepheline-syenites and marbles, as in sediments, e. g., in limestones, shell materials, and dolomites. Furthermore, carbonates can be a product of both inorganic and organic processes.

The most prominent carbonate minerals in sediments of all syngenetic and post-depositional environmental settings are the three anhydrous Ca- and Mg-carbonates: (1) calcite, (2) aragonite, and (3) dolomite. A few of the less common species listed in Table 9 may occasionally occur in association with evaporites, or they may form under restricted environmental conditions. For example, magnesite, trona and soda are common in evaporites; and siderite may form under moderate reducing conditions, for instance, in peatbog or iron-formation environments.

A general classification of pure end-member carbonate minerals of interest to sedimentologists is given in Table 9. A few details concerning structural and chemical properties of carbonates are included. For more comprehensive accounts on the mineralogy and chemistry of carbonates one may consult the following sources: Bragg (1937), Ewald and Hermann (1931), Palache et al. (1951), Graf and Lamar (1955), Goldsmith (1959), and Ingerson (1962).

Inasmuch as the bulk of all sedimentary carbonates is represented by the rhombohedral dolomite and the two polymorphs of $CaCO_3$, i.e., the rhombohedral calcite and orthorhombic aragonite, it is reasonable to focus attention in the forthcoming discussion predominately onto these three carbonate species. It may be pointed out that with increasing geologic age the metastable aragonite will be replaced by either calcite or dolomite.

2. Solution and Precipitation of Limestones

On their way through the atmosphere rain, snow, and ice will pick up some of the carbon dioxide present. Atmospheric precipitations can, therefore, be regarded as very dilute solutions of carbonic acid which may interact to a certain limited extent. By percolating through the soil, however, meteoric waters become chemically more and more aggressive as they take up CO_2 from the soil gases. This CO_2 is a product of organic activity and decay.

Whereas the CO_2 concentration in the atmosphere is about 0.03 Vol. % (Keeling, 1958), the CO_2 content in the soil gases is generally on the order of 0.5 to 5 Vol. % in humid regions; but concentrations between 10 and 15 Vol. % are also known (Meyer and Koepf, 1958, Vogel, 1959; Münnich and Vogel, 1962). The magnitude of CO_2 concentration in the soil gases largely depends on parameters such as climate, depth and nature of soil, microbial populations, flora, and

Table 9 CLASSIFICATION OF COMMON SEDIMENTARY CARBONATES.

STATE	SERIES/GROUP	SPECIES	CRYSTALLOCHEMICAL FORMULA	SPACE GROUP	STRUCTURE (SCHEMATIC)
Anhydrous	Calcite	Calcite Magnesite Siderite	$CaCO_3$ $MgCO_3$ $FeCO_3$	$R\bar{3}c$	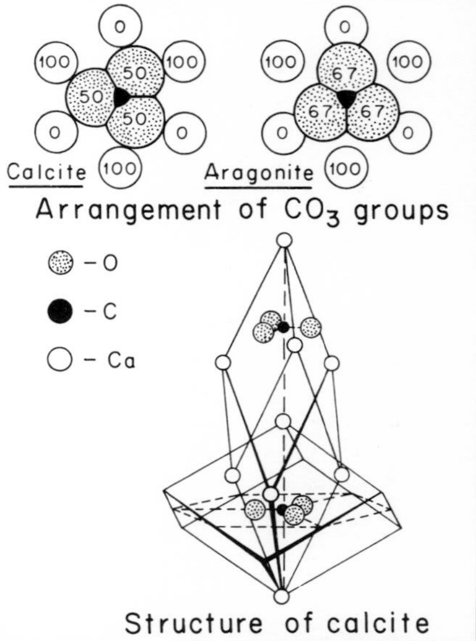
	Aragonite	Aragonite Strontianite	$CaCO_3$ $SrCO_3$	$Pmcn$	
	Dolomite	Dolomite Ankerite	$CaMg(CO_3)_2$ $CaFe(CO_3)_2$	$R\bar{3}$	
	Azurite	Azurite Malachite	$Cu_3\left[OH|CO_3\right]_2$ $Cu_2\left[(OH)_2|CO_3\right]$	$P2_1/c$ $P2_1/a$	
Hydrous	Soda	Soda Trona	$Na_2CO_3\cdot10H_2O$ $Na_3H(CO_3)\cdot2H_2O$	Monoclinic $C2/c$	

Calcite (100)   Aragonite (100)

Arrangement of CO_3 groups

○ – O   ● – C   ○ – Ca

Structure of calcite

type and amount of organic matter. CO_2 will be taken up by the percolating meteoric water till saturation. The equilibrium relationship between carbon dioxide and the dissolved bicarbonate is illustrated in Figure 21. It can be seen that rain water may only yield bicarbonate concentrations up to about 1.2 mMol/l. Inasmuch as the usual content of dissolved carbonates in ground waters of humid regions falls in the range of 3 to 10 mMol/l, most of it has to come from sources other than atmospheric CO_2.

It was stated above that meteoric waters obtain CO_2 from the biogenic soil gases. Limestones in contact with these CO_2 enriched waters will react in the following manner:

$$CaCO_3 + CO_2 + H_2O \rightleftarrows Ca^{+2} + 2\,HCO_3^-$$

This reaction actually involves a number of separate equilibria, i. e., the dissociation of calcite into calcium and carbonate atoms, and the subsequent formation of the bicarbonate from the various carbonate species present in the aqueous and gaseous phase (CO_3^{-2}, H_2CO_3, $CO_{2(gas)}$, and $CO_{2(H_2O)}$). In equilibrium the amount of calcium bicarbonate that can go into solution depends, therefore, on the partial pressure of CO_2 or on the quantities of dissolved CO_2 in the system.

Data on the solubility product of $CaCO_3$ in saline waters are more difficult to obtain, inasmuch as — aside from temperature and hydrostatic pressure — the solubility product is a function of the type and

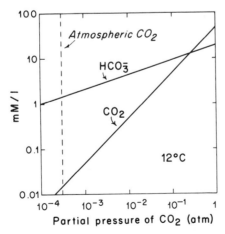

Fig. 21 Equilibrium concentrations of bicarbonate and carbon dioxide in water in contact with limestone as a function of the CO_2 partial pressure in the gas phase (after Vogel and Ehhalt, 1963)

of the amount of the various solutes present; also, the kinetics are different. In the case of sea water, however, information is plentiful (Wattenberg (1936), Zen (1960), Cloud (1962), Revelle and Fairbridge (1957), Kanwisher (1960), Garrels et al. (1960), Sverdrup et al. (1946), Ellis (1959), Pytkowicz (1964), and others). As a matter of fact, the ionic product ($[Ca^{+2}] \times [CO_3^{-2}]$) of sea water at $19^o/_{oo}$ chlorinity and $20°C$ is about 500 times that in distilled water; and aragonite is more soluble than calcite.

Sea water is always in near-equilibrium with atmospheric CO_2. The oceans are about saturated or just slightly super- or under-saturated with respect to $CaCO_3$ Revelle and Fleming (1934), Revelle and Fairbridge (1957), Wattenberg and Timmermann (1936), Sverdrup et al. (1946), Weyl (1959), Cloud (1962). In contrast there is not nearly enough magnesium carbonate for saturation.

Correlation of the data regarding the solubility of calcium carbonate indicates that alkalinity is by far the most important function among the several variables which affect solubility. Alkalinity is a measure of the milli-equivalents of H^+ ions required to release the ions of weak acids from 1 liter of water at $20°$ C. In sea water the magnitude of alkalinity is largely determined by the molar concentration of the bicarbonate and carbonate ions. An increase in alkalinity causes an increase in pH, or vice versa. The empirically determined relationship that exists between the ionic product $[Ca^{+2}] \times [CO_3^{-2}]$ and pH are plotted in Figure 22. Another very important factor is the ionic strength (salinity) of the solution. Increase in ionic strength is equal to an increase in solubility. Temperature and pressure follow next as influential factors acting on the carbon dioxide system. For example, waters which are saturated at the surface will become undersaturated when moved to the bottom of the deep sea; in contrast, saturated waters from the deep sea will become supersaturated when suddenly raised to the surface of the ocean.

All this is interpreted by most chemical oceanographers as indicating that $CaCO_3$ can be precipitated inorganically in the sea. That is, any condition such as an increase in temperature, agitation or aeration, or a decrease of the partial pressure in the atmosphere or surrounding gas system by inorganic or organic means, and which causes the removal of CO_2, increases the pH and thus favors the precipitation of lime. Also, salinity will affect the solubility of $CaCO_3$. Excess of calcium is equal to a decrease, and excess of foreign ions is equal to an increase in solubility of $CaCO_3$.

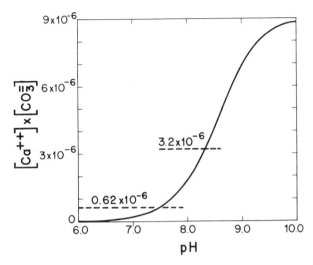

Fig. 22 Ionic product $[Ca^{+2}] \times [CO_3^{-2}]$ in sea water of $Cl =$ 19.00°/$_{00}$ at 20°C, as a function of pH. The horizontal lines indicate the solubility product according to Wattenberg (0.62×10^{-6}) and according to Revelle and Fleming (3.2×10^{-6}) (after Sverdrup et al., 1946)

This viewpoint is not accepted by Pytkowicz (1964) and Weyl (personal communication, 1964), who assume that sea water, even though it may be supersaturated with respect to $CaCO_3$ cannot bring on a spontaneous nucleation of aragonite or calcite. The reason for this "peculiar" behavior appears to be related to the presence of Mg which strongly interferes with the formation of $CaCO_3$ nuclei. This argument is supported by nucleation experiments in waters lacking Mg ions but otherwise of the same composition as sea water. The power dependence of the rate of nucleation increases from a second to a six order in the presence of magnesium. Inasmuch as the data suggest that inorganic precipitation in average sea water would require about 10^5 years, the inference is that $CaCO_3$ deposition in the oceans is largely a result of biogenic extraction. Inorganic precipitation of $CaCO_3$ may locally occur within a reasonable time either when organisms extract a considerable amount of CO_2, thus causing bicarbonate to dissociate to carbonate, or when carbonate seeds are stirred up from the sea floor by the action of organisms, water turbulence, etc. These particles then may act as nucleation sites for aragonite or calcite in $CaCO_3$ supersaturated waters. The sudden occurrence of "whitings," i.e., carbonate clouds in surface waters of the Persian Gulf (Wells and Illing, 1964) and elsewhere are not necessarily proofs for inorganic $CaCO_3$ precipitations as was assumed by Wells and Illing (1964). Instead, they may represent stirred up carbonate ooze, which then drifts as a cloud in the sea (Weyl, personal communication, 1964).

In summary: under normal fresh water conditions, where the water is saturated with respect to $CaCO_3$ and the Mg content is negligible, solution or precipitation can only take place as the solubility changes with changes in pressure, temperature or chemical composition of the moving water. $CaCO_3$ deposition can be brought about, for instance, when fresh waters move into open spaces where the partial pressure of CO_2 is lower than in the region in which the bicarbonate content originated. $CaCO_3$ deposition under marine conditions, however, appears to be governed largely by the activities of organisms that deposit calcite, aragonite or both during their life cycle. Whether inorganic precipitation of $CaCO_3$ from the saturated sea actually occurs by itself, i.e., without presence of "organic" carbonate nuclei, is questionable. More work of the type performed by Pytkowicz (1964) is needed to establish the true relationship in the carbon dioxide system of the sea.

When sea water evaporates, however, the situation is different, for inorganic precipitation of $CaCO_3$ may take place some time before the solubility product of $CaSO_4$ is exceeded. The effect which organic and inorganic complexing agents may have on the deposition mechanism of $CaCO_3$ in the sea is not fully understood. Magnesium ions seem to exercise some control. According to Garrels et al. (1961), the magnesium ion may be abnormally firmly hydrated, or it may form a stable ion pair. The reason that fresh waters behave so "normally" with respect to $CaCO_3$ solution and deposition is perhaps a result of their generally low magnesium content.

One may add that thermal decomposition of carbonate rocks can locally supplement CO_2 to the water system. The uptake is only limited by the amount of CO_2 that can go into solution at a given pressure and temperature.

3. Isotope Geochemistry of Carbonates

No other mineral group has been so thoroughly studied for the variations in isotopic compositions as the carbonate group. The reason for this is easy to understand. The common pure end-member carbonates, calcite, aragonite, and dolomite, are composed only of the four light elements: (1) carbon, (2) oxygen, (3) magnesium, and (4) calcium, all of which contain at least two stable isotopes that are relatively abundant. In the second place, the element carbon may have carbon[14] as a radioactive tracer constituent, with a half-life of 5730 ± 40 years.

(a) *Carbon*. The distribution of the two stable carbon isotopes C^{12} and C^{13}, of which the terrestrial ratio is about 90 to 1, is predominantly determined by (1) kinetic effects and (2) equilibrium processes. For instance, the C^{12} content in land plants which is about 2 per cent higher than in CO_2 in the atmosphere can be partly attributed to the more frequent collision of $C^{12}O_2^{16}$ with the photosynthesizing leaf as compared to $C^{13}O_2^{16}$ encounters. A comprehensive survey of the major factors that govern isotopic fractionations in nature has been presented by Epstein (1959).

In general, carbon isotope data are reported as per mil deviation relative to the PDB_I Chicago belemnite standard (Craig, 1953, 1957a):

$$\delta C^{13} = \left(\frac{R}{R_{standard}} - 1\right) \times 1000$$

$$R = C^{13}/C^{12} \text{ ratio in the sample}$$

$$R_{standard} = C^{13}/C^{12} \text{ ratio in the standard}$$

δO^{18} is defined similarly in terms of O^{18}/O^{16} ratio. The data for oxygen δ-values, however, will be lower by about $29.5\%_0$ when reported as per mil deviation relative to Standard Mean Ocean Water (S.M.O.W.). The relationship between $\delta O^{18}{}_{PDB_I}$ and $\delta O^{18}{}_{S.M.O.W.}$ is:

$$\delta O^{18}{}_{S.M.O.W.} = \delta O^{18}{}_{PDB_I} \times 1.03 + 29.5$$

Except for carbonates and organic materials the most commonly used oxygen isotope scale at present is Standard Mean Ocean Water.

Since publication of a detailed study on the distribution of stable carbon isotopes in nature by Craig (1953) many papers have appeared on this subject. With regard to carbonates, pertinent studies on C^{13}/C^{12} ratios include: Landergren (1954), Jeffrey et al (1955), Craig (1957a), Silverman and Epstein (1958), Vogel (1959), Compston (1960), Krejci-Graf and Wickman (1960), Degens and Epstein (1962, 1964), Eckelmann et al. (1962), and Münnich and Vogel (1962).

It was stated before that rain water can only pick up small amounts of atmospheric CO_2. The overwhelming portion of bicarbonate ions found in meteoric waters is derived from biogenic sources in the soil. According to Park and Epstein (1961), carbon isotope fractionation during photosynthesis may produce organic matter enriched in C^{12} by as much as about 30 per mil relative to atmospheric CO_2. Compared to a δC^{13} of about -8 for atmospheric CO_2, the δC^{13} content in average land plants is about -25. Thus, biogenic CO_2 in soil gases is expected to be enriched in C^{12} by about 2 per cent. This is based on the findings of Craig (1954b), Wickman (1952), Baertschi (1953), and others who maintain that apparently no significant isotope fractionation is involved, at least during decay and respiration of common land materials. Direct studies on the carbon isotopic composition of soil gases, however, are still lacking.

Biogenic CO_2, incorporated in the moving meteoric water, will eventually dissolve ancient carbonates which, in most instances, are of marine origin. The C^{13}/C^{12} ratio of the bicarbonate ion in the water will, therefore, be determined by the isotopic composition of the biogenic CO_2 and the marine limestone. Carbonates precipitated in a marine environment under equilibrium conditions are about 8 per mil heavier in C^{13} than atmospheric CO_2. The isotope relationship between $CO_{2(atm)}$, dissolved carbonate ions, and marine limestones are plotted in Figure 23.

Assuming the biogenic CO_2 in the soil gases has a δC^{13} of -24, and the limestone source one of 0, the resulting bicarbonate will have a δC^{13} of -12. Inasmuch as this bicarbonate may still stay in contact with biogenic CO_2, carbon isotope exchange will take place until equilibrium is attained. This will result in a lowering of the δC^{13} value in the bicarbonate by as much as 5 per mil (Fig. 23). In contact with atmospheric CO_2, on the other hand, equilibrium processes work in the opposite direction, i.e., fresh waters preferentially lose C^{12}. In the final stage, the bicarbonate in fresh waters exposed to the atmosphere will be isotopically similar to the dissolved carbonates in the sea. The speed of equilibration depends on a number of parameters which will be separately discussed in connection with radiocarbon studies. Fresh water carbonates, therefore, may yield a wide range of δC^{13} values from a low of about -20 to a high of $+2$ to $+3$. Most of the natural fresh water carbonate deposits, however, fall in the range of approximately -5 to -15 (Vogel, 1959; Clayton and Degens, 1959; Keith and Anderson, 1963; and others).

The thermal decomposition of a marine limestone will produce

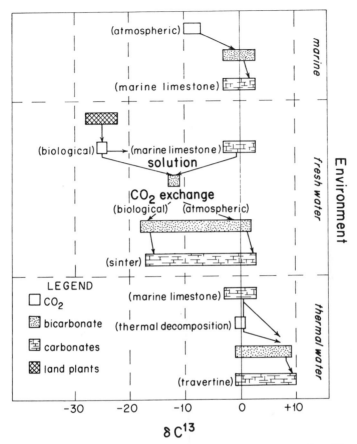

Fig. 23   C¹³/C¹² fractionation in the carbonate system under different environmental conditions (after Münnich and Vogel, 1962 and others)

a CO_2 of the same δC^{13} as the starting material (Fig. 23). In analogy to the marine and fresh water carbon dioxide system, the resulting bicarbonate will be enriched in C^{13} by about 7 per mil, and a carbonate forming from this source at room temperature will have a δC^{13} of about +8.

To sum up, equilibrium processes predominantly govern the distribution of stable carbon isotopes in the natural carbon dioxide system. Carbonates deposited in isotopic equilibrium with their surrounding water and gas phase will yield identical δC^{13} values, no matter whether they are of organic or inorganic origin. Fresh water carbonates, in general, are significantly different from marine carbonates. This is a result of C^{12}-enriched CO_2 contributions to the continental carbon dioxide system. Thus, isotope data may reveal information regarding the nature of ancient environments. Aquatic marine and fresh water organisms thriving on the dissolved carbonates will indirectly affect the carbon isotope distribution of marine and lacustrine carbonates. During assimilation and respiration, the C^{12} content in the dissolved carbonate fraction will decrease or increase respectively. The extent of organic activity and the available bicarbonate resources in the environment where the plants live will, therefore, determine the fluctuations in the δC^{13} of the bicarbonate from water samples taken during daytime (assimilation) and nighttime (respiration).

Radiocarbon is another useful tool (1) to trace the pathway of carbonate formation, (2) to measure the speed of equilibration in the various phases of the natural carbon dioxide system, and (3) to determine the age of natural waters and sediments up to about 40,000 years (Libby, 1955; Antevs, 1957; DeVries, 1959; Craig, 1954b, 1957, 1963; Broecker et al., 1960, 1961; Bien et al., 1960; Brinckmann et al., 1959; Münnich, 1963; Münnich and Vogel, 1959, 1962).

Approximately 96 per cent of all the carbon which participates in exchange reactions in the atmosphere and hydrosphere is dissolved in the sea. The remaining 4 per cent is equally distributed between the biosphere and the atmosphere. Consequently, the bulk of the C^{14} produced by cosmic radiation will eventually end up in the ocean and gradually decay there. Münnich (1963), in a review on the radiocarbon cycle in nature, indicates that due to the inner resistance of the sea water surface, the majority of the CO_2 molecules hitting the water surface will be bounced back into the atmosphere. As a result, more $C^{14}O_2$ molecules may accumulate in the atmosphere than one would expect. It has been calculated by Craig (1957), Münnich (1963), and a number of other investigators that the average CO_2 molecule will stay in the atmosphere for about 7 years before it is taken up by the sea. Inasmuch as the ocean has about 60 times as much CO_2 as the atmosphere, the average CO_2 molecule in the sea will be retained about $7 \times 60 \cong 400$ years. It has to be emphasized, however, that these are just approximate figures, because internal stratification patterns in the atmosphere and the oceans naturally will complicate the picture. As a matter of fact, there are exchange barriers similar to those that exist between the surface of the sea and the immediate overlying portion of the atmosphere. Furthermore, some of the radiocarbon in the sea will be extracted by organisms either as organic carbon or as $CaCO_3$. The carbon-14 age of recent marine sediments (Emery and Bray, 1962) can, therefore, be used to measure the rate of deposition. It is interesting to note that the top layers of marine sediments record C^{14}-ages of a few hundred to a few thousand years. In Figure 24, the C^{14} content of carbonate ions in sea water samples taken at various depths of the oceans are presented. Studies of this kind have recently been performed successfully on waters of both the Atlantic and Pacific (Burling and Garner, 1959; Broecker et al., 1960, 1961; Bien et al., 1960).

Of considerable geological interest is the so-called Suess-Effect (Suess, 1955). As a result of industrial activities, C^{14}-free carbon dioxide obtained from the combustion of coal, petroleum, and in calcining of limestone is continuously supplied to the atmosphere. It has been estimated (Fergusson, 1958; Revelle and Suess, 1957) that in the absence of an oceanic exchange reservoir the CO_2 content in

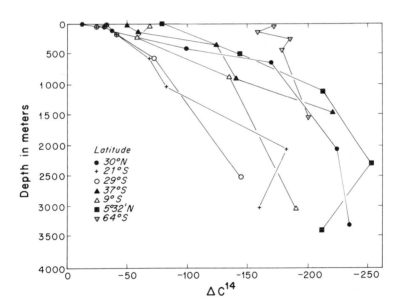

Fig. 24 C^{14} content in the bicarbonate of sea water taken at various depths of the Pacific. The $\triangle C^{14}$ represents the permil deviation from the NBS–Oxalic Acid Standard. The decrease in C^{14} content by 100 permil ($\triangle C^{14} = - 100$) is equivalent to an age of about 800 years. It should be noted that Atlantic deep sea water is only half as old as Pacific water of a corresponding depth (after Bien et al., 1960; and Münnich, 1963)

the atmosphere would have already increased by about 15 per cent by 1955. This increased supply of CO_2, however, has only partly been "digested" in the ocean. For due to the reluctance of the bicarbonate to act as an effective buffer for the dissolved CO_2 the partial pressure of CO_2 increased, and the capacity of the ocean for additional amounts of atmospheric CO_2 was lowered considerably. According to Münnich (1963), only 50 per cent of the industrial CO_2 has been picked up by the sea. The remaining 50 per cent has indeed increased the CO_2 content of the atmosphere. This fact has to be kept in mind, because changes in the atmospheric CO_2 level due to volcanic activities or vegetation have been used by some investigators to explain climatic changes in the geologic past (greenhouse effect) (Möller, 1963). Furthermore, Chilingar and Bissell (1963), Strakhov (1953), and many other scientists believe that dolomite will precipitate in the sea if the CO_2 level of the atmosphere could be raised, thus changing the alkalinity of the sea water.

The exchange rate of atmospheric CO_2 with the hydrosphere can be greatly increased if waters are vigorously stirred up by the action of wind, gravity (water flow), organisms, etc. For instance, a quiet ocean will exchange (within the same limit) about 100 to 500 times less CO_2 than a "roaring sea." This characteristic has to be kept in mind for environmental evaluations of carbonates in terms of fresh water versus marine water. Fresh water carbonates deposited in relatively old lakes (Great Salt Lake) where biological activity is low, or in young lakes and rivers where waters are turbulent, will most likely find and utilize a bicarbonate which is more or less isotopically equilibrated with the CO_2 of the atmosphere.

For the last 10 years the C^{14} level of the atmosphere has increased due to thermonuclear weapons and nuclear industries. The influence of the Suess Effect and that of thermonuclear weapons on the C^{14} content of our atmosphere is illustrated in Figure 25.

(b) *Oxygen.* Urey (1947), in his classical paper on the thermodynamic properties of isotopic substances, laid the foundation of modern isotope geochemistry. One of the first elements studied in detail during the early fifties for its isotope abundance in geological material was oxygen (McCrea, 1950; Urey et al., 1951; Baertschi and Silverman, 1951; Silverman, 1951; Dansgaard, 1953; Epstein and Mayeda, 1953; Epstein et al., 1953). Later studies, in particular by Epstein (1957, 1959) and his associates Clayton (1958, 1961) and

Taylor (1962), outlined the principal laws that govern oxygen isotope fractionations in natural systems. Based on their findings and those of the earlier workers a number of geological problems in the field of carbonate geochemistry have since been tackled.

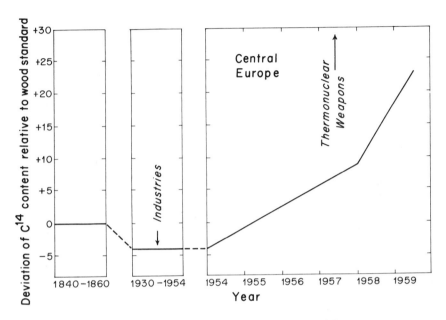

Fig. 25   Deviation of C^{14} content in plants of Central Europe over the last 100 years relative to the wood standard; (Münnich, 1963; Münnich and Vogel, 1958)

The temperature dependence of oxygen isotopes in the various molecular species of the CO_2-bicarbonate-carbonate system allowed paleotemperature determinations of the kind performed by Urey et al. (1951), Emiliani (1955, 1956, 1958), Epstein et al. (1953), Lowenstam and Epstein (1954), Compston (1960), Bowen (1964), and others. Their data indicate that it is possible to use the O^{18}/O^{16} ratio of preserved marine carbonates for the determination of water temperature fluctuations in the ancient sea. The results of the comprehensive isotope study by Emiliani (1958) are of particular geological interest. First of all, paleotemperatures deduced from the O^{18}/O^{16} data of carbonates ("Globigerina ooze" facies) in Pleistocene deep sea cores from the middle and equatorial Atlantic, the Caribbean, and the

Mediterranean, show similar patterns. Furthermore, a generalized curve of temperature variations of tropical surface oceanic waters during the last 300,000 years correlates well with continental temperature variations inferred from loess profiles and pollen profiles and with eustatic changes of the sea level (Fig. 26). Uncertainties in the reliability of paleotemperatures are introduced, however, as marine carbonates of older geologic periods are studied for O^{18}/O^{16} ratios. In most instances carbonates, unfortunately, are not preserved with geologic time; isotope equilibration with the surrounding meteoric or connate waters, often stimulated by a general increase in temperature (geothermal gradient), will make the marine limestones or shell carbonates progressively lighter (increase in O^{16}). Thus, the original O^{18}/O^{16} record, as laid down during deposition, is altered during diagenesis. The δO^{18} variation of a number of carbonates and coexisting cherts with geologic age is presented in Figure 18. However, certain post-depositional environments are known which apparently have preserved the original O^{18}/O^{16} record even of late Paleozoic carbonates. This can be inferred either by the presence of internal isotope variations, the occurrence of metastable aragonite, or the perfect structural preservation of the calcite material (Compston, 1960; Stehli 1956; Epstein and Lowenstam, personal communication).

The study of paleotemperatures and of diagenesis are only two fields among many in which the use of oxygen isotope methods is

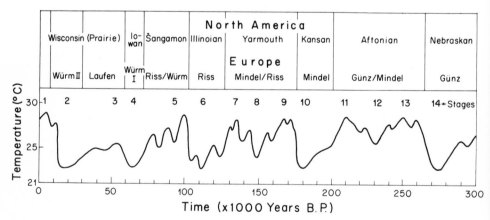

Fig. 26 Generalized temperature curve for tropical surface waters (O^{18}/O^{16} paleotemperature curve) and continental correlations (after Emiliani, 1958)

invaluable. In the following discussion of the general geochemistry of carbonates it will be seen how oxygen isotopes in general can be used to help us better to understand the entire field of carbonate geology and geochemistry.

(c) *Calcium and Magnesium.* Stable isotopes of calcium are different in mass up to 20% (Ca^{40} vs. Ca^{48}). Inasmuch as this is the largest relative mass difference for all the elements except hydrogen, studies on calcium isotopes appear promising.

Mass spectrometry studies by Hirt and Epstein (1964), however, indicate that there is a lack of large Ca-isotope variations in nature in contrast to oxygen, carbon, nitrogen, and sulfur. Samples of different origins, i.e., meteorites, crystalline rocks, limestones, shell materials, ocean waters, bones and teeth have about the same calcium isotope distribution. This may mean that elements in natural products which are bonded by ionic bonds show small isotopic variations compared to those light elements that are bonded by covalent bonds. In the light of these results a re-examination of magnesium isotopes would be relevant because Daughrty et al. (1962) report 5% variations in the Mg^{24}/Mg^{26} ratio in dolomites. Similarly, the isotope data on calcium by Corless (1963) and Corless et al. (1963) have to be re-evaluated in view of the results of Hirt and Epstein (1964).

4. CALCITE AND ARAGONITE

The phase relationships of the two polymorphs of $CaCO_3$, i.e., calcite and aragonite, have been thoroughly examined by Graf and Lamar (1955), Jamieson (1953), MacDonald (1956), Clark (1957), and Goldsmith (1959). The results have been summarized by Deer et al. (1962). From these data it appears that aragonite is thermally unstable with respect to calcite. Graf and Lamar (1955) state that although aragonite may remain stable indefinitely if kept in a dry environment, the transition to calcite will proceed relatively rapidly in hydrous environments and at elevated temperatures. Impurities such as $CaSO_4$ seem to increase the stability of aragonite. An increase in the calcite-aragonite ratio may also take place by dissolution of aragonite and precipitation of calcite, rather than by a single transition of one form to the other.

In most diagenetic environments, therefore, aragonite will be eliminated with time. Nevertheless, the presence of preserved aragonite in apparently dry sediments as old as the Paleozoic is well established (Stehli, 1956; Lowenstam, personal communication). Such environments, however, are extremely rare.

The factors which control the calcite-aragonite relationships in sedimentary environments, particularly in the ocean are still open to discussion. Many different opinions on this subject have been expressed (Lowenstam, 1954; Lowenstam and Epstein, 1957; Kitano, 1956; Daniels, 1961; Zeller and Wray, 1956; Wray and Daniels, 1957; Pobeguin, 1954; Monaghan and Lyttle, 1956; Togari and Togari, 1955; Siegel, 1960; Pytkowicz, 1964; Cloud, 1962; and others). The most widely accepted viewpoint is that calcite and aragonite can form in the ocean both inorganically and organically. The particular mineralogical state of $CaCO_3$ precipitates has been elaborately discussed by Cloud (1962). Briefly, Cloud regards the mineralogical state of the carbonate precipitate primarily as a function of the degree of supersaturation of the parent solution and thus of supersaturation kinetics. But he is also aware of other parameters that may affect the apparent thermodynamic state. Solutions of low ionic strength will usually produce calcite, except where the level of aragonite supersaturation is reached. Aragonite, the more soluble species at ordinary pressures and temperatures (Johnston et al., 1916), will precipitate from solutions that are supersaturated with respect to calcite and aragonite. Thus, differences in the solubility characteristics for calcite and aragonite will largely determine the mineralogical state of the final precipitate. The presence of greater amounts of Sr^{+2} in the crystal lattice of aragonite, as compared to calcite, has presumably only structural reasons since strontianite is isostructural with aragonite. There is no concrete evidence that certain trace constituents such as $SrCO_3$ have a controlling influence on primary mineralogy, as recently implied by a number of authors.

As a result of the work of Lowenstam (1954, 1957, 1961, 1963, 1964) and his associates Dodd (1961), Gross (1961), and Hare (1962, 1963), there is now a substantial body of knowledge regarding the factors that may determine the aragonite-calcite relationships in biological systems. The principal controlling factors in the aragonite-calcite system are biological species, temperature, and salinity. Hare (1963) further demonstrated that the organic matrix in shell carbonates of, e.g., molluscs, is partly responsible for the type of mineral species formed by the organisms. Perhaps future studies in this area of biogeochemistry may reveal in greater detail the factors that control the mineralization pattern in biological systems. In Figure 27 (Lowenstam, 1963), the complexity of biological mineralization becomes evident. This diagram also illustrates that calcite and aragonite are the most widespread mineral species in the plant and animal kingdom.

Aside from the aragonite-calcite relationship, many studies have explored the trace element composition of limestones and shell carbonates. The list of trace elements that can become incorporated into calcium and magnesium carbonates is rather limited; the principal cations incorporated are, of course, those whose ionic size and charge make them suitable substitutes for calcium and magnesium.

	Algae	Protozoa	Porifera	Coelenterata	Bryozoa	Brachiopoda	Annelida	Mollusca	Arthropoda	Echinodermata	Hemichordata	Chordata
Carbonates												
Aragonite	+	+		+	+		+	+	+		+	+
Calcite	+	+	+	+	+	+	+	+	+	+		
Arag. & Calcite		?	+	+			+	+	+			
"Amorphous"			+				+	+				
Silica												
Amorphous	+	+	+					?				
Phosphates												
Hydroxyapatite						+						+
Undefined								+	+			
+ Calcite									+			
Fe-Oxides												
Magnetite								+				
Goethite								+				
Magn. & Goethite								+				
Amorphous (Fe)		+						+				
+ Aragonite								+				
Sulfates												
Celestite		+										
Barite		?										

Fig. 27 Distribution of skeletal mineral species according to phylum (after Lowenstam, 1963)

Elements deserving investigation include strontium, cadmium, tin, and manganese (Goldberg, 1957).

One of the most promising trace elements is strontium; its distribution in limestones and calcareous fossils has been studied in some detail though most of the work has been done on marine sediments and shell materials (Lowenstam, 1963; Kulp et al., 1952; Turekian, 1955; Turekian and Kulp, 1956; Chilingar, 1956a; Dodd, 1961; Gross, 1961; Thompson and Chow, 1955). In the case of $CaCO_3$ polymorphs magnesium can also substitute for calcium (Chave, 1954a; Fairbridge, 1957).

In recent years a number of studies have been made of the biogeochemistry of magnesium and strontium in the skeletons of calcareous organisms (Pilkey and Hower, 1960). A certain correlation has been suggested between shell composition and chemical and physical environmental factors, such as salinity and temperature. According to Goldsmith (1959), the high concentration of $MgCO_3$ in solid solution in many of the marine organisms is obviously a non-equilibrium configuration; for instance, a great number of calcareous algae contain a quantity of $MgCO_3$ in solid solution that would only be stable at approximately 800°C. This fact will have an important bearing on the stability of high Mg-calcites during diagenesis and on the dolomite problem altogether.

It is rather remarkable that certain carbonate layers of a shell are sensitive to changes in temperature or salinity while others do not respond at all. These changes are reflected in the Sr/Ca and the Mg/Ca ratios.

As shown by Chave (1954a), Chilingar (1953, 1962) and others, the $MgCO_3$ content of certain fossils appears to be directly related to both water temperature and salinity. Besides temperature and salinity the phylogenetic level also has a contributing influence (Fig. 28). The greatest enrichment in $MgCO_3$, i.e., of ~ 30 per cent, has been reported from calcareous algae. Chave (1954a) states that the mineralogical form of the carbonate is the most critical factor in determining the amount of magnesium that can enter shell carbonates. The magnesium carbonate level of aragonites rarely exceeds 1 per cent, while biogenic calcites usually contain more than 1 per cent $MgCO_3$, and often have up to 20 to 30 per cent. It is highly questionable whether the magnesium and strontium content even of unaltered fossils can be used for the determination of paleotemperatures and salinities. For magnesium and, to a smaller degree, strontium, also can be affected by

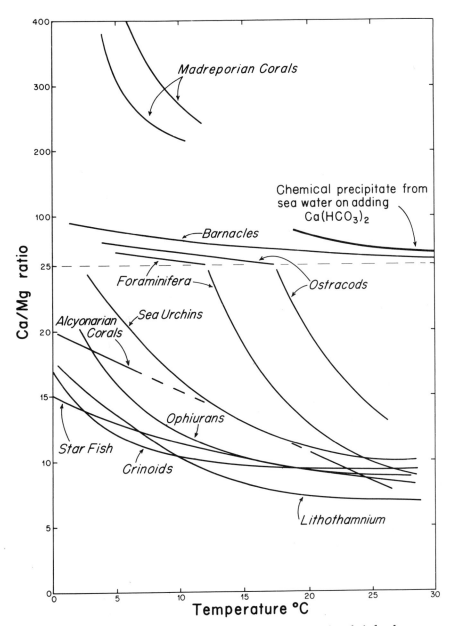

Fig. 28 Dependence on temperature of Ca/Mg ratio of skeletal structures of organisms and direct chemical precipitates out of sea water (after Chilingar, 1953, 1962; Clarke and Wheeler, 1922; and Chave 1954a)

at least six factors: (1) temperature, (2) salinity, (3) crystal structure (aragonite vs. calcite), (4) kind of layer in the fossil shell, (5) phylogenetic level, and (6) diagenesis. A critical review on the significance of trace elements in ancient unrecrystallized shell materials for geochemical and paleoecological studies has been made by Pilkey and Goodell (1964).

5. DOLOMITE

Perfectly ordered dolomites differ from the calcite-structure type carbonates in that exactly half of the Ca^{+2} positions in calcite are substituted for Mg^{+2} ions. Cation planes entirely populated by Ca^{+2} alternate with those completely occupied by Mg^{+2} ions. Thus, the triangular CO_3^{-2} groups are placed between one Ca^{+2} and one Mg^{+2} plane (Graf and Lamar, 1955; Goldsmith, 1959).

Experimental work by Graf and Goldsmith indicates that somewhat elevated temperatures ($\sim 200°C$) are necessary to produce — at least within reasonable time — a perfectly ordered dolomite. At lower temperatures, protodolomite is the only reaction product that comes close to a dolomite structure. Protodolomites are dolomite-like materials which contain up to about 10 mole per cent excess of $CaCO_3$ (Goldsmith and Graf, 1958).

Dolomite deposits, on the other hand, are widely distributed in the stratigraphic column. On the basis of geological and petrographical evidence, a number of these ancient dolomite deposits undoubtedly are of syngenetic origin (Sander, 1937), and a voluminous literature has accumulated on what is generally referred to as the "dolomite problem." This problem is mainly concerned with the failure of experimental dolomite precipitation at room temperature as against the ample occurrence of syngenetic dolomites in ancient marine sediments. For general references on this subject, one may consult Fairbridge (1957), Cloud and Barnes (1957), and Ingerson (1962).

Since Strakhov (1953) for the first time reported recent dolomites from Lake Balkhash, many reports have come in regarding recent dolomite deposits from many places all over the world. A selected list of localities follows: (1) Bahama evaporite ponds (Miller, 1961), (2) Florida Bay area (Taft, 1961), (3) South Australian lagoons (Alderman and Skinner, 1957; Skinner, 1960; Skinner et al., 1963; Alderman and von der Borch, 1960), (4) Persian Gulf (Wells, 1962; Wells and Illing, 1964), (5) Lake Bonneville (Graf et al., 1959, 1961; Bissell and Chilingar, 1962), (6) Deep Spring Lake, California (Peterson et al., 1963), and (7) South Africa caliche deposits (Gevers, personal communication). In all cases the geological field criteria and the petrographical relationship of coexisting CaCO₃ carbonates and dolomites are in support of the penecontemporaneous nature of both the dolomite and the various CaCO₃ species.

Whereas some of the investigators first assumed a syngenetic origin of the recent dolomite deposits with the dolomites being precipitated, the present consensus is that they are a product of early diagenetic metasomatism of calcite. By means of stable isotope investigations it was even possible to outline the mechanism of how these dolomites were formed. In view of the considerable importance of isotope data for the general understanding of the "dolomite problem" a few details are presented below.

The best approach involves a study of dolomite-calcite syngenetic pairs. Data by Clayton and Epstein (1958), Engel et al. (1958), and Epstein et al. (1964) suggest that dolomites precipitated in an aqueous environment at room temperature should be heavier by about 6 to 10 per mil in δO^{18} than cogenetic calcites and aragonites. In view of this considerable isotope fractionation between calcite and dolomite, it might be expected that dolomites and calcites precipitated in the same environment of deposition will also have a difference in δO^{18} values of about 6 to 10 per mil at room temperature.

Isotope data of recent dolomite-calcite pairs from some of the aforementioned localities, however, show no significant difference between calcite and dolomite (Degens and Epstein, 1964). The lack of such a relationship in the investigated sedimentary dolomite-calcite pairs and the consistent Δ-dolomite-calcite values* of about zero suggest that the dolomite did not precipitate from an aqueous solution (Fig. 29). Dolomite must have been produced by way of metasomatism of calcite, and dolomitization must have proceeded without significantly altering the O^{18}/O^{16} ratio of the precursor carbonate. That is, the transformation of the original calcareous ooze to dolomite must have taken place without chemically affecting the CO_3^{-2} unit. From this it can be inferred that the dolomite grew out of crystalline calcium carbonate under solid state conditions. It should be pointed out that

---

* Δ-dolomite-calcite is the difference between δO^{18} dolomite and δO^{18} calcite, and thus a measure of the magnitude of oxygen isotope fractionation between these two carbonate species.

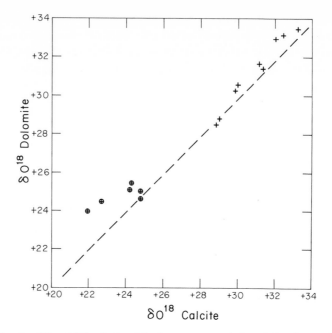

Fig. 29 The δO^{18} relationship between coexisting dolomites and calcites of recent age; + marine environment; ⊕ continental salt lake environment (after Epstein et al., 1964)

for structural reasons aragonite first has to become inverted to calcite before dolomitization may proceed.

In this connection the data of Fairbridge (1957) on the occurrence and origin of the famous Funafuti dolomite are of interest. According to his observation, calcareous algae enriched in $MgCO_3$ are geochemically reorganized into low Mg-calcite and dolomite during diagenesis. Sea water in this case presumably does not serve as a potential Mg-source for the newly formed dolomite. This opinion of the thermodynamic instability of $MgCO_3$ that is present in solid solution in $CaCO_3$ is also supported by the work of Chave (1954b), Lowenstam (1961), Seibold (1962), and Chilingar (1953, 1962). According to the isotope data by Epstein et al. (1963), the reorganization into calcite and dolomite seems to have no significant isotope effect on the Funafuti dolomite, and the δ-values of the dolomites seem to correspond to those originally fixed in the calcium carbonate at the time of its formation.

The formation of dolomites at the expense of calcite and aragonite in some recent marine environments agrees with thermodynamic considerations. For instance, Goldsmith (1959), Kramer (1959), and Garrels et al. (1960) concluded on the basis of solubility studies and calculations of free energies of formation that in a marine environment and at room temperature dolomite is the stable carbonate species with respect to calcite, aragonite, or magnesite. That dolomite does not spontaneously precipitate out of the sea at the present time, but is formed shortly afterwards in the calcareous muds, may, however, have kinetic reasons. It is interesting to note that some of the recent primary dolomites have carbon[14] ages of a few thousand years (Graf et al., 1952, 1961; Skinner et al., 1963; and others).

One may speculate that primary dolomite formation in ancient environments took place exclusively by way of $CaCO_3$ metasomatism. Daly (1907, 1909), Vinogradov et al. (1957), Sarin (1962), and a number of other investigators, however, express a different opinion on this subject. They assume that, for instance, the chemistry of the sea in terms of the Ca/Mg ratio, alkalinity, etc., or the amount of carbon dioxide in the atmosphere may have changed during the history of the earth. These authors also claim that such changes not only promoted a direct (syngenetic) precipitation of dolomite (primary dolomites), but also caused a fluctuation of the Ca/Mg ratio in fossil carbonate rocks; for the decrease in Ca/Mg ratio with increasing geologic age (Fig. 30) is linked to the evolution of dolomite. The slight inconsistency, i.e., a decrease in the Ca/Mg ratio, from the Cretaceous to the Present has been accounted for by the enforced extraction of lime from the sea by pelagic calcareous foraminifera and coccoliths.

Isotope studies by Degens and Epstein (1964) on ancient marine dolomite-calcite pairs of penecontemporaneous diagenetic and epigenetic origin from the Pre-Cambrian up to the Tertiary suggest different mechanism of dolomite formation. They reveal the following results.

(1) All sedimentary dolomites, independent of age (at least for the last 1000 million years), environment, and mode of formation (whether syngenetic, diagenetic, or epigenetic) are products of $CaCO_3$ metasomatism;

(2) dolomitization always proceeds under solid state conditions without chemically altering the CO_3^{-2} unit of the $CaCO_3$ precursor;

(3) in contrast to calcite and aragonite, dolomite is very reluctant to adjust isotopically to changes in temperatures and to the O^{18}/O^{16}

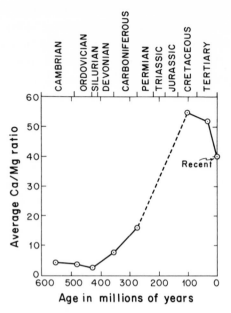

Fig. 30   Relationship between Ca/Mg ratios and geologic age (after Chilingar, 1956)

ratio of formation waters. This makes dolomites of marine origin a useful tool for the evaluation of paleotemperatures in the ancient sea;

(4) late diagenetic-epigenetic dolomitization is frequently a two-step process. The original limestone first recrystallizes into secondary calcite which subsequently is metasomatically replaced by dolomite. The occurrence of dolomitization pattern (e.g., veins) that cut across primary, sedimentary features can be explained this way.

It is at present not fully understood what kind of environmental conditions in terms of alkalinity, organic activity, salinity, temperatures, or other parameters have to exist for dolomite to be formed. It appears, however, that all sedimentary dolomites are similar in their mode of formation. Most probably the various $CaCO_3$ polymorphs are metastable in the majority of the diagenetic environments; gradually they are transformed into the more stable configuration, i.e., dolomite by straight-forward solid diffusion mechanism. Aragonites, however, first have to become inverted to calcite before dolomitization may proceed. The fact that the Ca/Mg ratio of carbonates generally decreases with increasing geologic age may have the simple explanation that progressively older rocks have —

statistically speaking — better chances of becoming dolomitized than comparatively younger sediments. It is also conceivable that in the Pre-Cambrian and Paleozoic Sea the organisms preferentially deposited high-magnesium calcite. Due to the metastability of magnesium calcite the diagenetic dolomite formation was favored. The sudden appearance of relatively advanced forms of life at about the start of the Cambrian, as evidenced by the detailed morphological shell structures, may also be linked to this phenomenon. Prior to the Cambrian, organisms deposited metastable mineral phases such as high-magnesium calcites, amorphous silica or certain iron oxyhydrates, which during transition into the stable modification, i.e., low magnesium calcite and dolomite, microcrystalline quartz, and hematite erased the biological record. Thus, organic tissues that once favored the deposition of metastable minerals now started to deposit stable modifications such as calcite or phosphates.

The speed of dolomitization appears to be greatly increased in hypersaline environments, as can be evidenced by the presence of penecontemporaneous dolomites in certain evaporite basins of deposition. Also, the greater abundance of $MgCO_3$ in solid solution enhances the chances of early dolomite formation. Perhaps alternating layers of dolomite and calcite (Bissell and Chilingar, 1962), even within a rock specimen, are a result of chemical differences in the original calcites in terms of $MgCO_3$ variations. That is, only the calcite layers with greater amounts of $MgCO_3$ in solid solution yielded dolomite; the others remained calcite.

Other geochemical aspects of dolomites and limestones which, however, will not be individually discussed, include porosity and permeability (Murray, 1960; Weyl, 1960; Chilingar, 1956b; Aschenbrenner and Chilingar, 1960), thermoluminescence (Angino, 1959; Daniels, 1961; Zeller and Roncor, 1963; Johnson, 1960; Zeller et al., 1957), microbial synthesis (Lalou, 1957; Neher and Rohrer, 1958), chemical composition of aqueous solution, both syngenetic and diagenetic, in the dolomite-forming system (Fairbridge, 1950, 1957; Adams and Rhodes, 1960; Teodorovich, 1961; Chave, 1960; Schoeller, 1956; and others), trace element studies (Graf, 1962), and classification systems (Chilingar, 1960; Folk, 1959).

6. MINOR VARIETIES

(a) *Magnesite*. Although most magnesite deposits represent alteration products of crystalline rocks, sedimentary magnesite is sporadically found in ancient lagoonal or salt lake deposits, in the zone of surface weathering in masses of ultrabasic rocks, in disseminated grains in evaporites, and also in association with anhydrite rocks (Teodorovich, 1961; Milton and Eugster, 1959; Nishihara, 1926; Schaller and Benderson, 1932; Stewart, 1949). Some of these sedimentary magnesite occurrences are believed to be primary in origin; but predominantly they are secondary products formed during diagenesis and epigenesis.

(b) *Siderite*. Aside from the importance of siderite as sedimentary iron ore (Taylor et al., 1952; Cohen, 1952; Teodorovich, 1961), its presence in sediments in the form of spherical concretions (spherosiderites), matrices or in a disseminated stage, can be used as an environmental indicator for low Eh-conditions. In this respect siderite resembles the rest of the iron minerals (e.g., goethite, lepidocrocite, pyrite, etc.) as a sensitive Eh- indicator mineral. It is, therefore, no accident that finely disseminated siderite is found along with iron sulfides, e.g., marcasite and pyrrhotite (Milton and Eugster, 1959), or asphaltic materials, oil shales, coals, and other organic constituents. Particularly in connection with geochemical studies on early Pre-Cambrian sediments, siderite and other iron minerals may be extremely helpful to pinpoint the time when the earth atmosphere and hydrosphere gradually changed from reducing to oxidizing conditions about two to three billion years ago.

(c) *Sodic carbonates*. The phase relationship in the system $NaHCO_3$-Na_2CO_3-H_2O has been determined by Milton and Eugster (1959). The results are illustrated in Figure 31. At elevated $CO_{2(atm)}$ pressures nahcolite is stable over the whole temperature range studied. Soda will preferentially precipitate in cooler environments, and trona lies between thermonatrite and nahcolite and will never form below 20°C. The stability field of thermonatrite is interesting because it may eventually allow us to estimate temperatures of deeply buried sediments which contain sodic carbonates.

(d) *Malachite and Azurite*. Malachite and azurite are characteristic minerals in the zone of oxidation of copper sulfide deposits, especially if these deposits contain carbonates or if they occur in limestones. Both minerals are also associated with sedimentary cupriferous sandstones in the German Triassic and the Permian of Russia (Teodorovich, 1961). Azurite apparently forms in environments somewhat less alkaline than malachite.

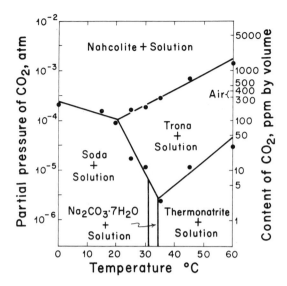

Fig. 31 $P_{CO_2}T$ diagram of the system $NaHCO_3–Na_2CO_3–H_2O$. The CO_2 content of present-day air has been indicated at the right (after Milton and Eugster, 1959)

7. Selected Topics of Carbonate Geochemistry

(a) *Concretions.* Concretions are the result of the transport of solutes in compacting sediments. As a matter of fact, most concretions are formed during the early stages of diagenesis, at a time when the, now lithified, muds were plastic enough to flow around them (Weeks, 1957). But occasionally late-diagenetic or epigenetic concretions may also have developed. The deposition of carbonate may be triggered off by decaying organic matter. For instance, central basin sediments in which most of the calcium concretion bearing shales were deposited, were not favorable to carbonate deposition. However, an alkalinity adequate for the precipitation of carbonates was locally created by the ammonia that evolved during the decomposition of organic matter, e.g., concretions enclosing fish originated this way. Lippmann (1955) and Seibold (1962) showed that concretions can also be formed shortly after deposition of the host strata when so-called "water-pillows" were developed in the compacting mud and when carbonates eventually replaced the water. The rate of formation of calcareous concretions has been considered by Pantin (1958).

(b) *Calcareous Ooliths.* Ooliths occur as surface deposits in various parts of the world. Among the deposits which have been reported in the literature are the Canary Islands, the Bahama Banks, the southern coast of Florida, the Red Sea, and the Great Salt Lake (Illing, 1954; Lengyel, 1937; Linck, 1903; Mathews, 1930; Thorp, 1939; Smith, 1940; Quiring, 1944; Rusnak, 1960; and others). Whereas all recent ooliths are aragonitic all ancient ones are calcitic.

According to the three principal theories of oolith formation ooliths are (1) chemical precipitates, (2) built by action of plant and animals, and (3) formed by physical aggregation of small particles rolling around on the bottom of the sea (Monaghan and Lytle, 1956; Oppenheimer, 1961, and others).

Controlled laboratory studies by Monaghan and Lytle (1956) show that calcareous ooliths can originate by (1) chemical precipitation from sea water and (2) the growth of sulfate reducing bacteria in sea water. The authors further assume that the presence of magnesium ions in sea water causes calcium carbonate to precipitate as aragonite rather than calcite. It should be noted that the carbonate ion concentration at the time of precipitation exceeded 0.002 mol per liter, which is a greater concentration than is normally observed in sea water.

(c) *Caliche Deposits.* Caliche underlies certain soils as a single, a double, or, in a few cases, as multiple layers (Brown, 1956; Bretz and Hornberg, 1949). Caliche is composed of varying but roughly equal parts of calcite or secondary silica, and clastic particles. The latter in general are non-adjoining. Without the carbonate cement from the rock the particles would collapse against one another. Caliche is the product of long continued deposition and results from the subsurface evaporation of soil moisture or from evaporation proceeding from surface outcrops. The ultimate source of $CaCO_3$ appears to be the bicarbonate liberated from limestone, loess, etc. This bicarbonate partially comes from atmospheric CO_2 picked up by rain water; but predominantly, it is derived from biologically generated CO_2. Bicarbonate solutions are chemically very aggressive and can dissolve even quartz and feldspars. In exchange, carbonates will be deposited. Some of the dissolved materials will be carried away in solution; others will become re-precipitated as secondary silica or authigenic overgrowth on detrital feldspars (Knetsch, 1937; Rutte, 1958; Welte, 1962). Solution, metasomatism, and redeposition of silica or carbonates may frequently take place within an area not larger than a thin section. In other words, the caliche environment represents a place where authigenic quartz and feldspar formation is presently going on. A knowledge of the chemical composition of the participating aqueous solutions may, therefore, be helpful to comprehend the process of quartz and feldspar solution and deposition in the course of diagenesis. Inasmuch as carbonate can easily replace quartz or vice versa, one ought to be able to understand why in one case calcareous fossils are metasomatically replaced by silica, and in another case the original silica of fossils is replaced by calcite.

Some caliche deposits have been formed continuously over hundreds of years and the process may still be alive. Microlayering is rather common and may reflect seasonal or annual deposition cycles. Stable isotope studies may give the answer. Caliche will form under arid to semi-arid conditions. Mineralogically, the carbonate can be calcite as well as dolomite. According to Welte (1962), the latter is preferentially formed when hypersaline solutions represent the aqueous phase during the caliche formation. For a full account of the geochemistry and geology of caliche deposits, one may consult Rutte (1958) and Welte (1962).

(d) *Stylolite Development.* Stylolites are crenulated rock structures or seams that in appearance somewhat resemble cranial sutures. They frequently can be seen on polished faces of marbles and limestone. The formation mechanism of stylolites has been the subject of many hypotheses. Pertinent literature has been reviewed by Dunnington (1954) and Brown (1959).

The "solution-pressure theory" (Stockdale, 1922, 1943, and others) of their origin is, with some modification, commonly regarded as the most likely mechanism of stylolite formation. According to this theory, hard rock is removed by solution, with simultaneous deposition of insoluble residue, in situ. Waters responsible for stylolite formation may be unsaturated meteoric waters which are charged with carbon dioxide (Dunnington, 1954). But connate waters also may participate, although these may be already saturated with electrolytes. Thus, stylolites may be considered to be the result of local supersaturation due to local high stress, invoking the "Rieke principle" in one or another of its multiple disguises (Dunnington, 1954). The dissolved material must be precipitated somehow, and redeposition can occur almost instantaneously, filling pores with secondary material. The same saturated solvent, therefore, could have served innumerable times as the transport medium; thus, stylolite formation can continue until the original porosity is almost obliterated. The semilithographic appearance of stylolite limestones supports this inference.

The formation of stylolites is by no means restricted to carbonate rocks, although they are macroscopically most impressive there. In sandstones and conglomerates they are also very common, and there is no reason to believe that the mechanism may not operate even in fine-grained clastic materials. Nevertheless, carbonate minerals and quartz appear to be the most sensitive common minerals to be affected by this type of solution-deposition phenomenon which sometimes will find its macroscopic expression in the formation of stylolites.

(e) *Age Determination.* Aside of the radiocarbon method there is so far no reliable technique developed to determine the absolute age of fossil carbonates. Preliminary studies by Broecker and his associates (personal communication), however, suggest the usefulness of, for instance, the uranium isotopes U^{238}/U^{234} and some other radiogenic isotopes for the purpose of carbonate age dating.

8. Summary

The importance of carbonate minerals for geochemical studies is well documented by the voluminous literature that has accumulated on this subject over the last 30 years. In the previous discussion a few major topics of carbonate geochemistry were selected to outline the principal mechanisms involved in carbonate solution and deposition. Emphasis was placed particularly on oxygen and carbon isotope studies in view of the fact that from these significant information can be obtained on major problems of carbonate geochemistry, such as paleotemperature evaluations, environments, mineralization phenomena in biological systems, phase relationships, diagenesis, dolomite formation, age determinations, etc. Other aspects of carbonate geochemistry have been included as comprehensively as possible within the limits of this book in order to demonstrate the wide application and potentiality of carbonate research to the general field of sedimentology.

Selected References

Adams, J. E. and M. L. Rhodes, "Dolomitization by Seepage Reflux Ion." Bull. Amer. Assoc. Petrol. Geol., **44** (1960), 1912–1920.

Alderman, A. R. and von der Borch, "Occurrence of Hydromagnesite in Sediments in South Australia." Nature, **188** (1960), 931.

Alderman, A. R. and H. C. W. Skinner, "Dolomite Sedimentation in the South-East of South Australia." Amer. J. Sci., **255** (1957), 561–567.

Angino, E. E., "Pressure Effects on Thermoluminescence of Limestone Relative to Geologic Age." J. Geophys. Research, **64** (1959), 569–573.

Antevs, E., "Geological Tests of the Varve and Radio-carbon Chronologies." J. Geol., **65** (1957), 129–148.

Aschenbrenner, B. C. and G. V. Chilingar, "Teodorovich's Method for Determining Permeability from Pore-space Characteristics of Carbonate Rocks." Bull. Amer. Assoc. Petrol. Geol., **44** (1960), 1421–1424.

Baertschi, P., "Die Fraktionierung der natürlichen Kohlenstoffisotopen im Kohlendioxydstoffwechsel grüner Pflanzen." Helv. Chim. Acta, **36** (1953), 773–781.

Baertschi, P. and S. R. Silverman, "The Determination of Relative Abundances of the Oxygen Isotopes in Silicate Rocks." Geochim. et Cosmochim. Acta, **1** (1951), 317–328.

Bien, G. S., N. W. Rakestraw, and H. E. Suess, "Radiocarbon Concentration in Pacific Ocean Water." Tellus, **12** (1960), 436–443.

Bissell, H. J. and G. V. Chilingar, "Evaporite Type Dolomite in Salt Flats of Western Utah." Sedimentology, **1** (1962), 200–210.

Bowen, R., "O^{18}/O^{16} Ratio Isotopic Paleotemperature Measurements on Cretaceous Fossils and their Significance in the Determination of the Paleoclimatology of this Period." In *Advances in Organic Geochemistry*, edited by U. Colombo and G. D. Hobson. New York: The Macmillan Company (1964), 271–283.

Bragg, W. L., *Atomic Structure of Minerals*. Ithaca, N. Y.: Cornell Univ. Press, 1937.

Bretz, J. H. and L. Hornberg, "Caliche in Southeastern New Mexico." J. Geol., **57** (1949), 491–511.

Brinkmann, R., K. O. Münnich, and J. C. Vogel, "C^{14} Altersbestimmung von Grundwasser." Naturwissenschaften, **46** (1959), 10–12.

Broecker, W. S., R. D. Gerards, M. Ewing, and B. C. Heezen, "Geochemistry and Physics of Ocean Circulation." In *Oceanography,* ed. M. Sears, Amer. Assoc. Advanc. Sci., Publ. No. **67** (1961), 301–322.

Broecker, W. S., R. Gerards, M. Ewing, and B. C. Heezen, "Natural Radiocarbon in the Atlantic Ocean." J. Geophys. Research, **65** (1960), 2903–2931.

Brown, C. N., "The Origin of Caliche in the Northeastern Llano Estacado, Texas." J. Geol., **64** (1956), 1–15.

Brown, W. W. M., "The Origin of Stylolites in the Light of a Petro-fabric Study." J. Sed. Petr., **29** (1959), 254–259.

Burling, R. W. and D. M. Garner, "A Section of C^{14} Activities of Sea Water between 9° S and 66° S in the Southwest Pacific Ocean." New Zealand J. Geol. Geophys., **2** (1959), 799–823.

Chave, K. E., "Aspects of the Biochemistry of Magnesium-1: Calcareous Marine Organisms." J. Geol., **62** (1954a), 266–283.

Chave, K. E., "Aspects of the Biogeochemistry of Magnesium-2: Calcareous Sediments and Rocks." J. Geol., **62** (1954b), 587–599.

Chave, K. E., "Evidence on History of Sea Water from Chemistry of Deeper Surface Waters of Ancient Basins." Bull. Amer. Assoc. Petrol. Geol., **44** (1960), 357–370.

Chave, K. E., K. S. Deffeyes, P. K. Weyl, R. M. Garrels, and M. E. Thompson, "Observations on the Solubility of Skeletal Carbonates in Aqueous Solution." Science, **137** (1962), 33–34.

Chilingar, G. V., "Use of Ca/Mg Ratios in Limestones as a Geologic Tool." The Compass of Sigma Gamma Epsilon, **30** (1953), 202–209.

Chilingar, G. V., "Relationship between Ca/Mg Ratios and Geologic Age." Bull. Amer. Assoc. Petrol. Geol., **40** (1956a), 2256–2266.

Chilingar, G. V., "Use of Ca/Mg Ratio in Porosity Studies." Bull. Amer. Assoc. Petrol. Geol., **40** (1956b), 2489–2493.

Chilingar, G. V., "Notes on Classification of Carbonate Rocks on Basis of Chemical Composition." J. Sed Petr., **30** (1960), 157–158.

Chilingar, G. V., and H. J. Bissell, *Dolomites.* In "Ente Nationale Idrocarburi, Petroleum Encyclopedia." Rome: University of Rome, 1963.

Chilingar, G. V., "Dependence on Temperature of Ca/Mg Ratio of Skeletal Structures of Organisms and Direct Chemical Precipitates Out of Sea Water." Bull. South. Calif. Acad. Sci., **61** (pt. 1), (1962), 45–60.

Chilingar, G. V., "Possible Loss of Magnesium from Fossils to the Surrounding Environment." J. Sed. Petr., **32** (1962), 136–139.

Clark, S. P., "A Note on Calcite-Aragonite Equilibrium." Amer. Mineralogist, **42** (1957), 564–566.

Clayton, R. N., "Oxygen Isotope Fractionation between O^{18}/O^{16} Ratios in Calcium Carbonate and Water." J. Chem. Phys., **34** (1961a), 724–726.

Clayton, R. N. and E. T. Degens, "Use of Carbon-Isotope Analyses for Differentiating Fresh-water and Marine Sediments." Bull. Amer. Assoc. Petrol. Geol., **43** (1959), 890–897.

Clayton, R. N. and S. Epstein, "The Relationship between O^{18}/O^{16} Ratios in Coexisting Quartz, Carbonate and Iron Oxides from Various Geological Deposits." J. Geol., **66** (1958), 352–373.

Clayton, R. N. and S. Epstein, "The Use of Oxygen Isotopes in High-Temperature Geological Thermometry." J. Geol., **69** (1961), 447–452.

Cloud, P. E., Jr., "Behaviour of Calcium Carbonate in Sea Water." Geochim. et Cosmochim. Acta, **26** (1962), 867–884.

Cloud, P. E. and V. E. Barnes, "Early Ordovician Sea in Central Texas." Geol. Soc. Amer. Memoir, **67** (1957), 163–214.

Cohen, E., "The Nature of Silicates and Carbonates of Iron in the Northampton Sand Ironstone of Central England." In *Symposium sur les gisements de fer du monde, vol. 2,* **19**th Int. Geol. Congr., Algiers, 1952.

Compston, W., "The Carbon Isotopic Compositions of Certain Marine Invertebrates and Coals from the Australian Permian." Geochim. et Cosmochim. Acta, **18** (1960), 1–22.

Corless, J. T. "Variations of the Ratio $Ca^{48}/$ (total Ca) in the Natural Environment." Ph.D. Thesis, Massachusetts Inst. Techn., July, 1963.

Corless, J. T., K. A. Rahn, and J. W. Winchester, "Variations in the Ratio $Ca^{48}/$(total Ca) in Natural Materials." Trans. Amer. Geophys. Union, **44** (1963), 69–70.

Craig, H., "The Geochemistry of the Stable Carbon Isotopes." Geochim. et Cosmochim, Acta, **3** (1953), 53–92.

Craig, H., "Carbon-13 in Plants and the Relationships between Carbon-13 and Carbon-14 Variations in Nature." J. Geol., **62**, (1954b), 115–149.

Craig, H., "Geochemical Implications of the Isotopic Composition of Carbon in Ancient Rocks". Geochim. et Cosmochim. Acta, **6**, (1954a) 186–196.

Craig, H., "The Natural Distribution of Radiocarbon and the Exchange of Carbon Dioxide between Atmosphere and Sea." Tellus, **9** (1957a), 1–17.

Craig, H., "Isotopic Standards for Carbon and Oxygen and Correction Factors for Mass-spectrometric Analysis of Carbon Dioxide." Geochim et Cosmochim. Acta, **12** (1957b), 133–149.

Craig, H., "The Natural Distribution of Radiocarbon: Mixing Rates in the Sea and Residence Times of Carbon and Water." In *Earth Science and Meteoritics,* Editors: H. Craig, S. L. Miller, and G. J. Wasserburg. Amsterdam: North-Holland Publishing Company, (1964) 103–114.

Curtis, R., G. Evans, D. J. J. Kinsman, and D. J. Shearman, "Association of Dolomite and Anhydrite in the Recent Sediments of the Persian Gulf." Nature, **197** (1963), 679–680.

Daly, R. A., "The Limeless Ocean of Pre-Cambrian Time." Amer. J. Sci., **23** (1907), 93–115.

Daly, T. A., "First Calcareous Fossils and the Evolution of Limestone." Geol. Soc. Amer. Bull., **20** (1909), 153–170.

Daniels, F., "Kinetics and Thermoluminescence in Geochemistry." Geochim. et Cosmochim. Acta, **22** (1961) 65–74.

Dansgaard, W., "The Abundance of O^{18} in Atmospheric Water and Water Vapour," Tellus, **5** (1953), 461–469.

Daughtry, A. C., D. Perry, and M. Williams, "Magnesium Isotope Distribution in Dolomite." Geochim. et Cosmochim. Acta, **26** (1962) 857–866.

Deer, W. A., R. A. Howie, and J. Zussman, "Rock-forming Minerals." Vol. 5, London: Longmans, Green and Co., 1962.

Degens, E. T. and S. Epstein, "Oxygen and Carbon Isotope Ratios in Coexisting Calcites and Dolomites from Recent and Ancient Sediments." Geochim. et Cosmochim. Acta, **28** (1964), 23–44.

Degens, E. T. and S. Epstein, "Relationship between O^{18}/O^{16} Ratios in Coexisting Carbonates, Cherts and Diatomites." Bull. Amer. Assoc. Petrol. Geol., **46** (1962) 534–542.

De Vries, H., "Measurement and Use of Natural Radiocarbon." In *Researches in Geochemistry,* edited by P. H. Abelson. New York: John Wiley & Sons, Inc. (1959) 169-189.

Dodd, J. R., *Paleoecological Implications of the Mineralogy, Structure, and Strontium and Magnesium Contents of the West-Coast Species of the Genus Mytilus.* Ph.D. Thesis, California Institute of Technology, July, 1961.

Dunnington, H. V., "Stylolite Development Post-dates Rock Induration." J. Sed. Petr., **24** (1954), 27–49.

Ellis, A., "The Solubility of Calcite in Carbon Dioxide Solutions." Amer. J. Sci., **257** (1959), 354–365.

Eckelmann, W. R., W. S. Broecker, D. W. Whitlock, and J. R. Allsup, "Implications of Carbon Isotopic Composition of Total Organic Carbon of Some Recent Sediments and Ancient Oils." Bull. Amer. Assoc. Petrol. Geol., **46** (1962), 699–704.

Emery, K. O. and E. E. Bray, "Radiocarbon Dating of California Basin Sediments." Bull. Amer. Assoc. Petr. Geol. **46** (1962) 1839–1856.

Emiliani, C., "Oligocene and Miocene Temperatures of the Equatorial and Subtropical Atlantic Ocean." J. Geol., **64** (1956), 281–288.

Emiliani, C., "Paleotemperature Analysis of Core 280 and Pleistocene Correlations." J. Geol., **66** (1958), 264–275.

Emiliani, C., "Pleistocene Temperatures." J. Geol., **63** (1955), 538–578.

Engel, A. E. J., R. N. Clayton, and S. Epstein, "Variations in Isotopic Composition of Oxygen and Carbon in Leadville Limestone and in its Hydrothermal and Metamorphic Phases." J. Geol., **66** (1958), 374–393.

Epstein, S., "Nuclear Processes in Geologic Settings." Washington, D. C., Natl. Acad. Sci., U. S.-Natl. Research Council, Publ. **400**, 1957.

Epstein, S., "The Variations of the O^{18}/O^{16} Ratio in Nature and Some Geologic Implications." In *Researches in Geochemistry*, edited by P. H. Abelson. New York: John Wiley & Sons, Inc., (1959), 217–240.

Epstein, S., R. Buchsbaum, H. A. Lowenstam, and H. C. Urey, "Revised Carbonate Water Isotopic Temperature Scale." Bull. Geol. Soc. Amer., **64** (1953), 1315–1326.

Epstein, S., D. L. Graf, and E. T. Degens, "Oxygen Isotope Studies on the Origin of Dolomites." In *Isotopic and Cosmic Chemistry*, edited by H. Craig, S. L. Miller, and G. J. Wasserburg. Amsterdam: North-Holland Publishing Company, (1964), 169–180.

Epstein, S. and T. Mayeda, "Variation of O^{18} Content of Waters from Natural Sources." Geochim et Cosmochim. Acta, **4** (1953), 213–224.

Ewald, P. P. and C. Hermann, Strukturbericht 1913–1928 (Ergänzungsband der Ztschr. Krist.), Leipzig: 1931.

Fairbridge, R. W., "Recent and Pleistocene Coral Reefs of Australia." J. Geol., **58** (1950), 330–401.

Fairbridge, R. W., "The Dolomite Question." *Symp. Regional Aspects of Carbonate Decomposition*, edited by R. J. LeBlanc and J. G. Breeding. Soc. Econ. Paleo. Min. Special Publication No. **5** (1957), 125–178.

Fergusson, G. J., "Reduction of Atmospheric Radiocarbon Concentration by Fossil Fuel Carbon Dioxide and the Mean Life of Carbon Dioxide in the Atmosphere." Proc. Roy. Soc. (London), **243** (1958), 561–574.

Folk, R. L., "Practical Petrographic Classification of Limestones." Bull. Amer. Assoc. Petr. Geol., **43** (1959), 1–38.

Garrels, R. M., *Mineral Equilibria at Low Temperature and Pressure*. New York: Harper and Brothers, Publishers, 1960.

Garrels, R. M., "Rates of Geochemical Reactions at Low Temperatures and Pressures." In *Researches in Geochemistry*, edited by P. H. Abelson. New York: John Wiley & Sons, Inc., (1959), 25–37.

Garrels, R. M. and R. M. Dreyer, "Mechanism of Limestone Replacement at Low Temperatures and Pressures." Geol. Soc. Amer. Bull., **63** (1952), 325–379.

Garrels, R. M., M. E. Thompson, and R. Siever, "Control of Carbonate Solubility by Carbonate Complexes." Amer. J. Sci., **259** (1961), 24–25.

Garrels, R. M., M. E. Thompson, and R. Siever, "Stability of Some Carbonates at 25° C and One Atmosphere Total Pressures." Amer. J. Sci., **258** (1960), 402–418.

Goldberg, E. D., "Biogeochemistry of Trace Metals." Geol. Soc. Amer., Mem., **67** (1957), 345.

Goldsmith, J. R., "Some Aspects of the Geochemistry of Carbonates." In *Researches in Geochemistry,* edited by P. H. Abelson. New York: John Wiley & Sons, Inc., (1959), 336–358.

Goldsmith, J. R. and D. L. Graf, "Structural and Compositional Variations in Some Natural Dolomites." J. Geol., **66** (1958), 678–693.

Graf, D. L., "Minor Element Distribution in Sedimentary Carbonate Rocks." Geochim. et Cosmochim. Acta, **26** (1962), 849–856.

Graf, D. L. and J. R. Goldsmith, "Some Hydrothermal Syntheses of Dolomite and Protodolomite." J. Geol., **64** (1956), 173–186.

Graf, D. L. and J. E. Lamar, "Properties of Calcium and Magnesium Carbonates and their Bearing on Some Uses of Carbonate Rocks." Econ. Geol., Fiftieth Anniversary Vol. (1959), 639–713.

Graf, D. L., A. L. Eardley, and N. F. Shimp, "A Preliminary Report on Magnesium Carbonate Formation in Glacial Lake Bonneville." J. Geol., **69** (1961), 219–223.

Graf, D. L., A. L. Eardley, and N. F. Shimp, "Dolomite Formation in Lake Bonneville, Utah." (Abstract): Bull. Amer. Geol. Soc., **70** (1959), 1610.

Gross, M. G. Jr., *Carbonate Sedimentation and Diagenesis of Pleistocene Limestones in the Bermuda Islands.* Ph.D. Thesis, California Institute of Technology, July 1961.

Hare, P. E., *The Amino Acid Composition of the Organic Matrix of Some Recent and Fossil Shells of Some West Coast Species of Mytilus.* Ph.D. Thesis, California Institute of Technology, Div. Geol. Sci., July 1962.

Hare, P. E., "Amino Acids in the Proteins from Aragonite and Calcite in the Shells of *Mytilus Californianus.*" Science, **139** (1963), 216–217.

Hirt, B. and S. Epstein, *A Search for Isotopic Variations in Some Terrestrial and Meteoritic Calcium.* (in press), 1964.

Illing, L. V., "Bahaman Calcareous Sands." Bull. Amer. Assoc. Petr. Geol., **38** (1954), 1–95.

Ingerson, E., "Problems of the Geochemistry of Sedimentary Carbonate Rocks." Geochim. et Cosmochim. Acta, **26** (1962), 815–847.

Jamieson, J. C., "Phase Equilibrium in the System Calcite-Aragonite." J. Chem. Phys., **21** (1953), 1385–1390.

Jeffrey, P. M., W. Compston, D. Greenhalgh, and J. de Laeter, "On the Carbon-13 Abundance of Limestones and Coals." Geochim. et Cosmochim. Acta, 7 (1955), 255–286.

Johnson, N. M., "Thermoluminescence in Biogenic Calcium Carbonates." J. Sed. Petr., 30 (1960), 305–313.

Johnston, J., H. S. Merwin, and E. D. Williamson, "The Several Forms of Calcium Carbonate." J. Amer. Sci., Ser. 4, 41 (1916), 473.

Kanwisher, J., "pCO₂ in Sea Water and Its Effect on the Movement of CO₂ in Nature." Tellus, 12 (1960), 209–215.

Kaye, C. A., "The Effect of Solvent Motion on Limestone Solution." J. Geol., 65 (1957), 35–46.

Keeling, C. D., "The Concentration and Isotopic Abundance of Atmospheric Carbon Dioxide in Rural Areas." Geochim. et Cosmochim. Acta, 13 (1958), 322–334.

Keith, M. L. and G. M. Anderson, "Radiocarbon Dating: Fictitious Results with Mollusk Shells." Science, 141 (1963), 634–637.

Kitano, Y., "Polymorphism of Calcium Carbonate." Kôgyô Kagaku Zasshi, 59 (1956), 1346–1350 (cited from: Chem. Abstr., 52, 14438).

Knetsch, C., "Beiträge zur Kenntnis von Krustenbildungen." Ztschr. Deutsch. geol. Ges., 89 (1937), 177–192.

Kramer, J. R., "Correction on Some Earlier Data on Calcite and Dolomite in Sea Water." J. Sed. Petr., 29 (1959), 465–469.

Krejci-Graf, K. and F. E. Wickman, "Ein geochemisches Profil durch den Lias alpha (Zur Frage der Entstehung des Erdöls)." Geochim. et Cosmochim. Acta, 18 (1960), 259–272.

Kulp, J. L., K. Turekian, and D. W. Boyd, "Strontium Content of Limestones and Fossils." Bull. Geol. Soc. Amer., 63 (1952), 701–716.

Lalou, C., "Studies of Bacterial Precipitation of Carbonates in Sea Water." J. Sed. Petr., 27 (1957), 190–195.

Landergren, S., "On the Relative Abundance of the Stable Carbon Isotopes in Marine Sediments." Deep-Sea Research, 1 (1954), 98–120.

Lengyel, E., "Zum Problem der Sphärokristalle." Ztschr. Krist., 97 (1937), 67–87.

Libby, W. F., Radiocarbon Dating, 2nd ed. Chicago: University of Chicago Press, 1955.

Linck, G., "Die Bildung der Oolithe und Rogensteine." N. Jb. Min., 16 (Beilage Band) (1903), 495–513.

Lippmann, F., "Ton, Geoden und Minerale des Barrême von Hoheneggelsen." Geol. Rdsch., **43** (1955), 475–503.

Lowenstam, H. A., "Factors Affecting the Aragonite: Calcite Ratios in Carbonate-secreting Marine Organisms." J. Geol., **62** (1954), 284–322.

Lowenstam, H. A., "Mineralogy, $O^{18}/^{16}$ Ratios, and Strontium and Magnesium Contents of Recent and Fossil Brachipods and their Bearing on the History of the Oceans." J. Geol., **69** (1961), 241–260.

Lowenstam, H. A., "Biological Problems Relating to the Composition and Diagenesis of Sediments." In *The Earth Sciences*, edited by T. W. Donnelly. Chicago and London: The University of Chicago Press, (1963), 137–195.

Lowenstam, H. A., "Sr/Ca Ratio of Skeletal Aragonites from the Recent Marine Biota at Palau and from Fossil Gastropods." In *Isotopic and Cosmic Chemistry*, Edited by H. Craig, S. L. Miller, and G. J. Wasserburg. Amsterdam: North-Holland Publishing Co. (1964), 114–132.

Lowenstam, H. A. and S. Epstein, "On the Origin of Sedimentary Aragonite Needles of the Great Bahama Banks." J. Geol., **65** (1957) 364–375.

Lowenstam, H. A. and S. Epstein, "Paleotemperatures of the Post-Aptian Cretaceous as Determined by the Oxygen Isotope Method." J. Geol., **62** (1954), 207–248.

MacDonald, G. J. F., "Experimental Determination of Calcite-Aragonite Equilibrium Relations at Elevated Temperatures and Pressures." Amer. Mineralogist, **41** (1956), 744–756.

Mathews, A. A. L., "Origin and Growth of Great Salt Lake Ooliths." J. Geol., **38** (1930), 633–642.

McCrea, J. M., "On the Isotopic Chemistry of Carbonates and the Paleotemperature Scale." J. Chem. Phys., **18** (1950), 849–857.

Meyer, L. and H. Koepf, *Das Kohlendioxyd und die Kohlensäure im Boden.* Handbuch der Pflanzenphysiologie, Vol. V. Heidelberg: Springer Verlag, 1958.

Miller, D. N., Jr., "Early Diagenetic Dolomite Associated with Salt Extraction Process, Inagua, Bahamas." J. Sed. Petrol., **31** (1961), 473–476.

Milton, C. and H. P. Eugster, "Mineral Assemblages of the Green River Formation." In *Researches in Geochemistry*, edited by P. H. Abelson. New York: John Wiley & Sons, Inc., (1959), 118–150.

Möller, F., "On the Influence of Changes in the CO_2 Concentration in Air on the Radiation Balance of the Earth's Surface and on the Climate." J. Geophys. Research, **68** (1963), 3877–3886.

Monaghan, P. H. and M. L. Lytle, "The Origin of Calcareous Ooliths." J. Sed. Petr., **26** (1956), 111–118.

Münnich, K. O. and J. C. Vogel, "Untersuchungen an pluvialen Wässern der Ost-Sahara." Geol. Rdsch., **52** (1962), 611–624.

Münnich, K. O., "Der Kreislauf des Radiokohlenstoffs in der Natur." Naturwissenschaften, **50** (1963) 211–218.

Münnich, K. O. and J. C. Vogel, "C-14-Altersbestimmung von Süsswasser-Kalkablagerungen." Naturwissenschaften, **46** (1959), 168–169.

Murray, R. C., "Origin of Porosity in Carbonate Rocks." J. Sed. Petr., **30** (1960), 59–84.

Neher, J. and E. Rohrer, "Dolomitbildung unter Mitwirkung von Bakterien." Eclog. Geol. Helvet., **51** (1958), 213–215.

Nishihara, H., "Magnesite Deposits of Manchuria." Econ. Geol., **21** (1926), 190.

Oppenheimer, C. H., "Note on the Formation of Spherical Aragonitic Bodies in the Presence of Bacteria from the Bahama Bank." Geochim. et Cosmochim. Acta, **23** (1961), 295–296.

Pantin, H. M., "Rate of Formation of a Diagenetic Calcareous Concretion." J. Sed. Petr., **28** (1958), 366–371.

Palache, C., H. Berman, and C. Frondel, 1951, *Dana's System of Mineralogy,* Vol. 2, 7th ed. New York: John Wiley & Sons, Inc., 1951.

Park, R. and S. Epstein, "Carbon Isotope Fractionation During Photosynthesis." Geochim. et Cosmochim. Acta, **21** (1961), 110–126.

Peterson, M. N. A., C. S. Bien, and R. A. Berner, "Radiocarbon Studies of Recent Dolomite from Deep Spring Lake, California." Jour. Geophys. Research, **68** (1963), 6493–6505.

Pilkey, O. H. and J. Hower, "The Effect of Environment on the Concentration of Skeletal Magnesium and Strontium in *Dendraster*." J. Geol., **68** (1960), 203–216.

Pilkey, O. H. and H. G. Goodell, "Comparison of the Composition of Fossil and Recent Mollusk Shells." Geol. Soc. Am. Bull., **75** (1964), 217–228.

Pobeguin, T., "Contribution a l'Etude des Carbonates du Calcium, Precipitation du Calcaire par les Vegetaux, Comparison Avec le Monde Animal." Ann. Sci. Nat. Bot., **15** (1954), 29–109.

Pytkowicz, R. M., *Rates of Inorganic Calcium Carbonate Nucleation.* (in press) 1964.

Quiring, H., "Oolithentstehung." Ztschr. deut. Geol. Ges., **96** (1944), 75–87.

Revelle, R. and H. E. Suess, "Carbon Dioxide Exchange between Atmosphere and Ocean and the Question of an Increase of Atmospheric CO_2 during the Past Decades." Tellus, **9** (1957), 18–27.

Revelle, R. and R. Fairbridge, "Carbonates and Carbon Dioxide." In *Treatise on Marine Ecology and Paleocology*, Vol. 1, Geol. Soc. Amer. Memoir, **67** (1957), 239–295.

Revelle, R. and R. H. Fleming, "The Solubility Product Constant of Calcium Carbonate in Sea Water." Fifth Pacific Sci. Congr., Canada, 1933, Proc., **3** (1934), 2089–2092.

Rusnak, G. A., "Some Observations of Recent Oolites." J. Sed. Petr., **30** (1960), 471–480.

Rutte, E., "Kalkkrusten in Spanien." N. Jb. Geol. Paläontol., Abh., **106** (1958), 52–138.

Sander, B., "Beiträge zur Kenntnis der Anlagerungsgefüge; Rhytmische Kalke und Dolomite der Trias." Min. Petr. Mitt., **48** (1937), 27–139.

Sarin, D. D., "Cyclic Sedimentation of Primary Dolomite and Limestone." J. Sed. Petr., **32** (1962), 451–471.

Schaller, W. T. and E. P. Benderson, "Mineralogy of Drill Cores from the Potash Field of New Mexico and Texas." U. S. Geol. Surv. Bull., **833** (1932).

Schoeller, H., "Geochimie des eaux souterraines." Rev. Inst. Franc. Petr. Ann. Comb. Liquid. Paris (1956), 21–28.

Seibold, E., "Kalk-konkretionen und karbonatisch gebundenes Magnesium." Geochim. et Cosmochim. Acta, **26** (1962), 899–909.

Shternina, E. B. and E. V. Frolova, "The Solubility of Calcite in the Presence of CO_2 and NaCl." Izv. fiz.-khim. anal. Akad. Nauk S.S.S.R., **21** (1952), 271–287 (cit. Chem. Abstr., **48**, 6224a).

Siegel, F. R., "The Effect of Strontium on the Aragonite-Calcite Ratios of Pleistocene Corals." J. Sed. Petr., **30** (1960), 297–304.

Silverman, S. R., "The Isotope Geology of Oxygen." Geochim. et Cosmochim. Acta, **2** (1951), 26–42.

Silverman, S. R. and S. Epstein, "Carbon Isotopic Compositions of Petroleums and Other Sedimentary Organic Materials." Bull. Amer. Assoc. Petrol. Geol., **42** (1958), 998–1012.

Skinner, H. C. W., "Formation of Modern Dolomitic Sediments in South Australian Lagoons." (Abstract): Bull. Geol. Soc. Amer., **71** (1960), 1976.

Skinner, H. C. W., B. J. Skinner, and M. Rubin, "Age and Accumulation Rate of Dolomite-bearing Carbonate Sediments in South Australia." Science, **139** (1963), 335–336.

Smith, C. L., "The Great Bahama Bank, I and II." J. Mar. Research, **3** (1940), 147–189.

Stehli, F. G., "Shell Mineralogy in Paleozoic Invertebrates." Science, **123** (1956), 1031–1032.

Stewart, F. H., "The Petrology of the Evaporites of the Eksdale No. 2 Boring, East Yorkshire. Part I. The Lower Evaporite Bed." Min. Mag., **28** (1949), 621.

Stockdale, P. B., "Stylolites: their Nature and Origin." Indiana Univ. Studies. IX, (1922), 1–97.

Stockdale, P. B., Stylolites: Primary or Secondary? J. Sed. Petr., **13** (1943), 3–12.

Strakhov, N. M., "Diagenesis of Sediments and its Significance for Sedimentary Ore Formation." Izv. Akad. Nauk S.S.S.R., **5** (1953), 12–49.

Strunz, H., *Mineralogische Tabellen* (third edition). Leipzig: Akademische Verlagsgesellschaft, Geest und Portig, (1957).

Suess, H. E., "Radiocarbon Concentration in Modern Wood." Science, **122** (1955), 415–417.

Sverdrup, H. U., M. W. Johnson, and R. H. Fleming. *The Oceans: Their Physics, Chemistry and General Biology.* Englewood Cliffs, N. J.: Prentice-Hall, Inc., 1946.

Taft, W. H., "Authigenic Dolomite in Modern Carbonate Sediments Along the Southern Coast of Florida." Science, **134** (1961), 561–562.

Taylor, H. P. Jr., and S. Epstein, "Relationship between O^{18}/O^{16} Ratios in Coexisting Minerals of Igneous and Metamorphic Rocks. Part 1. Principles and Experimental Results; Part 2. Application to Petrologic Problems." Bull. Geol. Soc. Amer. **73** (1962), 461–480; 675–693.

Taylor, J. H., W. Davies, and R. J. M. Dixie, "The Petrology of the British Mesozoic Ironstones and its Bearing on Problems of Beneficiation." In *Symposium sur les gisements de fer du monde, vol. 2.* **19**th Int. Geol. Congr., Algiers (1952).

Teodorovich, G. I., *Authigenic Minerals in Sedimentary Rocks.* Consultants Bureau Enterprise, Inc., New York, (1961). (The Russian text was published by the USSR Academy of Sciences Press, Moscow, 1958.)

Thompson, T. G. and T. J. Chow, "The Strontium-Calcium Atom Ratio in Carbonate Secreting Marine Organisms." Papers in Marine Biol. and Oceanogr., Deep-Sea Research, Suppl. to Vol. 3, (1955), 20.

Thorp, E. M., "Florida and Bahama Marine Calcareous Deposits." Amer. Assoc. Petrol. Geol., Spec. Vol. "Marine Sediments." (1939), 283–297.

Togari, K. and S. Togari, 1955, "Conditions Controlling the Crystal Form of Calcium Carbonate Minerals. Part I. On the Influence of the Temperature and the Presence of the Magnesium Ion." Hokkaido Univ., J. Fac. Sci., (Ser. 4, **9** (1955), 55–65.

Turekian, K. and J. L. Kulp, "The Geochemistry of Strontium." Geochim. et Cosmochim. Acta, **10** (1956), 245–296.

Turekian, K., "Paleoecological Significance of the Strontium-Calcium Ratio in Fossils and Sediments." Bull. Geol. Soc. Amer., **66** (1955), 155–158.

Turner, R. C., "A Theoretical Treatment of the pH of Calcareous Soils." Soil Science, **86** (1958), 32–34.

Urey, H. C., "The Thermodynamic Properties of Isotopic Substances." J. Chem. Soc., (1947), 562–581.

Urey, H. C., H. A. Lowenstam, S. Epstein, and C. R. McKinney, "Measurement of Paleotemperatures and Temperatures of the Upper Cretaceous of England, Denmark, and the Southeastern United States." Bull. Geol. Soc. Amer., **62** (1951), 399–416.

Vinogradov, A. P., A. B. Ronov, and V. M. Ratynskii, "Variation in the Chemical Composition of Carbonate Rocks of Russian Platform." Geochim. et Cosmochim. Acta, **12** (1957), 273–276.

Vogel, J. C., "Über den Isotopengehalt des Kohlenstoffs in Süsswasser-Kalkablagerungen." Geochim. et Cosmochim. Acta, **16** (1959), 236–242.

Wattenberg, H., "Kohlensäure und Kalziumkarbonat im Meere." Fortschr. Mineral. Kristal. Petrogr., **20** (1936), 168–195.

Wattenberg, H. and E. Timmermann, "Über die Sättigung des Seewassers an $CaCO_3$ und die anorganogene Bildung von Kalksedimenten." Ann. Hydrogr. Marit. Meteorol. Z. Seefahrt-Meereskunde, **64** (1936), 23–31.

Weeks, L. G., "Origin of Carbonate Concretions in Shales, Magdalena Valley, Colombia." Bull. Geol. Soc. Amer., **68** (1957), 95–102.

Weyl, P. K., "The Solution Kinetics of Calcite." J. Geol., **66** (1958), 163–176.

Weyl, P. K. "The Change in Solubility of Calcium Carbonate with Temperature and Carbon Dioxide Content." Geochim. et Cosmochim. Acta, **17** (1959), 214–225.

Weyl, P. K., "Porosity through Dolomitization: Conservation-of-mass Requirements." J. Sed. Petr., **30** (1960), 85–90.

Wickman, F. E., "Variations in the Relative Abundance of the Carbon Isotopes in Plants." Geochim. et Cosmochim. Acta, **2** (1952), 243–254.

Wray, J. L. and F. Daniels, "Precipitation of Calcite and Aragonite." J. Amer. Chem. Soc., **79** (1957), 2031–2034.

Wells, A. J., and L. V. Illing, "Present Day Precipitation of Calcium Carbonate in the Persian Gulf." In *Deltaic and Shallow Marine Deposits,* edited by L. M. J. U. van Straaten. Amsterdam-London-New York: Elsevier Publishing Company, (1964), 429–435.

Wells, A. J., "Recent Dolomite in the Persian Gulf." Nature (London), **194** (1962), 274–275.

Welte, D. H., "Sedimentologische Untersuchungen uranhaltiger Keuper-sedimente aus der Umgebung von Lichtenfels bei Coburg." Geologica Bavarica, **49** (1962), 91–123.

Zeller, E. J. and J. L. Wray, "Factors Influencing Precipitation of Calcium Carbonate." Bull. Amer. Assoc. Petrol. Geol., **40** (1956), 140–152.

Zeller, E. J. and L. B. Ronca, "Reversible and Irreversible Thermal Effects on the Thermoluminescence of Limestone." In *Earth Science and Meteoritics*. Amsterdam: North Holland Publishing Company, (1963), 282–294.

Zen, E., "Carbonate Equilibria in the Open Ocean and their Bearing on the Interpretation of Ancient Carbonate Rocks." Geochim. et Cosmochim. Acta, **18** (1960), 57–71.

Phosphates

1. CLASSIFICATION, STRUCTURE, AND CHEMISTRY

The minerals of the phosphate class all have the PO_4^{-3} ion as a fundamental structural unit. Phosphates can be classified according to the absence or presence of water and of foreign anions such as Cl^-, OH^-, F^-, SO_4^{-2} and others (Strunz, 1957). Vanadates (VO_4^{-3}) and arsenates (AsO_4^{-3}) resemble phosphates structurally and can be classified similarly.

Of the more than 150 known phosphates, the only ones which are abundant in sedimentary environments are the calcium phosphates; among these, apatite and apatite varieties are the most common minerals. A comprehensive list of sedimentary rock phosphates, including structural and chemical details, has been prepared by McConnell (1950).

The four prominent pure end-member phosphate species of the apatite group are presented in Table 10. Isomorphous series exist between individual apatites. According to Altschuler et al. (1953) and McConnell (1952a, 1952b, 1958), carbonate apatite must be considered as a distinct variety of apatite rather than as a mixture of $CaCO_3$ (calcite or aragonite) and fluor apatite. CO_3 is truly present in the structure and does not occur as a coexisting carbonate or in an adsorbed state.

The term fluor apatite is frequently substituted for the term apatite; but in case one is dealing with any of the other three varieties of apatite, the appropriate prefix chlor, hydroxy, or carbonate should

Table 10 CLASSIFICATION OF COMMON PURE END-MEMBER SEDIMENTARY PHOSPHATES.

GROUP	SPECIES	CRYSTALLOCHEMICAL FORMULA	SPACE GROUP	STRUCTURE (SCHEMATIC)
APATITE	Fluor-apatite (apatite)	$Ca_5(PO_4)_3F$	$C6_3/m$	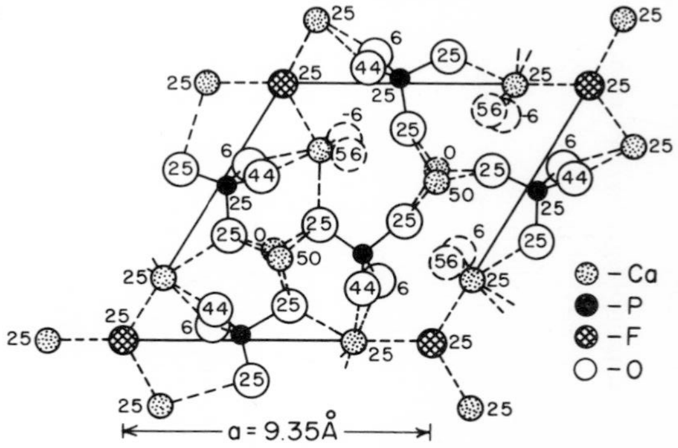
	Chlorapatite	$Ca_5(PO_4)_3Cl$		
	Hydroxyapatite	$Ca_5(PO_4)_3OH$		
	Carbonate-apatite (francolite) *	$Ca_5(PO_4,CO_3OH)_3F$		

Fluor-apatite

$a = 9.35\text{Å}$

Ca — ●
P — ●
F — ●
O — ○

* Carbonate-apatite with less than 1% fluorine is termed dahllite (carbonate-hydroxyapatite)

be employed. In Table 10, PO_4 groups can be recognized as deformed tetrahedra in the apatite structure. Each fluorine atom is surrounded by three calcium atoms on the same level, and Ca-O columns are linked with PO_4 groups to form a hexagonal network (Náray-Szabó, 1930; Mehmel, 1930, and others).

2. GEOCHEMISTRY OF PHOSPHORUS

(a) *Origin.* Among the authigenic calcium phosphates in sediments, the carbonate apatites dahllite (hydroxyl-) and francolite (fluorine-) are quantitatively the most important ones. Sediments in which carbonate phosphates are a major mineral constituent are generally called phosphorites. Those of economic importance are restricted to marine environments. Phosphorite deposits cover wide areas in North Africa (Morocco), Russia (Kara-Tau area) and the western United States. In order to give some idea of the extent of their regional distribution, it may be mentioned that the Permian marine phosphorites of the western United States, for instance, are spread across a territory of approximately 135,000 square miles in Montana, Wyoming, Utah and Nevada (McKelvey et al., 1953).

The various phosphate minerals of the phosphorite strata are generally of a cryptocrystalline nature, thoroughly mixed and virtually isotropic in nature. The word "collophane" is frequently employed as a collective term for such a complex mixture of phosphate minerals. This is analogous to the adoption of the name "limonite" for the cryptocrystalline mineral assemblage of different iron oxides and hydroxides.

Although earth scientists now agree on the whole that CO_3^{-2} is part of the structure of carbonate apatite, there is still considerable controversy regarding the mode of phosphorite formation. A summary of the different viewpoints with respect to the mineralogical and geochemical aspects of carbonate apatites has been made by Ames (1959). The main geochemical question is whether carbonate apatites should be considered as a regular chemical precipitate formed upon supersaturation of natural waters (Kazakov, 1937, 1950; McKelvey et al., 1953), a biogeochemical product formed, for instance, by the action of micro-organisms (Cayeux, 1936), or a simple replacement product caused by the introduction of PO_4 units into pre-existing calcareous materials (Bushinksy, 1935, 1964; Ames, 1959).

The first theory is at present widely accepted among geologists, though it appears that the replacement of $CaCO_3$ by phosphate solutions is the most probable mode of formation of large marine phosphorite deposits. This assumption is based on the fact that the conversion of calcite into carbonate apatite may take place at PO_4^{-3} and Ca^{+2} concentrations considerably below those required for apatite precipitation. Furthermore, in contrast to (F, OH, Cl)-apatite, the carbonate phosphates do not precipitate from aqueous solutions as determined experimentally by Klement et al. (1942). Thus, a supersaturation would only result in the precipitation of (F, OH, Cl)-apatite (Arnold, 1950). In this respect, carbonate apatites resemble closely the so-called primary dolomites which are exclusively products of early diagenesis.

The formation of carbonate apatite by calcite replacement in the system $Na_3PO_4 - CaCO_3 - H_2O$ at low temperature has been investigated in detail by Ames (1959). The mechanism of calcite-phosphate exchange was studied both under equilibrium and non-equilibrium conditions. In principle, the experiments involved a treatment of calcite with dilute Na_3PO_4 solutions at room temperature. Care was taken that the system was Ca-saturated with respect to its HCO_3^- content. In the course of the experiments, changes were made with regard to the molar concentrations of the phosphate solution, crystal size of the calcite minerals, pH, temperature, time of reaction and other parameters. Tracer techniques (radioactive isotopes) allowed the determination of the replacement rate as well as the mechanism of metasomatism.

Ames' data show that phosphate is removed from the solution at a relatively rapid rate following the reaction scheme:

$$NaOH + 3\ Na_3PO_4 + 5\ CaCO_3 \leftrightarrows Ca_5(PO_4)_3\ OH + 5\ Na_2CO_3$$

The amount of Sr^{90} removed per unit time allows a quantitative estimate of the effect of pH on the relative rate of carbonate apatite formation by replacement of calcite (Fig. 32). A pH greater than 7 is seen to be required to achieve substantial exchange rates. In the apatite lattices CO_3^{-2} can be accommodated in amounts up to about 10 per cent by weight. When CO_3^{-2} exceeds the 10 per cent level, the surplus amount of CO_3^{-2} will coexist as true carbonate, (e.g., calcite). Thus, alkaline phosphate solutions will cause rapid metasomatic replacement of calcite; the resulting carbonate apatites will have varying CO_3^{-2} contents. The essential environmental conditions required for the deposition of natural phosphates include (1) a pH greater than 7, (2) presence of calcareous materials and a system that is Ca-saturated with respect to its HCO_3^- content, (3) PO_4^{-3} concentrations exceeding 0.1 ppm, and (4) a nondepositional environment.

The replacement is little affected by large quantities of alkalies; also, the redox potential apparently does not control the exchange rate to a significant extent. Only the trace element assemblage of the carbonate apatite appears to be affected by Eh (Arrhenius, 1963). An increase in the grain size of the $CaCO_3$ precursor material, however, will reduce the efficiency of phosphate metasomatism, while an increase in temperature will speed up the reaction.

To sum up, one can say that the formation of carbonate apatite is a result of the incomplete replacement of CO_3^{-2} by PO_4^{-3}. It is suggested that if the diagenetic environment permits, the chemical composition of a completely phosphatized limestone consisting of carbonate apatite will gradually change in the direction of a regular apatite, which means a loss of CO_3^{-2} groups and a gain in OH^- or F^- with time.

(b) *Distribution and geological significance.* The literature on phosphorites is plentiful and has been reviewed by Cayeux (1939, 1941, 1950), Jaffe (1951), Gulbrandsen (1960) and Bushinski (1964). Pertinent studies of Russian phosphorites

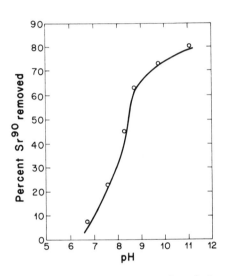

Fig. 32   The effect of pH on the relative rate of carbonate apatite formation by the replacement of calcite. The replacement rate is determined by the amount of Sr^{90} removed per unit time (after Ames, 1959)

have been made by Bushinski (1935, 1964), Gimmelfarb et al. (1959), and Tuschina (1960). The occurrence of extensive phosphorite deposits at the bottom of the sea is interesting, insofar as the conditions of their formation can be studied in great detail (Dietz et al., 1942). A critical evaluation of the published data on natural phosphorites reveals that geologic field observations and petrographic studies (Carozzi, 1960) are in excellent agreement with the experimental findings of Klement et al. (1942), and Ames (1959) who maintained that phosphorites are alteration products of calcareous materials.

Geologically speaking, the phosphorite facies is restricted to marine environments where the areas are neither too shallow nor too deep (platform facies), with access to the open sea at one side. In general, the phosphorus content in the sediments will increase up to a certain point with increasing distance from the shore line, and then fall off sharply. In this respect, the gradient coincides with that of the associated organic matter which also increases in the same direction. Inasmuch as the distribution of phytoplankton in the sea depends on the availability of dissolved mineral constituents such as phosphate or nitrate and is greatest in areas of upwelling, cold, phosphate-rich waters (McKelvey et al., 1953), early investigators suggested that the formation of phosphorites is somehow governed by organic activities. Others assumed that both the luxuriant growth of marine organisms and the precipitation of carbonate apatite were caused by the same phenomenon, that is, the great abundance of phosphorus in the environment of deposition. As such, these authors conclude, the observed relationship of phosphorus and organic matter in the sediments of the Phosphoria formation is just an accident and has no genetic implication whatsoever.

The present concensus, however, is that a great part of the phosphorus in the carbonate apatite was initially collected by photosynthesizing marine organisms. Upon the death of the organisms, the phosphorus was carried to the ocean floor via organic detritus (tripton). During decay, much of the phosphorus was released and became available for the phosphate formation. An increase in pH, caused by the formation of ammonia in the course of decomposition, may have accelerated the rate of phosphate exchange with the surrounding limestone materials. At present no quantitative estimates can be made of how much of the phosphorus has come from organic debris and of how much was directly extracted (inorganically) during exposure of the carbonates to the PO_4^{-3}-enriched sea water. It is conceivable that enzymatic-derived PO_4^{-3} is different from sea-water derived PO_4^{-3} with respect to its O^{18}/O^{16} ratio, for there is no exchange mechanism in the sea which could effectively modify the oxygen isotope distribution in the phosphate ion once it has been set. Thus, sea water PO_4^{-3} initially obtained during the weathering of igneous and metamorphic rocks should differ considerably from PO_4^{-3} produced by the hydrolysis of adenosine triphosphate. Oxygen isotope studies of phosphates, however, are just at the beginning (Tudge, 1960).

The total amount of collophane within a single phosphorite deposit can be rather significant. McKelvey et al. (1953), in a study of the marine phosphorites of the western United States, calculated the amount of phosphorus that had been extracted from the Permian sea. They obtained a figure of approximately 1.7×10^{12} metric tons of P_2O_5. This represents more than five times the 0.32×10^{12} tons of P_2O_5 at present distributed in the ocean (0.23 mg P_2O_5 per kg of sea water). According to Kazakov (1950), about one million tons of P_2O_5 are brought to the sea annually. Less conservative are the estimates for the continental phosphorus run off made by Clarke (1924) and Conway (1942), and which give a rough figure of about 4.5 million tons of P_2O_5 per year. At Kazakov's rate, and over a period of 15 million years, which is equivalent to about half of the Permian period, 15×10^{12} metric tons of P_2O_5 would be brought to the sea. This represents about ten times as much phosphorus as has accumulated during the deposition of the Phosphoria formation. Because of the low content of phosphorus in the sea of today and the high influx rate from the continents, there must be an effective mechanism which constantly reduces the phosphorus level of the oceans. Thorough oceanographic investigation of the sea floor in areas of upwelling waters may reveal similar or even greater phosphorite accumulations than those already discovered off the shore of California (Dietz et al., 1942). Marine areas with luxuriant plankton growth, nondepositional environments and abundant calcium carbonate in the top layers of the sea bottom sediments, represent the most likely localities where modern phosphorite deposits may be discovered.

The fluorine content in the present sea is about six times as high as that of the phosphorus—that is, 1.4 mg/kg compared to 0.23 mg/kg (McKelvey et al., 1953). This is sufficient to account for the fluorine in the collophane minerals. Under certain circumstances, even fluorite can be associated with the phosphorites.

Aside from the development of extensive phosphorite deposits, phosphatization of all kinds of organic residue such as shell materials, wood, fecal pellets, teeth, etc., is a common feature in marine environments (Goldberg and Parker, 1960; Adams et al., 1961; Arrhenius, 1963; and others).

On the continents there is no phosphorus reservoir comparable in magnitude to that in the ocean which would continuously supply phosphorus and cause the formation of phosphorites. Also, by and large, fresh water environments do not have the alkalinities favorable for carbonate apatite deposition. Aside from biological debris (bones), sediments of the red bed facies can be moderately enriched in P_2O_5. This observation is in line with the close relationship of phosphorus and a number of iron minerals; P_2O_5 concentrations of 0.5 to 2 per cent are rather common (Pettijohn, 1957; Schneiderhöhn, 1955, p. 248).

In order to illustrate the close association of iron minerals with phosphates, a radiograph of Triassic red bed sediments is presented in Figure 33 (Knetsch et al., 1960). The thin section (Figure 29a; schematic) starts, from bottom to top, with a 3 to 5 mm clay layer and continues with alternating bands of sandstone-type material and of limonite—the latter having a maximum thickness of 1 mm. The limonite layers contain small spherules of carbonate apatite which have a uranium content ranging between 1000 and 5000 ppm. A thin-section radiograph shows tracks of α-particles which are restricted to the phosphate containing limonite bands (Figure 33b), and which outline to some extent structures exhibited in the sediment specimen. An enlargement of the α-tracks reveals a rosette pattern for the distribution of the phosphate minerals in the limonite layers (Figure 33c).

A great number of different phosphates are found in with coal beds. They may occur in nodules (ironstones), veins, and thin layers (Deans,1938, and others). The variety of phosphate minerals in coals is largely due to the metastability of certain coexisting minerals, the high abundance of organic phosphorus and the great number of elements available during the maturation of coal and the formation of phosphates. Inasmuch as most of the phosphorus is organic in origin (pyrophosphate), oxygen-isotope studies on coal phosphates are promising.

In comparison to carbonate apatites the other three apatite species are less common, at least as authigenic minerals, while detrital fluor apatites are rather abundant. Hydroxyapatite plays an important role in biological mineralization systems. The present state of research on this subject is well documented by papers presented at a conference in Washington (Sognnaes, 1960) and New York (Moss et al., 1963). It is well established that certain organic tissues can nucleate hydroxyapatite, and that they do so even if they are reconstituted experimentally (Glimcher, 1960). Some native type reconstituted collagen fibrils from normally unmineralized tissues are also able to precipitate apatite from metastable calcium-phosphate solutions. A few highlights on biological mineralizations are presented elsewhere (p. 220 − 224).

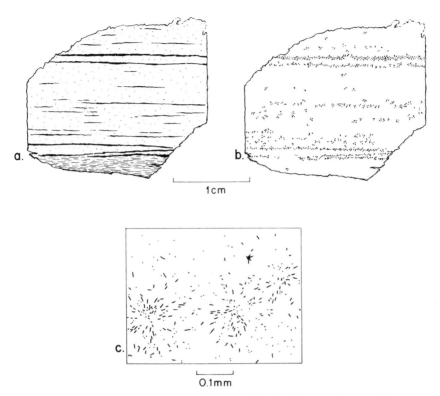

Fig. 33   (a) Thin section of Triassic red bed sediment (Buntsand-
stein) of South-west Germany (schematic); (b) radiograph of the
same section, showing tracks of α-particles; (c) enlargement of
rosette-pattern of α-particles (after Knetsch et al., 1960)

(c) *Trace elements.* Phosphate rocks owe some of their rare
metals to co-existing organic matter and sulfides rather than to phosphates themselves. Only a few elements are present in significant
quantities; these are strontium, arsenic, uranium, the rare earths,
lead, zirconium, and possibly beryllium and niobium (Krauskopf,
1955; Arrhenius, 1963; McKelvey et al., 1955; Rösler, 1961). Of
particular economic interest is the high uranium content in some
phosphate deposits. The rare earth concentration in some phosphorites which often runs to a few 100 ppm (Rösler, 1961), also is occasionally sufficient to allow economic exploitation.

Phosphates have a tendency to pick up some of their trace constituents long after burial. This has to be kept in mind when inter-

preting trace element assemblages of "syngenetic" phospate deposits. Age determinations of bones by means of the small potassium and argon amounts, agree reasonably well with the true ages of the bone deposits (Lippolt and Gentner, 1962).

3. GUANO

Guano deposits represent accumulations of vertebrate excretion. Depending on their biological source, one may distinguish between bird guano, sea-lion guano, or bat guano. A comprehensive study of the biogeochemistry of guano deposits has been made by Hutchinson (1950), and the pertinent literature may be obtained from this source.

Chemically speaking, there are two types of guano deposits: (1) nitrogenous deposits and (2) phosphatic deposits. The phosphatic guano is geochemically the more mature concentrate which has lost part of its nitrogen content in some way, for example, by volatilization or leaching processes. Hutchinson (1950) and Clarke (1924) present numerous examples of the formation of phosphates within the guano and in the rock formation underlying the deposits. Although at least twenty different phosphates are known to be genetically derived from guano constituents, the carbonate apatites are by far the most abundant species. Not only can underlying limestones become partly or completely phosphatized, but even igneous materials will be altered into phosphates. The type of precursor material will, to a certain extent, influence the type of phosphate to be formed. For instance, a decomposing feldspar may furnish Al to the reacting phosphate system, resulting in the formation of Al-phosphates, while a limestone will produce carbonate apatite. This adds further strength to the assertion that the formation of carbonate apatites is a metasomatic replacement phenomenon rather than a precipitation process.

Selected References

Adams, J. K., J. J. Groot, and N. W. Hiller, Jr., "Phosphatic Pebbles from the Brightseat Formation of Maryland." J. Sed. Petrol., **31** (1961), 546–552.

Altschuler, Z. A., C. A. Cisney, and U. H. Barlow, "X-ray Evidence of the Nature of Carbonate Apatite." 19th Int. Geol. Cong., Algiers, Compt. Rend., **XI** (1953), 9.

Ames, L. L., Jr., "The Genesis of Carbonate Apatites." Econ. Geol., **54** (1959), 829–841.

Arnold, P. W., "The Nature of Precipitated Calcium Phosphates." Trans. Faraday Soc., **46** (1950), 1061–1072.

Arrhenius, G., "Pelagic Sediments." In *The Sea. Ideas and Observations on Progress on the Study of the Seas,* edited by M. N. Hill. New York: Interscience Publishers, Inc., (1963), 655–727.

Bushinsky, G. I., "Structure and Origin of the Phosphorites of the U.S.S.R." J. Sed. Petrol., **5**, (1935), 81–92.

Bushinsky, G. I., "On Shallow-Water Origin of Phosphorite Sediments." In *Developments in Sedimentology,* Vol. I, edited by L. M. J. U. van Straaten. Amsterdam-London-New York: Elsevier Publishing, (1964), 62–70.

Carozzi, A. V., *Microscopic Sedimentary Petrography.* New York and London: John Wiley & Sons, Inc., 1960.

Cayeux, L., "Phosphates Sédimentaires et Bactéries." Compt. Rend., **203** (1936), 1198–1200.

Cayeux, L., *Les Phosphates de Chaux Sédimentaires de France* (France métropolitaine et d'outremer): Etude des gîtes minéraux de la France, Service Carte géol. France, Paris: Imprimerie Nationale, I (1939), II (1941), III (1950).

Clarke, F. W., *The Data of Geochemistry* (fourth edition). Washington, D. C.: Government Printing Office, 1924.

Conway, E. J., "Mean Geochemical Data in Relation to Oceanic Evolution." Proc. Royal Irish Acad., **48B** (1942), 119–159.

Deans, T., "Francolite from Sedimentary Ironstones of the Coal Measures." Min. Mag., **25** (1938), 135.

Dietz, R. S., K. O. Emery, and F. P. Shepard, "Phosphorite Deposits on the Sea Floor Off Southern California." Bull. Geol. Soc. Amer., **53** (1942), 815–848.

Gimmelfarb, B. M., N. A. Krasilnikowa, and A. M. Tuschina, "Classification of Phosphorites." Dokl. Akad. Nauk U.S.S.R., **128** (1959), 1258–1261.

Glimcher, M. J., "Specificity of the Molecular Structure of Organic Matrices in Mineralization." In *Calcification in Biological Systems,* ed. R. F. Soggnaes. Amer. Assoc. Advanc. Sci. Washington, D. C.: Publ. No. **64** (1960), 421–487.

Goldberg, E. D. and R. H. Parker, "Phosphatized Wood from the Pacific Sea Floor." Bull. Geol. Soc. Amer., **71** (1960), 631–632.

Gulbrandsen, R. A., "Petrology of the Meade Peak Phosphatic Shale Member of the Phosphoria Formation at Coal Canyon, Wyoming." U. S. Geol. Surv. Bull., **1111-C** (1960), 71–146.

Hutchinson, G. E., "Survey of Existing Knowledge of Biochemistry: 3. The Biogeochemistry of Vertebrate Excretion." Bull. Amer. Mus. Nat. Hist., **96** (1950), 1–544.

Jaffe, E. B., "Abstracts of the Literature on Synthesis of Apatites and Some Related Phosphates." U. S. Geol. Surv. Circ. **135** (1951).

Kazakov, A. V., "The Phosphorite Facies and the Genesis of Phosphorites." Trans. Sci. Inst. of Fertilizers and Insects-Fungicides, Moscow, **142** (1937), 95–113 (published for the 17th Session Int. Geol. Congr.).

Kazakov, A. V., "Fluorapatite-system Equilibria under Conditions of Formation of Sedimentary Rocks." Akad. Nauk U.S.S.R., Trudy Inst. Geol. Nauk, Vyp., **114,** (1950) Geol. Ser. No. 40, 1–21.

Klement, R., F. Hüter, and K. Köhrer, "Bildet sich Karbonat-Apatit in wässrigen Systemen?" Ztschr. Elektrochem. angew. phys. Chem., **48** (1942), 334–336.

Knetsch, G., E. Degens, D. Welte, and H. Reuter, "Untersuchungen und Schlüsse zur Verteilung von Strahlungsträgern in Sedimenten Frankens." Glückauf, **96** (1960), 172–182.

Krauskopf, K. B., "Sedimentary Deposits of Rare Metals." **50**th Anniversary Volume, (1955), 411–463.

Lippolt, H. J. and W. Gentner, "Argonbestimungen an Kalium-Mineralien.-X. Versuche der Kalium-Argon-Datierung von Fossilien." Geochim. et Cosmochim. Acta, **26** (1962), 1247–1253.

McConnell, D., "The Petrography of Rock Phosphates." J. Geol., **58** (1950), 16–23.

McConnell, D., "The Problem of the Carbonate Apatites. IV. Structural Substitutions Involving CO_3 and OH." Bull. Soc. Franc. Minér. Crist., **75** (1952a), 428–445.

McConnell, D., "The Nature of Rock Phosphates, Teeth, and Bones." J. Washington Acad. Sci., **42** (1952b), 36–38.

McConnell, D., "The Apatitelike Mineral of Sediments." Econ. Geol., **53** (1958), 110–111.

McKelvey, V. E., R. W. Swanson, and R. P. Sheldon, "The Permian Phosphorite Deposits of Western United States." 19th Int. Geol. Congr. Algiers, Compt. Rend., **XI** (1953), 45–64.

McKelvey, V. E., D. L. Everhart, and R. M. Garrels. "Origin of Uranium Deposits." Econ. Geol. **50**th Anniversary Volume (1955), 464–533.

Mehmel, M., "Über die Struktur des Apatits." Ztschr. Krist., **75** (1930), 323.

Moss, M. L., H. E. Whipple, and S. Silverzweig, eds., *Comparative Biology of Calcified Tissue.* Ann. New York Acad. Sci., **109** (1963), 1–410.

Náray-Szabó, S., "The Structure of Apatite." Ztschr. Krist., **75** (1930), 387.

Pettijohn, F. J., *Sedimentary Rocks* (second edition). New York: Harper and Row, Publishers, 1957.

Rösler, H. J., "Einige Bemerkungen zum Chemismus paläozoischer Phosphorite aus Thüringen und dem Harz." Geologie, **10** (1961), 131–140.

Schneiderhöhn, H., *Erzlagerstätten*. Stuttgart: Gustav Fischer Verlag, 1955.

Soggnaes, R. F., ed., *Calcification in Biological Systems*. Amer. Assoc. Advanc. Sci. Washington, D. C.: Publ. No. **64** (1960), 511 pp.

Strunz, H., *Mineralogische Tabellen*. Leipzig: Akademische Verlagsgesellschaft, Geest und Portig K.-G., 1957.

Tudge, A. P., "A Method of Analysis of Oxygen Isotopes in Orthophosphate—its Use in the Measurement of Paleotemperatures." Geochim. et Cosmochim. Acta, **18** (1960), 81–93.

Tuschina, A. M., "Phosphate-ooliths and -spherulites of the Kara-Tau." Sap. Wses. Miner. Obschtsch, **89** (1960), 46–51.

Sulfides

1. CLASSIFICATION, STRUCTURE, AND CHEMISTRY

A number of sulfides occur in sedimentary rocks in a manner which is compatible with the assumption that they were formed more or less contemporaneously with sedimentation. About 30 different sulfide species are known to be present as authigenic low temperature minerals in sedimentary rocks. Quantitatively most important are the two polymorphs of FeS_2, i.e., pyrite and marcasite. Other sulfides commonly encountered in sediments include those of nickel, copper, lead and zinc (Table 11).

Pyrite with its cubic structure is frequently found as cubes and pyritohedra. The orthorhombic marcasite is mostly tabular or pyramidal in appearance (Strunz, 1957). The phase relationship in the system: Fe-S, Ni-S, Fe-Ni-S, Cu-Fe-S, Fe-Zn-S and related sulfide type systems has been studied by Rosenthal (1956), Roseboom and Kullerud (1958), Kullerud and Yoder (1959), Kullerud (1959), Arnold (1957), Barnes (1960), Clark and Kullerud (1963), and others. These studies have yielded detailed information about the stability of sulfide minerals and mineral assemblages, their solid solution relationship and the temperature of formation. For example, the FeS-ZnS thermometer, based on the iron content in sphalerites coexisting with pyrrhotite, can be extremely helpful to reconstruct the temperature at the time the minerals were formed. An increase in iron content indicates an increase in temperature (Kullerud, 1959).

Table 11   CLASSIFICATION OF COMMON SEDIMENTARY SULFIDES.

GROUP	SPECIES	CRYSTALLOCHEMICAL FORMULA	SPACE GROUP	STRUCTURE (SCHEMATIC)
Iron-Nickel Sulfides	Pyrrhotite	Fe_7S_8-FeS	$P6_3/mmc$	
	Millerite	NiS	$R3m$	
	Pyrite	FeS_2	$\left.\begin{array}{c} \\ \end{array}\right\} Pa3$	
	Bravoite	$(Fe,Ni)S_2$		
	Marcasite	FeS_2	$Pnnm$	$\leftarrow a=5.42\text{Å}\rightarrow$ Pyrite O-S · -Fe ⊙-Cu ⊘-Zn
Copper-Iron Sulfides	Chalcocite	Cu_2S	$Abm2$ Orthorhombic (pseudocubic)	
	Bornite	Cu_5FeS_4		
	Covellite	CuS	$C6/mmc$	
	Chalcopyrite	$CuFeS_2$	$I\bar{4}2d$	$\leftarrow a=5.25\text{Å}\rightarrow$ Chalcopyrite
Lead and Zinc Sulfides	Galena	PbS	$Fm3m$	
	Sphalerite	ZnS	$F\bar{4}3m$	$\leftarrow a\approx5.41\text{Å}\rightarrow$ Sphalerite

The metastability of certain sulfides at elevated temperatures makes them excellent indicators also for low temperature environments. Bravoite, for example, is a stable phase only below $\sim 140°$ C (Kullerud and Yoder, 1959). No such precise temperature boundaries, however, can be delineated for the pyrite-marcasite stability fields. According to Kullerud and Yoder (1959), temperatures as high as 400° C are necessary to cause, within experimentally reasonable time (2 weeks), the inversion of marcasite to pyrite. In view of the fact that even the grinding of marcasite results in the conversion to pyrite (Anderson and Chesley, 1933), it is likely that moderate temperatures will bring about the inversion of marcasite to pyrite. Perhaps the sluggish nature of the inversion is responsible for the failure to produce, experimentally, stable pyrite from metastable marcasite at temperatures much lower than 400° C. This would seem to agree with the geological observation that marcasite is practically restricted to sediments and low-temperature ore deposits and absent from magmatic and metamorphic rocks.

2. GEOCHEMISTRY OF SULFIDES

Of the more than thirty ionic and molecular species of sulfur that are chemically important, only five are thermodynamically stable at room temperature in quantities to be geologically significant. These are elemental sulfur, H_2S, HS^-, HSO_4^- and SO_4^{-2}. In Eh-pH diagrams the distribution of these five individual species at equilibrium have been determined by Garrels and Naeser (1958). The required Eh-pH conditions for the formation of sulfur containing minerals can be obtained from these diagrams.

Whereas there is reasonable agreement in terms of Eh-pH conditions between the outlined stability fields and the natural occurrence of sedimentary sulfides and sulfates, the presence of elemental sulfur in marine environments is unexpected. The sulfur content in the sea is only 0.03 M, which is too low to enter the field of elemental sulfur stability upon reduction. More acid or higher sulfur concentrations are required to do so. It was, therefore, suggested by Garrels and Naeser (1958) that the formation of marine elemental sulfur is a result of the reduction of sea water sulfate to bisulfide or of organic H_2S production, with concomitant lowering of the pH. Subsequent oxidation may finally move the reactions into the elemental sulfur stability field. This hypothesis agrees with the inference made from sulfur isotope studies by Thode et al. (1953) and Kaplan et al. (1963).

A number of investigations over the last ten years have sought to determine exactly the forms and quantities of sulfur present in sediments and their genetic relationship to one another; studies include those of Sugawara et al. (1953), Ostroumov and Fomina (1959), Rittenberg et al. (1955), Emery and Rittenberg (1952), and Kaplan et al. (1960, 1963). The distribution of sulfur species in reducing and oxidizing sediments off the shore of California has been thoroughly studied and the data are plotted in Figure 34. It should be pointed out that the sulfate ion is the only form of dissolved sulfur present in the sea water above. These data show that sulfate reduction is the major phenomenon in the geochemistry of sulfur at this early stage of diagenesis. All sediments contain more sulfur than could possibly be contributed by the sulfate ions in the interstitial waters. Organic sulfur can also be excluded as a major source, inasmuch as organic matter contains only about 1 per cent sulfur per dry weight of sample. Instead, the results of Kaplan et al. (1963) indicate that most

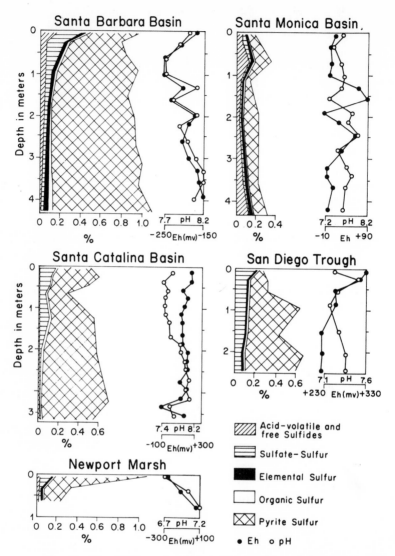

Fig. 34 Distribution of various sulfur species and the *p*H-Eh relationship in off-shore Californian sediments (Kaplan et al., 1963)

of the sulfides originated at the sediment-water interface by utilizing sea-water sulfate. The decrease in sulfate in the interstitial waters with increase of depth of burial (Fig. 34) may mean that small amounts of sulfides can form within the sediment by thriving on the sulfate in the connate waters. It is interesting to observe that although the most strongly reducing sediments (Santa Barbara Basin) contain most of the sulfides, the highly oxidizing San Diego Trough sediments are also greatly enriched in pyrite. Emery and Rittenberg (1952) and Kaplan et al. (1963) explain this feature to be a result of reducing micro-environments in the generally oxidizing sedimentary environment. The mechanism that causes the greater abundance of sulfides in the highly oxidizing environments of the San Diego Trough as against the moderate concentration in some less oxidizing environments (Fig. 34), however, is not yet fully understood. The fact that elemental sulfur, which plays a significant part in the formation of pyrite, is obtained via H_2S upon oxidation is perhaps linked to this process.

In this connection, the pyrite-marcasite relationship should also be considered. Geologic field data indicate that marcasite is widespread in fresh water, brown coal, peat and swamp environments which, for the most part, are acid in nature. In contrast, pyrite is abundant in marine sediments that provide a neutral or alkaline environment. Low temperature experiments in the Fe-S system show that marcasite forms from acid solutions whereas pyrite requires neutral to alkaline conditions. In view of the close agreement in the pH requirements between natural and experimental iron-sulfide formation, one may suspect that pH is the major factor in determining the mode of crystallization.

The paragenetic sequence of various sulfides in a single deposit may also be pH-Eh dependent. For instance, Wiese (1957), in a study on mineralized organic matter in Nova Scotia, observed the following coexisting low temperature minerals: pyrite, chalcopyrite, tetrahedrite-tennantite, sphalerite, galena, bornite, chalcocite and covellite. He offers the explanation that the paragenetic sequence of pyrite, followed by chalcocite and then bornite and chalcopyrite may represent the effects of a progressively more reducing environment. Mineralizations of organic materials similar to those observed by Wiese (1957) are known from many sedimentary deposits.

Whereas the sea can be regarded as the main source of sulfur for the sulfides in marine sediments, the origin of iron is less well known. The amount of iron in the sea is only about 0.01 Fe/l. The iron content of marine organisms which amounts to about 0.1 per cent, is also too small to be of great significance (Noddack and Noddack, 1939). Kaplan et al. (1963) and Keith and Degens (1959) assumed, therefore, that the bulk of the iron for the pyrite formation did come from minerals within the sediments. Sulfate reducing bacteria for instance, are known to mobilize iron from the clay minerals (Carroll, 1958); fine-grained hydrous ferric oxide is unstable under the reducing conditions developed in bottom muds high in organic matter, and there are a great number of other detrital constituents (amphiboles, pyroxenes, biotites, etc.) that can release iron for the sulfide formation.

The dimorphs of FeS_2, i.e., pyrite and marcasite, are obtained by the interaction of $FeS \cdot nH_2O$ (hydrotroilite) and elemental sulfur (Kaplan et al., 1963). Thus, the highly metastable hydrotroilite has to be regarded as the initial iron sulfide which, in the presence of elemental sulfur, will be rapidly altered into more stable sulfide modifications; depending on the acidity of the environment, either pyrite (alkaline) or marcasite (acid) will be the endproduct (Goldschmidt, 1954; Harmsen, 1954; Kaplan et al., 1963). The elemental sulfur essential for the formation of FeS_2 will be obtained by the oxidation of free sulfide. A commonly accepted alternative for the formation of FeS_2 involves the loss of Fe from hydrotroilite (Goldschmidt, 1954). In a study on the low temperature formation of a number of iron sulfides, Berner (1964) observed that in many occurrences hydrotroilite is a poorly crystallized tetragonal FeS. The water suggested by the prefix "hydro" is adsorbed or nonessential water.

The central question in recent extensive discussions on sedimentary sulfides was whether pyrite spheres or grains in sediments are a product of microbial synthesis or whether they should be considered simply as a result of inorganic precipitation mechanisms (Love, 1957, 1962a, 1962b; Love and Zimmermann, 1961; Zimmermann, 1962; Neuhaus, 1940; Schneiderhöhn, 1923; Schouten, 1946; Fabricius, 1962; Davidson, 1962; Ramdohr, 1960; Steinike, 1963; and others). Love (1957, 1962a) demonstrated that pyrite spheres are frequently associated with carbonaceous shales throughout the stratigraphic column. The external and internal pattern (arrangement) of the individual sulfide grains and agglomerations has been explained by him (as well as by other investigators) as representing the fossilized residues of former micro-organisms, e.g., *Pyritosphaera barbaria*, (Love, 1957). According to Love, pyrite became deposited within the micro-organisms, most likely as an amorphous sulfide resulting from the secretion of hydrogen sulfide by the organisms.

Steinike (1963) and Vallentyne (1962) express a different opinion. According to their findings, pyrite spheres, structurally identical to those reported by Love and other investigators, may come into existence by simple inorganic precipitation phenomena. It is particularly noteworthy that sulfide spheres of this type have also been reported from volcanic rocks and hydrothermal deposits (Steinike, 1963; Ramdohr, 1960).

There is no doubt that the presence of micro-organisms and decaying organic matter will promote the deposition of sulfides. Baas Becking and Moore (1961) have succeeded in producing experimentally most of the common sedimentary sulfides by the action of sulfate reducers, *Desulphovibrio desulfuricans* or *Clostridium desulfuricans*. This anaerobe may generate Eh potentials as low as -500 millivolts and can exist in the *p*H range between 4.2 and about 10. Rather than to assume a direct biological deposition of sulfides resulting in the preservation of detailed microbial structures as proposed by Love (1957, 1962a), it appears more likely that the occurrence of sulfides in spheres or layers in sediments is mainly determined (1) by the Eh condition in the strata which in turn is largely a function of microbial activities, and (2) the sulfate reducing capacities of the bacterial populations present. The deposition of sedimentary sulfides should be regarded in all instances as an inorganic process and not as a biological mineralization phenomenon. This would mean that the "biologic" structures reported by Love and others are probably sulfide mineral agglomeration phenomena of abiotic origin.

Just as the iron sulfides, so do other sedimentary sulfides also obtain their cations predominantly from the surrounding rock strata, unless they are truly epigenetic in origin, i.e., formed after rock induration. In this connection, a rather interesting but controversial sulfide deposit of the Permian "Kupferschiefer" and the Marl Slate should be mentioned (Schneiderhöhn, 1923, 1926, 1955; Love, 1962; Richter, 1941; Wedepohl, 1964). Among the great variety of sulfides and metals that are coexisting, the sulfides of iron, copper, zinc and lead are the most common ones. It has been suggested that the bulk of the complex primary sulfide material has been precipitated by micro-organisms in the sediments of the foul-bottomed early Zechstein sea (Love, 1962a; and others). Davidson (1962), however, presents convincing information which indicates that the amount of copper necessary to produce the copper sulfides in the above mentioned Permian deposits could not have been derived from the sea; the amount of ionic copper required in the ancient sea to account for the quantities of sedimentary copper sulfides would have been toxic to all bacteria. Instead, Davidson assumes that the copper was epigenetically introduced after the microbial activity had ceased in the strata, and that copper sulfides replaced the primary iron sulfides. However, since organic matter and sulfides in the "Kupferschiefer" each amount to about 10 per cent of the total sediment, one may alternatively suggest that copper and other trace elements were initially concentrated by the organic detritus or potential mineral collectors such as iron and manganese oxides and hydroxides. During the early stages of diagenesis and under the reducing conditions established at the bottom of the Zechstein sea, metastable minerals and the organic detritus gradually released most of their incorporated cations to the neighboring environment where they became available for sulfide deposition. This concept would largely agree with Davidson's statement that the sulfur was supplied from the sea above by sulfate reducers; the copper as well as other cations, however, were not necessarily introduced epigenetically, but may have been diagenetically released from coexisting detrital materials at a time when microbes were still alive in the sediment. It should be emphasized again that the bacterial populations made the sea water sulfur available for sulfide formation only by furnishing the right molecular or ionic species; simultaneously they produced the favorable conditions in terms of Eh and pH to initiate the inorganic sulfide deposition. Micro-organisms as such, however, did not become mineralized in the manner which was proposed earlier.

In comparison to sea water most fresh waters contain only small amounts of sulfate ions. Fresh water sediments therefore yield in general fewer sulfides than marine deposits of the same age, area and lithology (Keith and Degens, 1959). This statement supports the inference made earlier that the sulfate ions in the sea should be considered the major sulfur source for the syngenetic and early diagenetic sulfides in the underlying marine sediments. Williams and Keith (1963), in a geochemical study of Pennsylvanian coal beds, present further information on the effect of environment on the sulfur distribution. Coals in the areas of marine overburden are higher in sulfur than the same coal beds overlaid by fresh water sediments. The conclusion is submitted that the presence or absence of marine waters was one of the principal factors for the regional variation of sulfur in coals. Spackman (cited by Williams and Keith, 1963) in studies on fresh water and marine peat bogs in Florida, reports that the fresh water peats contain on an average about six times less sulfur than the corresponding marine peats.

3. TRACE ELEMENTS

In contrast to all naturally occurring silicates and oxides which chiefly show ionic bonding, the bulk of the sulfides have mainly — although not entirely — covalent bonding in which the atoms are bonded by the mutual sharing of electrons. This difference in the type of bonding and the complexity of bonding pattern, i.e., metallic, ionic and covalent bonding, make it difficult to predict isomorphous substitutions for most of the individual sulfide species.

A review of the trace element distribution in sulfides has been made by Fleischer (1955) and Krauskopf (1955). In principle, trace elements in sulfides can be accommodated in two ways: (1) in the lattice position as isomorphous substitutes, and (2) as trace minerals in the main sulfide mineral. Trace element investigations are plentiful only for high temperature sulfides, and the concentrations are often considerably high. It appears that sedimentary sulfides do not allow as much lattice substitution as the comparable high temperature counterpart, for the simple reason that low temperature environments do not favor initial lattice expansion.

The only sedimentary sulfides for which minor element concentrations are known in some detail are the dimorphs, pyrite and marcasite. Keith and Degens (1959) studied a series of Paleozoic iron sulfides of fresh water and marine origin for their trace element distribution. The data are presented in Figure 35. The fact that the trace element assemblage in sedimentary pyrites and marcasites is similar to that in the associated organic fraction may support the inference made before that some of the trace constituents were initially collected by organic matter. Elements notably concentrated in both the organic and the sulfide fractions include nickel, cobalt, copper and lead. Arsenic is concentrated in the sulfides but not in the organic matter. It appears possible, therefore, that arsenic was initially collected by the hydrous oxides of iron and manganese which are known to be effective collectors of arsenic. It is also interesting to note that the trace element spectra of iron sulfides are greatly dependent on the nature of the host rock. For iron sulfides from a sandstone have a very limited content of trace elements, while those from shales and limestones are often highly enriched in some elements (Fig. 35).

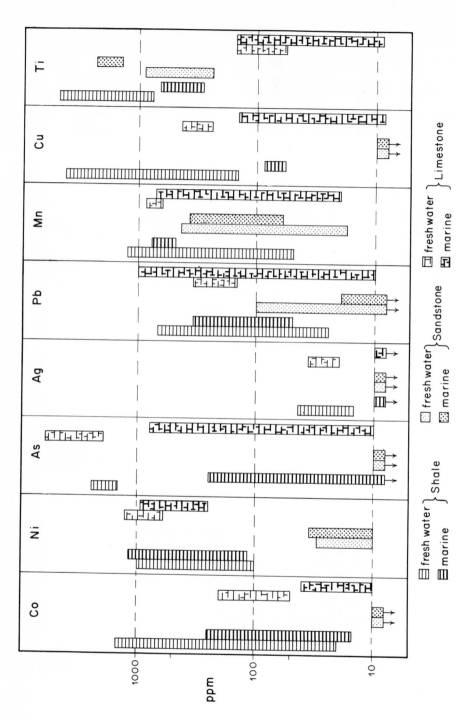

Fig. 35 Range in trace-element content of sedimentary pyrite and marcasite (after Keith and Degens, 1959)

Also, the environment exercises some control over the type and the concentration of the trace elements. The higher the abundance of sulfides in a normal sediment, the lower the trace element content in the sulfides. Since marine sediments contain on the average more sulfides than fresh water sediments of the same age and the same lithology, marine sulfides are generally less enriched in trace elements (dilution effect). All these criteria can be used as further evidence that the bedrock will control the syngenetic sulfide formation by supplying (with the exception of sulfur) all essential ions to the reacting system.

4. Sulfur Isotopes

Sulfur has four stable isotopes, i.e., S^{32}, S^{33}, S^{34}, and S^{36}, in a ratio of about 95.08 : 0.75 : 4.22 : 0.02 (meteoritic troilite). Sulfur isotope values are commonly expressed in terms of δS^{34}, which is the per mil deviation of the S^{34}/S^{32} ratio relative to a meteorite standard (Fig. 36). Previously, the isotope data were reported in terms of S^{32}/S^{34} values which is an abundance ratio relative to an assumed value for meteoritic sulfur of 22.21 ($\delta S^{34}=0.0$). In the present survey the δS^{34} scale has been adopted.

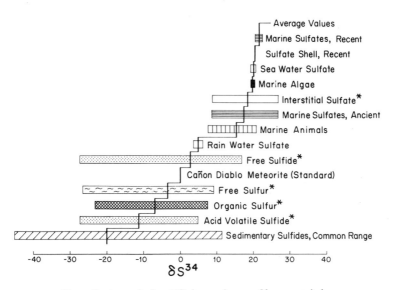

Fig. 36 Compilation of the δS^{34} in various sulfur-containing materials; data with asterisk are obtained from the same environmental set-up (Kaplan et al., 1963; Ault, 1959; Ault and Kulp, 1959; Thode et al., 1961)

The S^{34}/S^{32} ratio varies by as much as ~ 11 per cent in nature; sulfates in the cap rock of salt domes are the heaviest, and sedimentary sulfides are the lightest in S^{34}/S^{32}. Pertinent geochemical studies of the distribution of sulfur isotopes include those of Thode et al. (1949, 1953, 1954, 1961), Feely and Kulp (1957), Vinogradov et al. (1956), Ault and Kulp (1959), Sakai (1957), Kaplan (1962), Kaplan et al. (1960, 1963). Reviews of the isotope geochemistry of sulfur have been prepared by Ault (1959), Ault and Kulp (1959) and Thode et al. (1961). From these sources additional literature quotations can also be obtained.

Sulfur may undergo a valence change from -2 to $+6$ during oxidation-reduction processes. A valence change such as that between sulfate and sulfide causes isotope fractionation. The heavier, less energetic isotope S^{34} will be concentrated in the more tightly bound sulfate, while the lighter, more energetic isotope S^{32} is being favored by the sulfide.

The greatest sulfur reservoir on the surface of the earth is the ocean. Oceanic sulfur is continuously extracted to be deposited mainly as sulfide, sulfate or organic sulfur. Besides the recycled sea water sulfate, volcanic exhalations and rocks and ore deposits eroded on the continents are potential sources for the sulfur in the sea. The bulk of the sulfur in the ocean is present as sulfate ion which is remarkably uniform in isotope ratio with a mean δS^{34} value of $+20.1$ $\pm$ 0.3 per mil (Thode et al., 1961), which indicates that there is practically no isotope fluctuation in the sea. By using the δS^{34} value of sea water sulfate as a basis we may thus determine the magnitude of sulfur isotope fractionations between various complex biochemical and chemical sulfur systems in the marine environment.

Biological sulfate mineralization (shell material) introduces no significant isotope fractionation (Thode et al., 1961; Kaplan et al., 1963). This is true also for the sulfates precipitated in the course of the evaporation of ocean water (Thode et al., 1961; Ault and Kulp, 1959). Nor does the conversion of gypsum to anhydrite during diagenesis apparently have a significant effect on the original sulfur isotope value of the hydrated sulfate species. Total sulfur in marine organisms shows generally only a slight enrichment in S^{32} relative to sea water sulfate (Kaplan et al., 1963). This may suggest that the δS^{34} of fossil marine shell and evaporite sulfates are indicative of the δS^{34} of the ancient sea. It is well established, however, that the sulfur isotope ratios even of contemporaneous ancient anhydrite and gypsum deposits differ greatly among each other (Ault and Kulp, 1959; Macnamara and Thode, 1950; Feely and Kulp, 1957). In the absence of fresh water influx and of volcanic activities the wide variation can possibly be attributed to bacterial reduction of sulfate and the production of reduced sulfur compounds which are enriched in S^{32}. Thus, the remaining sea water sulfate and the sulfate mineral precipitating from this source will be enriched in S^{34} relative to mean ocean water. The amount of enrichment, of course, depends on the magnitude and efficiency of bacterial reduction. Sulfates from calcite cap rock of Gulf Coast salt domes for instance are known to have a δS^{34} as high as +66, which represents an enrichment of about 45 per mil relative to mean ocean water (Feely and Kulp, 1957). Thode et al. (1961), therefore, tentatively concluded that ancient sulfates should be either identical or heavier in S^{34} relative to the ancient mean ocean water sulfate. Thus, the lowest δS^{34} value for a sulfate of any geologic period should give the closest approximation to the sea water isotope level at that time. Nielsen and Ricke (1964) present tentative δS^{34} values for sea water sulfate in the Permian (+ 11.5), Muschelkalk (+21), Keuper (+17.5), Jurassic (+18 to +19) and Tertiary (+16 to +17).

If fresh water is the main source for the sulfate minerals, as is the case in some inland seas and lakes, lower δS^{34} values are expected. The origin of the sulfate ions in fresh water is partly related to the weathering of sulfur containing minerals, and the isotope ratio of the sulfate ion so obtained is identical to that of the original mineral. Rain water may also contribute sulfate ions to the system; the enrichment of rain water sulfate in S^{32} has been the subject of some speculation. According to Thode et al. (1961), loss of gaseous sulfur compounds, e.g., H_2S, as a result of bacterial reduction of sulfate from the sea, may account for this enrichment in S^{32}. This is so because subsequent oxidation of H_2S enriched in S^{32} will produce relatively light rain water sulfate.

Since the influence of bacterial reduction and fresh water influx on the δS^{34} oceanic sulfate cannot be quantitatively determined for ancient times it is difficult to use the δS^{34} of fossil sulfate deposits as a reliable indicator for the δS^{34} of the former sea. Perhaps this is the reason for some of the conflicting results obtained by Thode et al. (1953), Vinogradov et al. (1956), and Ault and Kulp (1959) on the age effect of δS^{34} in sulfates and sulfides.

Sulfur isotopic fractionation in low temperature environments is achieved mainly by the action of sulfate reducers in the ocean. With respect to sea water sulfate all reduced sulfur compounds are markedly enriched in S^{32}. Kaplan et al. (1963) were able to show that the various reduced inorganic forms of sulfur coexisting in a sediment are similar isotopically. Basically, coexisting free sulfide, acid volatile sulfide, elemental sulfur and pyrite have the same δS^{34} value. The similarity indicates that these compounds are interrelated and suggests a common origin. It is noteworthy that in some of the studied basin sediments off the shore of California the reduced sulfur compounds markedly increase in S^{34} with depth of burial. This feature is explained by Kaplan et al. (1963) to be a result of a decreasing sulfate reservoir. On the other hand, sulfates obtained by oxidation of pyrite materials during the various stages of diagenesis will be enriched in S^{32} sometimes to the same extent as their pyrite precursor.

In conclusion, sulfate reduction is the most important factor in the geochemistry of sulfur compounds. The 11 per cent variation of the sulfur isotope ratio in nature can essentially be accounted for by the action of sulfate-reducing bacteria. Oxidation and reduction phenomena also explain why marine sulfate minerals can be lighter or heavier than the sulfate ions in the sea. The complexity of the reactions that determine sulfur isotope fractionation processes in nature suggests that isotope data of fossil materials which contain sulfur should be analyzed rather cautiously before any interpretation is made regarding age effects, environmental evaluations and other geologic phenomena.

The application of sulfur isotope studies to aspects of economic geology is a wide open field. For instance, Thode et al. (1958) investigated the sulfur isotope distribution in a number of crude oils, and Buschendorf et al. (1963) studied the genesis of the low temperature sulfide-sulfate ore deposits of Meggen/Germany.

Selected References

Anderson, H. V. and K. G. Chesley, "X-ray Study of the Transformation of Marcasite into Pyrite." Amer. J. Sci., **25** (1933), 315–324.

Arnold, R. G., "The NiS-NiS$_2$ Join." Carnegie Inst. Washington Year Book, **56** (1957), 197–198.

Ault, W. U., "Isotopic Fractionation of Sulfur in Geochemical Processes." In *Researches in Geochemistry*, edited by P. H. Abelson. New York: John Wiley & Sons, Inc., (1959), 241–259.

Ault, W. U. and J. L. Kulp, "Isotopic Geochemistry of Sulphur." Geochim. et Cosmochim. Acta, **16** (1959), 201–235.

Baas Becking, L. G. M. and D. Moore, "Biogenic Sulfides." Econ. Geol., **56** (1961), 259–272.

Barnes, H. L., "Ore Solutions." Carnegie Institution, Washington, Ann. Report Dir. Geophys. Lab., **59** (1959–1960), 137.

Berner, R. A., "Iron Sulfides formed from Aqueous Solution at Low Temperatures and Atmospheric Pressure." J. Geol., **72** (1964), 293–306.

Buschendorf, F., H. Nielsen, H. Puchelt, and W. Ricke, "Schwefel-Isotopen-Untersuchungen am Pyrit-Sphalerit-Baryt-Lager Meggen Lenne (Deutschland) und an verschiedenen Devon Evaporiten." Geochim. et Cosmochim. Acta, **27** (1963), 501–523.

Carroll, D., "Role of Clay Minerals in the Transportation of Iron." Geochim. et Cosmochim. Acta, **14** (1958), 1–27.

Clark, L. A., and G. Kullerud, "The Sulfur-rich Portion of the Fe-Ni-S System." Econ. Geol., **58** (1963), 853–885.

Davidson, C. F., "Further Remarks on Biogenic Sulfides." Econ. Geol., **57** (1962), 1134–1137.

Emery, K. O. and S. C. Rittenberg, "Early Diagenesis of California Basin Sediments in Relation to Origin of Oil." Bull. Amer. Assoc. Petrol. Geol., **36** (1952), 735–806.

Fabricius, F., "Die Strukturen des "Rogenpyrits" (Kössener Schichten, Rät) als Beitrag zum Problem der "Vererzten Bakterien." Geol. Rdsch. **51** (1962), 647–657.

Feely, H. W. and J. L. Kulp, "Origin of Gulf Coast Saltdome Sulfur Deposits." Bull. Amer. Assoc. Petrol. Geol., **41** (1957), 1802–1853.

Fleischer, M., "Minor Elements in Some Sulfide Minerals." Econ. Geol., **50**th Anniversary Volume (1955), 970–1024.

Garrels, R. M. and C. R. Naeser, "Equilibrium Distribution of Dissolved Sulphur Species in Water at 25°C and 1 atm Total Pressure." Geochim. et Cosmochim. Acta, **15** (1958), 113–130.

Goldschmidt, V. M., *Geochemistry*. Oxford: Clarendon Press, 1954.

Harmsen, G. W., "Observations on the Formation and Oxidation of Pyrite in the Soil." Plant and Soil, V (1954), 324–348.

Kaplan, I. R., *Sulphur Isotope Fractionations During Microbial Trans-formations in the Laboratory and in Marine Sediments.* Ph.D. Thesis, University of Southern California, Los Angeles, 1962.

Kaplan, I. R., K. O. Emery, and S. C. Rittenberg, "The Distribution and Isotopic Abundance of Sulphur in Recent Marine Sediments off Southern California." Geochim. et Cosmochim, Acta **27** (1963), 297–331.

Kaplan, I. R., T. A. Rafter, and J. R. Hulston, "Sulphur Isotopic Variations in Nature. 8. Application to Some Biogeochemical Problems." New Zealand J. Sci., **3** (1960), 338–361.

Keith, M. L. and E. T. Degens, "Geochemical Indicators of Marine and Fresh-water Sediments." In *Researches in Geochemistry,* edited by P. H. Abelson. New York: John Wiley & Sons, Inc., (1959), 38–61.

Krauskopf, K. B., "Sedimentary Deposits of Rare Metals." Econ. Geol., **50**th Anniversary Volume, (1955), 411–463.

Kullerud, G., "Sulfide Systems as Geological Thermometers." In *Researches in Geochemistry,* edited by P. H. Abelson. New York: John Wiley & Sons, Inc., 1959, 301–355.

Kullerud, G. and H. S. Yoder, "Pyrite Stability Relations in the Fe-S System." Econ. Geol., **54** (1959), 533–572.

Love, L. G., "Biogenic Primary Sulfide of the Permian *Kupferschiefer* and Marl Slate." Econ. Geol., **57** (1962a), 350–366.

Love, L. G., "Further Studies on Micro-organisms and the Presence of Syn-genetic Pyrite." Palaeontology, **5** (1962b), 444–459.

Love, L. G., "Micro-organisms and the Presence of Syngenetic Pyrite." Geol. Soc. London, Quart. J., **113** (1957), 429–440.

Love, L. G. and D. O. Zimmerman, "Bedded Pyrite and Micro-organisms from Mount Isa Shale." Econ. Geol., **56** (1961), 873–896.

Macnamara, J. and H. G. Thode, "Comparison of the Isotopic Constitution of Terrestrial and Meteoritic Sulfur." Phys. Rev., **78** (1950), 307–308.

Neuhaus, A. "Über die Erzführung des Kupfermergels der Hasseler und Grödlitzer Mulde in Schlesien." Ztschr. angew. Miner., **2** (1940), 304–343.

Nielsen, H. and M. W. Ricke, "Schwefel-Isotopenverhältnisse von Evaporiten aus Deutschland; Ein Beitrag zur Kenntis von δS^{34} im Meerwasser-Sulfat." Geochim. et Cosmochim. Acta, **28** (1964), 577–591.

Noddack, I. and W. Noddack, "Die Häufigkeiten der Schwermetalle in Meerestieren," Arch. Zool., **32A** (1939), 1–35.

Ostroumov, E. A. and L. S. Fomina, "On the Forms of Sulphur Compounds in the Bottom Deposits of the Marianas Trench." Dokl. Akad. Nauk S.S.S.R., **126** (1959), 382–384.

Ramdohr, P., *Die Erzmineralien und ihre Verwachsungen:* Berlin, Akademie-Verlag, (1960).

Richter, G., "Geologische Gesetzmässigkeiten in der Metallführung des Kupferschiefers." Arch. f. Lagerstättenforschung, **73** (1941), 61 pp.

Rittenberg, S. C., K. O. Emery, and W. L. Orr, "Regeneration of Nutrients in Sediments of Marine Basins." Deep-Sea Research, **3** (1955), 23–45.

Roseboom, E. H. and G. Kullerud, "The Solidus in the System Cu-Fe-S Between 400° and 800°C." Carnegie Institution, Washington, Ann. Report Dir. Geophys. Lab., **57** (1957–1958), 222.

Rosenthal, G., "Versuche zur Darstellung von Markasit, Pyrit und Magnetkies aus wässerigen Lösungen bei Zimmertemperatur." Heidelberger Beiträge zur Mineralogie and Petrographie, **5** (1956), 146–164.

Sakai, H., 1957, "Fractionation of Sulphur Isotopes in Nature." Geochim. et Cosmochim. Acta, **12** (1957), 150–169.

Schneiderhöhn, H., "Chalkographische Untersuchung des Mansfelder Kupferschiefers." N. Jb. Mineral., **B 47** (1923), 1–38.

Schneiderhöhn, H., "Erzführung und Gefüge des Mansfelder Kupferschiefers." Metall und Erz, **23** (1926), 143–146.

Schneiderhöhn, H., *Erzlagerstätten.* Stuttgart: Gustav Fischer Verlag, 1955.

Schouten, C., "The Role of Sulfur Bacteria in the Formation of the So-called Sedimentary Copper Ore and Pyritic Ore Bodies." Econ. Geol., **41** (1946), 517–538.

Steinike, K., "A Further Remark on Biogenic Sulfides." Econ. Geol., **58** (1956), 998–1000.

Strunz, H., *Mineralogische Tabellen.* Leipzig: Akademische Verlagsgesellschaft Geest und Portig K.-G., 1957.

Sugawara, K., T. Koyama, and A. Kozawa, "Distribution of Various Forms of Sulphur in Lake-, River-, and Sea-muds." J. Earth Sci., Nagoya Univ., **1** (1953), 17–23.

Thode, H. G., J. Macnamara, and C. B. Collins, "Natural Variations in the Isotopic Content of Sulphur and their Significance." Canad. J. Research, **27 B** (1949), 361–373.

Thode, H. G., J. Macnamara, and W. H. Fleming, "Sulphur Isotope Fractionation in Nature and Geological and Biological Time Scales." Geochim. et Cosmochim. Acta, **3** (1953), 235–243.

Thode, H. G., R. K. Wanless, and R. Wallouch, "The Origin of Native Sulphur Deposits from Isotope Fractionation Studies." Geochim. et Cosmochim. Acta, **5** (1954), 286–298.

Thode, H. G., J. Monster, and H. B. Dunford, "Sulphur Isotope Abundances in Petroleum and Associated Materials." Bull. Amer. Assoc. Petrol. Geol., **42** (1958), 2119–2141.

Thode, H. G., J. Monster, and H. B. Dunford, "Sulphur Isotope Geochemistry." Geochim. et Cosmochim. Acta, **25** (1961), 159–174.

Vallentyne, J. R., "Concerning Love, Microfossils, and Pyrite Spherules." Trans. New York Acad. Sci., Ser. II, **25** (1962), 177–189.

Vinogradov, A. P., M. S. Chupakhin, V. A. Grinenko, and A. F. Trofimov, "The Isotopic Composition of Sulphur in Connection with the Growth of Pyrites of Sedimentary Origin." Geokhimiya, No. **1** (1956), 97–108.

Wedepohl, K. H., "Untersuchungen am Kupferschiefer in Nordwestdeutschland; Ein Beitrag zur Deutung der Genese bituminöser Sedimente." Geochim. et Cosmochim. Acta, **28** (1964), 305–364.

Wiese, R. G., "On Occurrence of Mineralized Organic Material of Nova Scotia." Econ. Geol., **52** (1957), 76–82.

Williams, E. G., and M. L. Keith, "Relationship between Sulfur in Coals and the Occurrence of Marine Roof Beds." Econ. Geol., **58** (1963), 720–729.

Zimmermann, D. O., "Pyrite Spheres in Sediments." Econ. Geol., **57** (1962), 459–460.

Sulfates and Halides

1. INTRODUCTION

The bulk of the sulfates and halides belong to a group of sediments commonly known as evaporites, but not all sulfates and halides are evaporite minerals. Some species, such as barite, celestite or fluorite, are frequently associated with normal marine or continental sediments as well. Nevertheless, the close genetic relationship of both classes of compounds during evaporation of natural waters furnishes an excellent basis for a simultaneous discussion of sulfates and halides.

Evaporation of natural waters will ultimately result in the precipitation of the dissolved mineral constituents. The sequence of precipitation is mainly determined by the solubility characteristics of the saline compounds. The least soluble material will deposit first, and the most soluble compound last of all. The processes, however, are not as simple as they appear to be. They are complicated by the fact that the solubility of a salt is affected by the nature and amount of its coexisting solutes, the water temperature, and the vapor pressure of the system. In a qualitative manner, the Gibbs' phase rule expresses the phase relationship in complex salt systems, namely, that the pressure-temperature conditions and the number and concentration of all participating components will determine the number of phases. A comprehensive account of the significance of the Gibbs' phase rule and its application to natural systems has been presented by Findlay (1958).

Although any aqueous solution will yield upon evaporation salt deposits, the various mineral systems of the sea are geologically most significant and best studied from a physical-chemical point of view. The main sulfates and halides are listed in Table 12. A full account on major continental evaporite deposits is given by Lotze (1957).

2. MARINE EVAPORITES

(a) *Chemical Composition of the Sea and Classification of Sulfates and Halides.* In Table 13 the chemical composition of present day ocean water is presented. The data are taken from Sverdrup et al. (1946), and Braitsch (1962). It appears that only six major elements occur in the sea, i.e., (1) sodium, (2) magnesium, (3) calcium, (4) potassium, (5) chlorine, and (6) sulfur. Accordingly, the bulk of the oceanic salt deposits are composed of Na-Mg-Ca-K chlorides and sulfates. More than thirty major evaporite minerals are known from marine evaporite deposits of which the more important ones are listed in Table 12. Aside from chlorides and sulfates about thirty different borates have been reported, with boracite $(Mg, Fe, Mn)_3$ ClB_7O_{13} being the most abundant mineral species.

Models have been presented to account for the mineralogical diversity of marine evaporites. In this connection the pioneering work of van't Hoff (1905, 1909) and Jänecke (1923) should be mentioned. Reviews of this subject, including pertinent literature quotations, have been prepared by Lotze (1957), Waljaschko (1958), Borchert (1959), d'Ans and Kühn (1960), and Braitsch (1962).

The reaction products obtained under static isothermic evaporation of ocean water at $25°C$, assuming stable equilibrium conditions, are illustrated in Figure 37. The chemical composition (in mol/$\times$mol H_2O) and the weight of the residual solution (in grams) at the start of the gypsum, halite, bloedite, etc., precipitation, are indicated. It is the nature of the sea water system, however, that causes in many

Table 12 CLASSIFICATION OF PRINCIPAL SEDIMENTARY SULFATES AND HALIDES.

CLASS	STATE	SPECIES	CRYSTALLOCHEMICAL FORMULA	SPACE GROUP	STRUCTURE (SCHEMATIC)
SULFATES	Anhydrous	Anhydrite	$CaSO_4$	$Bbmm$	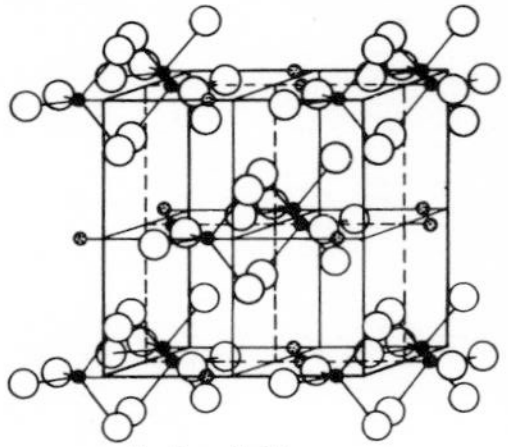
		Barite	$BaSO_4$	$\left.\begin{array}{l} \\ \end{array}\right\} Pnma$	
		Celestite	$SrSO_4$		
	Hydrous	Kieserite	$MgSO_4 \cdot H_2O$	$C2/c$	
		Gypsum	$CaSO_4 \cdot 2H_2O$	$A2/a$	
		Polyhalite	$Ca_2K_2Mg(SO_4)_4 \cdot 2H_2O$	$F\bar{1}$ or $F1$	
		Bloedite	$Na_2Mg(SO_4)_2 \cdot 4H_2O$	$P2_1/a$	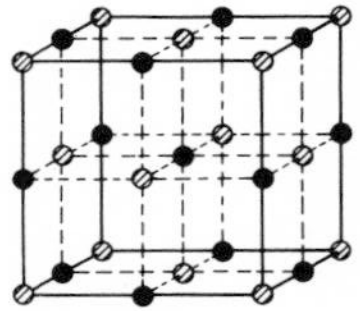
		Hexahydrite	$MgSO_4 \cdot 6H_2O$	$C2/c$	
		Epsomite	$MgSO_4 \cdot 7H_2O$	$P2_12_12_1$	
		Kainite	$K_4Mg_4[Cl|SO_4] \cdot 11H_2O$	$C2/m$	
HALIDES	Anhydrous	Halite	$NaCl$	$\left.\begin{array}{l} \\ \end{array}\right\} Fm3m$	
		Sylvite	KCl		
		Fluorite	CaF_2		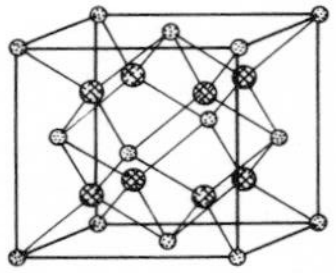
	Hydrous	Bischofite	$MgCl_2 \cdot 6H_2O$	$C2/m$	
		Carnallite	$KMgCl_3 \cdot 6H_2O$	$Pban$	

Anhydrite

Halite

Fluorite

O—O
—Ca
$\bullet$—S
$\bullet$—Cl
—Na
—F

0 1 2 3 4 5 Å

Table 13   MAJOR CONSTITUENTS OF SEA WATER (STANDARD CHLORINITY $= 19^0/_{00}$)
(AFTER SVERDRUP ET AL., 1942; AND BRAITSCH, 1962).

Ion		$^0/_{00}$	CALCULATED MOLECULAR COMPOSITION (WEIGHT PERCENT)	
Sodium,	Na^+	10.56	78.03	NaCl
Magnesium,	Mg^{++}	1.27	0.01	NaF
Calcium,	Ca^{++}	0.40	2.11	KCl
Potassium,	K^+	0.38	9.21	$MgCl_2$
Strontium,	Sr^{++}	0.013	0.25	$MgBr_2$
Chloride,	Cl^-	18.98	6.53	$MgSO_4$
Sulfate,	SO_4^{--}	2.65	3.48	$CaSO_4$
Bicarbonate,	HCO_3^-	0.14	0.05	$SrSO_4$
Bromide,	Br^-	0.065	0.33	$CaCO_3$
Fluoride,	F^-	0.001		
Boric acid,	H_3BO_3	0.026	100.00	

cases the deposition of metastable mineral phases. This is due to the fact that quite often the stable mineral phases are not precipitated within their stability field for kinetic reasons. Thus, paragenetic salt sequences develop that differ considerably from the model outlined in Figure 37. Little is known concerning the time required for the conversion of the metastable into the stable conformation. The only thing that is clear is that the concentration of the participating electrolytes, the chemical nature of the metastable product, the temperature, and the overburden pressure are essential factors in controlling the inversion time. For a full account of the phenomenon of metastable-stable equilibria in sea water systems, one may consult Braitsch (1962).

(b) *Gypsum and Anhydrite.* Upon evaporation of sea water the first salt to separate is calcium carbonate. As evaporation proceeds calcium sulfate appears. In order to evaluate calcium sulfate deposition under marine conditions, it is helpful to consider first of all the solubility characteristics in the system $CaSO_4$-H_2O, that is, in the absence of foreign ions. The relationship has been determined by Kelley et al. (1941), Posnjak (1940), MacDonald (1953), D'Ans et al. (1955), and others. Based on Figure 38, it is apparent that the solubility of gypsum is little affected by an increase in temperature while the solubility decreases for anhydrite with a rise in temperature; both curves intersect at $42°C$. Hemihydrates (bassanite, $CaSO_4$ · $\frac{1}{2}H_2O$) intersect gypsum at about $100°C$, but they are more soluble

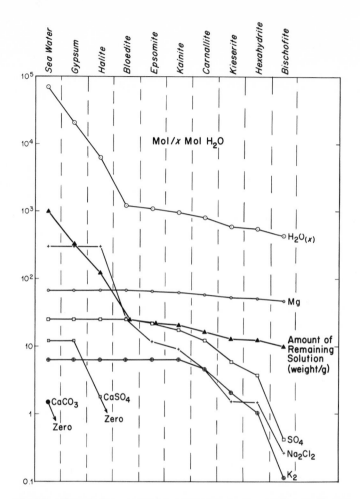

Fig. 37 Chemical composition of ocean water under isothermic evaporation at 25°C, and at the start of precipitation of the individual mineral species (after Braitsch, 1962)

than anhydrite for any given temperature. It is inferred, therefore, that gypsum is the stable form below 42°C whereas anhydrite is stable above this temperature. Bassanite can develop from gypsum only above 100°C, but cannot be derived via anhydrite at any temperature; however, bassanite can be altered into anhydrite.

A somewhat different picture is obtained when foreign electrolytes are present. Several investigators have postulated that certain salt solutions decrease the solubility of anhydrite relative to gypsum

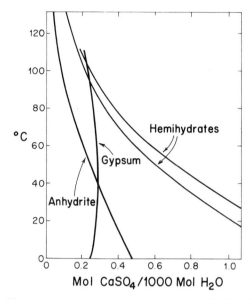

Fig. 38 Phase relationships in the system $CaSO_4$-H_2O (after Braitsch, 1962)

to the point where anhydrite enters a stable phase well below 42°C. MacDonald (1953), for instance, suggested that concentrated saline solutions, for instance evaporating bodies of sea water, precipitate anhydrite at temperatures as low as 7°C. Posnjak (1940), Madgin and Swales (1956), D'Ans et al. (1955), and Braitsch (1962) give graphical representations of the solubility of gypsum and anhydrite in evaporating salt solutions. According to their findings, gypsum starts to precipitate when the salinity has been increased by evaporation to 3.35 times the normal value (at 30°C). Nearly one-half of the total amount of $CaSO_4$ present will be deposited as gypsum before the concentration is reached at which the anhydrite solubility curve intersects that of the gypsum (about 5 times the salinity of normal sea water). From there on anhydrite is the stable phase.

Based on the work of Conley and Bundy (1958), however, who studied the mechanism of gypsification, it becomes clear that primary precipitation of anhydrite from sea water at temperatures encountered in evaporating basins is improbable. The relative ease of crystallization of metastable gypsum within the anhydrite stability field prevents sufficient supersaturation for the nucleation of anhydrite. This feature is in line with the interpretation offered in the case of some other common mineral systems, for instance, aragonite-calcite-dolomite, gibbsite-boehmite-diaspore, or amorphous silica-quartz, where metastable mineral phases can form within the stability field of their stable modifications, so that there is at least a temporary stability.

Activating constituents contained in sea water will bring about almost immediate conversion of anhydrite crystallites to gypsum in a sea water brine. Salinities up to 200 parts per thousand still convert anhydrite to gypsum. Based on these findings, Conley and Bundy (1958) conclude that, given sufficient time, anhydrite is formed after burial when gypsum is subjected to direct stresses and increased temperatures. In the absence of saline solutions in the rock strata, gypsum may be stable up to about 800 meter depth of burial; below that, anhydrite will form. On the other hand, the hydration of anhydrite is accelerated by certain acids, bases and salts. Most effective among the activators are the alkali sulfates.

As a result of the inefficiency of anhydrite nucleation anhydrite is not found in recent salinar deposits of either continental or marine environments. It represents, however, the most important sulfate species in ancient rock formation. Richter-Bernburg (cited in Braitsch, 1962) reports anhydrite deposits from the Upper Miocene of Sicily, Italy, which so far are geologically the youngest occurrences known. It is noteworthy that hydration of gypsum does not alter the original stratification pattern of saline beds. In their appearance these beds occasionally resemble varves (Richter-Bernburg, 1960) and allow stratigraphical correlations over a few hundred miles throughout their basin of evaporation, e.g., Zechsteinbecken, Germany. Furthermore, they may be used as a varve chronology.

(c) *Evaporites (exclusive of carbonates, gypsum and anhydrite)*. When ocean water is reduced by evaporation to about one-tenth of the original amount the mineral halite will precipitate. The model of a static isothermic evaporation of sea water at $25°C$ presented in Figure 37 may be expanded by comparing the mineral sequences obtained under (1) metastable equilibrium conditions, (2) stable equilibrium conditions without reaction at the phase boundaries, and (3) stable equilibrium conditions with complete reaction at the phase boundaries (Fig. 39). This picture illustrates that even at constant water temperature the type of salt minerals and the total amount of salts obtained during complete evaporation of sea water will be different. It should be noted that a deposit of about 0.4

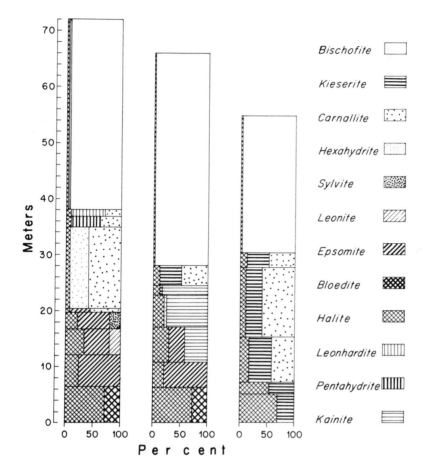

Fig. 39 Static evaporation of ocean water at 25°C; (a) metastable equilibrium; (b) stable equilibrium, without reaction at the phase boundaries; (c) stable equilibrium, with complete reaction at the phase boundaries (after Braitsch, 1962)

meter limestone, 4.8 meter gypsum, and 100 meter halite will form before the salts seen in Figure 39 will precipitate upon isothermic evaporation at 25°C. To produce such a layer of salt, however, a water column of 8500 meters of mean ocean water composition has to evaporate. But evaporites of completely unchanged sea water composition are not known in nature. The previously proposed model, therefore, can only be used as a simple example to acquaint students with the principal mechanism of salt mineral formation. There are so many factors in nature which determine the type of salt deposits that it is impossible to include even the major mineral systems within the scope of this book. Braitsch (1962), in his work on the origin and mineral composition of oceanic salt deposits, thoroughly discusses the manifold possibilities of salt mineral formation that may arise in the course of evaporation of ocean water and subsequent diagenesis.

According to Braitsch (1962), the bulk of the marine evaporites falls into two major categories, i.e., into those deposits which are slightly, and into others that are often completely impoverished in $MgSO_4$. Factors that determine the type of salt to be formed in a marine evaporation basin include: (1) Microbial activities which extract and reduce some of the sulfate ions, particularly in the initial stages of evaporation; (2) Interactions of the brine with the detritus and the underlying rock strata (dolomitization is one of the results); (3) Infiltration of fresh water or sea water and extraction of brine solutions by differential density current flow (wedging effect); the exchange of saline by less saline waters or vice versa may take place across reefs or through permeable rock barriers and change the chemistry of the evaporite system; (4) Internal temperature changes within the basin of deposition; they can produce facies changes in the sense that, for example, gypsum will deposit in the shallow environment (warm), while halite precipitates in the deeper parts of the basin (cold); (5) Diagenesis, and solution- and thermo-metamorphosis at moderate temperatures (below $100°C$) that may effectively alter the mineral composition of an evaporite deposit; for instance, paragenetic kieserite-sylvite is definitely a secondary product caused by a metamorphic alteration; or connate waters, e.g., enriched in $CaCl_2$, may diagenetically modify the primary precipitates.

Tectonic deformation may not only mobilize the salt deposit, as evidenced by the warping pattern of salt layers or the formation of diapirs (Trusheim, 1960), but cause structural-chemical alterations in some of the participating salts. The geology of salt deposits has been discussed and reviewed by Struton (1953), Sloss (1953), Lotze (1957), Richter-Bernburg (1953), Krumbein (1951), Briggs (1958), Borchert (1959), Groves (1958), Bersticker et al. (1962), and in abstracts presented at the International Conference on Saline Deposits, Houston, Texas (1962).

3. Minor Varieties

(a) *Celestite*. In studies on the solubility of celestite in sea water, Müller and Puchelt (1961) conclude that celestite will precipitate upon evaporation of sea water to about $\frac{1}{4}$ its volume. This may be the explanation for the paragenesis of celestite-carbonate or celestite-carbonate-calcium sulfate, as frequently observed in primary celestite deposits (Müller, 1960). This observation agrees with a report of Skinner (1960) on the occurrence of celestite (up to 3 per cent of the total sediment) in South Australian Lagoons, in which dolomites and various calcium carbonates coexist.

Braitsch (1960) and Herrmann (1961, 1962), however, identified celestite crystals in the sodium and potassium salts of marine evaporites. It is interesting to note that in this case celestite does not occur in the earlier deposits, which means not in association with carbonates or calcium sulfates. No reasonable interpretation is at present available to account for the early celestite deposition in one case (Müller, 1960), and the comparatively late precipitation in another case (Braitsch, 1960; Herrmann, 1961, 1962). Perhaps future studies on the strontium sulfate content in waters and mineral deposits of the South Australian Lagoons (Skinner, 1960) will give more insight into the mechanism of celestite formation.

A protozoan group, the acantharid radiolaria, mineralize biologically a celestite skeleton with small amounts of barite in solid solution (Arrhenius, 1963). The skeleton of dartlike spines is built of radially arranged celestite microcrystals. Upon the death of the organism the spines become detached from each other and sink to the ocean floor. Due to the undersaturation of ocean water with respect to celestite the $SrSO_4$ microcrystals rapidly corrode and dissolve. Analogous to the behavior of silica biologically extracted from a solution undersaturated with respect to amorphous silica, it is conceivable that a similar mechanism may provide local concentration of strontium in the sea which will cause inorganic precipitation of celestite upon slight evaporation of the ocean water.

(b) *Barite*. The barium content of the sea lies between 10 and $70 \mu g/l$ (Chow and Goldberg, 1960; Goldberg, 1961); thus, the ocean is slightly undersaturated with respect to the precipitation of barium sulfate. But favorable micro-environments may locally develop around decaying organic matter (Goldberg, 1961; Arrhenius, 1959, 1963) where barium sulfate will become deposited. The wide occurrence of radioactive celestobarite on the ocean floor supports this assumption. Strontium, radium and lead substitute in larger quantities in this sulfate (Arrhenius et al., 1957; Arrhenius, 1963). Bowen (1956), Arrhenius (1963), Koczy (1950, 1958), and Chow and

Goldberg (1960) give data on the quantities of barium, strontium, lead and other elements that can be carried by organic debris to the bottom of the sea in the form of shell or tissue material. Aside from cation substitution, replacement of SO_4 by BF_4 and possibly CrO_4 is indicated by the high amounts of boron and chromium in the celestobarite, all of which naturally affect the solubility characteristics of the mineral.

The extensive corrosion observed when celestobarite is placed for short periods of time in distilled water at room temperature, and the lack of such etching in specimens obtained from the bottom of the sea indicates that the dissolution of celestobarite does not take place in the aqueous environment from which the minerals were taken. Arrhenius (1963) discusses the dissolution-precipitation mechanism of marine celestobarite in some detail.

It is still uncertain whether protozoa can precipitate barite.

(c) *Fluorite.* Fluorite is one of the first compounds to precipitate upon evaporation of ocean water. It is commonly found in association with dolomites, limestones and occasionally with phosphorites. In studies of the geochemistry of fluorine Correns (1956, 1957) found fluorine in anhydrite deposits in amounts up to about 900 ppm. In view of the low concentration of P_2O_5, he suggested tentatively that most of the fluorine is present in the form of fluorite. It is conceivable that organisms during their lifetime may concentrate fluorine to such a degree that upon decay of organic matter the level of fluorine can be raised to the extent that fluorite will deposit.

The genesis of fluorite in sedimentary environments has been discussed by Bushinsky (1936) and Teodorovich (1961).

Selected References

D'Ans, J., D. Bretschneider, H. Eick, and H. E. Freund, "Untersuchungen über die Calziumsulfate." Kali und Steinsalz, 1 (1955), 17–38.

D'Ans, J., and R. Kuhn, "Bemerkungen zur Bildung und zu Umbildungen ozeaner Salzlagerstätten." Kali und Steinsalz 3 (1960), 69–84.

Arrhenius, G., "Pelagic sediments." In *The Sea. Ideas and Observations on Progress in the Study of the Seas,* edited by M. N. Hill. New York: Interscience Publishers, Inc., (1963), 655–727.

Arrhenius, G., "Sedimentation on the Ocean Floor." In *Researches in Geochemistry*, edited by P. H. Abelson, New York: John Wiley & Sons, Inc., (1959), 1–24.

Arrhenius, G., M. N. Bramlette, and E. Picciotto, "Localization of Radioactive and Stable Heavy Nuclides in Ocean Sediments." Nature, **180** (1957), 85–86.

Bersticker, A. C., K. E. Hoekstra, and J. F. Hall, eds., *Symposium on Salt.* Cleveland, Ohio: The Northern Ohio Geological Society, Inc., 1963.

Borchert, H., *Ozeane Salzlagerstätten.* Berlin-Nikolassee: (1959) Gebrüder Borntraeger.

Bowen, H. J. M., "Strontium and Barium in Sea Water and Marine Organisms." J. Mar. Biol. Assoc., U.K., **35** (1956), 451–460.

Briggs, L. I., "Evaporite facies." J. Sed. Petrol., **28** (1958), 46–56.

Braitsch, O., "Mineralparagenesis und Petrologie der Stassfurtsalze in Reyershausen." Kali und Steinsalz, **3** (1960), 1–14.

Braitsch, O., *Entstehung und Stoffbestand der Salzlagerstätten.* "Mineralogie und Petrographie in Einzeldarstellungen," edited by W. v. Engelhardt and J. Zemann, Dritter Band. Berlin-Göttingen-Heidelberg: Springer Verlag, 1962.

Bushinsky, G. I., "On the Genesis of Fluorite in Sedimentary Rocks." Acad. Sci. USSR, B. Ser. Geol., **5** (1936), 775–793.

Chow, T. J. and E. D. Goldberg, "On the Marine Geochemistry of Barium." Geochim. et Cosmochim. Acta, **20** (1960), 192–198.

Conley, R. F. and W. M. Bundy, "Mechanism of Gypsification." Geochim. et Cosmochim. Acta, **15** (1958), 57–72.

Correns, C. W., "The Geochemistry of the Halogens." In *Physics and Chemistry of the Earth,* Vol. 1, ed. L. H. Ahrens, K. Rankama, and S. K. Runcorn (1956), 181–233.

Correns, C. W., "Uber die Geochemie des Fluors und Chlors." N. Jb. Mineral. Abh., **91** (1957), 239–256.

Findlay, A., *"Die Phasenregel und ihre Anwendungen."* Weinheim: Verlag Chemie, 1958.

Goldberg, E. D., "Chemistry in the Oceans." In *Oceanography,* edited by M. Sears. Washington, D. C.: Amer. Assoc. Advanc. Sci., **67** (1961), 583–597.

Groves, A. W., *Gypsum and Anhydrite.* London: Overseas Geological Surveys, Mineral Resources Division, 1958.

Herrmann, A. G., "Zur Geochemie des Strontiums in den salinaren Zechsteinablagerungen der Stassfurt-Serie des Südharzbezirkes." Chemie der Erde, **21** (1961–62), 137–194.

van't Hoff, J. H., *Zur Bildung der ozeanischen Salzablagerungen.* Braunschweig: Fr. Vieweg 1905, 1909.

Jänecke, E., *Die Entstehung der deutschen Kalisalzlager,* 2 Aufl. Braunschweig: Fr. Vieweg, 1923.

Koczy, F. F., "Die bodennahen Wasserschichten der Tiefsee." Naturwissenschaften, **37** (1950), 360.

Koczy, F. F., *Natural Radium as a Tracer in the Ocean.* Proceedings of the Second United Nations International Conference on the Peaceful Uses of Atomic Energy, Geneva, 1958, Vol. 18, 351–357, printed in Great Britain.

Kelley, K. K., J. C. Southard, and C. T. Anderson, "Thermodynamic Properties of Gypsum and its Dehydration Products." U. S. Bur. Mines Techn. Papers, **625** (1941).

Krumbein, W. C., "Occurrence and Lithologic Associations of Evaporites in the United States." J. Sed. Petrol., **21** (1951), 63–81.

Lotze, F., *Steinsalz und Kalisalze.* Berlin-Nikolassee: Gebrüder Borntraeger, 1957.

MacDonald, G. J. F., "Anhydrite-Gypsum Equilibrium Relations." Amer. J. Sci., **251** (1953), 884–898.

Madgin, W. M. and D. A. Swales, "Solubilities in the System $CaSO_4$-$NaCl$-H_2O at 25° and 35°." J. Appl. Chem. (London), **6** (1956), 482–487.

Müller, G., "Eine sedimentäre Coelestin-Lagerstätte im Oberen Malm NW-Deutschlands." Fortschr. Mineral., **38** (1960), 189.

Müller, G. and H. Puchelt, "Die Bildung von Coelestin ($SrSO_4$) aus Meerwasser." Naturwissenschaften, **48** (1961), 301–302.

Posnjak, E., "Deposition of Calcium Sulfate from Sea Water." Amer. J. Sci., **238** (1940), 559–568.

Richter-Bernburg, G., "Über salinare Sedimentation." Ztschr. deutsch. geol. Ges., **105** (1953), 593–645.

Richter-Bernburg, G., "Zeitmessung geologischer Vorgänge nach Warvenkorrelationen im Zechstein." Geol. Rdsch., **49** (1960), 132–148.

Skinner, H. C. W., "Formation of Modern Dolomitic Sediments in South Australian Lagoons." Bull. Geol. Soc. Amer. (Abstract), **71** (1960), 1976.

Sloss, L. L., "The Significance of Evaporites." J. Sed. Petrol., **23** (1953), 143–161.

Sruton, P. C., "Deposition of Evaporites." Bull. Amer. Assoc. Petrol. Geol., **37** (1953), 2498–2512.

Sverdrup, H. U., M. W. Johnson, and R. H. Fleming, *The Oceans: Their Physics, Chemistry and General Biology*. Englewood Cliffs, N. J.: Prentice-Hall, Inc., 1946.

Teodorovich, G. I., "Authigenic Minerals in Sedimentary Rocks." New York: Consultants Bureau Enterprise, Inc., 1961. (The Russian text was published by the USSR Academy of Sciences Press, Moscow, 1958.)

Trusheim, F., "Mechanism of Salt Migration in Northern Germany." Bull. Amer. Assoc. Petrol. Geol., **44** (1960), 1519–1540.

Waljaschko, M. G., "Die wichtigsten geochemischen Parameter für die Bildung der Kalisalzlagerstätten." Freiburger Forschungshefte, **A 123** (1958), 197–233.

4

Mobile Phases

Water

1. INTRODUCTION

One of the more significant topics of modern theoretical and applied geology concerns the water cycle in nature. Aside from the importance of water studies for all purposes of human and industrial consumption, geologists are also interested in understanding the role of water at the earth's surface and within the earth's crust. Inasmuch as water is the main agent during physical and chemical weathering, the carrier and transporter of most sediment material in the dissolved or particulate state, and the environment of most life processes, the complexity of the problem is well demonstrated. Furthermore, water makes up two-thirds of the living matter and is essential for a number of minerals such as clays and hydroxides to balance their structure. It is safe to conclude that without water, life and most sediments would not exist on earth.

2. CLASSIFICATION

Waters can be classified in a number of ways. Most commonly they are grouped according to (1) origin in terms of meteoric, connate, or juvenile water, (2) chemistry, e.g., bicarbonate, sulfate, or chloride water, and (3) total salinity, i.e., fresh water, salinized water, or brine water.

The prefix "meteoric" applies to water that has gone through the meteorological cycle, that is evaporation, condensation, and finally, precipitation. All continental surface waters such as rivers, lakes, or glaciers fall into this general category. Because meteoric water may subsequently seep into the underlaying rock strata, it will also be found at various depths of the lithosphere.

The ocean, although it continuously receives the continental run-off of meteoric waters as well as rain, is by general agreement not regarded as being of "meteoric" nature. Instead, the ocean represents in some approximation the chemically stable and original water reservoir enduring over geological periods of time. Therefore, the sea water entrapped in sediments during deposition is called "connate water" in order to make a clear cut distinction from meteorologically derived waters. Some authors use the term connate water for all syngenetic waters independent of whether they are enclosed in fresh water or marine sediments. In the present context, only sea water entrapped in marine sediments at the time of burial will be designated as connate water, since all fresh waters — buried or infiltrated — are ultimately meteoric in origin.

Juvenile waters are those that have come from inner sources of the earth where they originated. Unfortunately, geologists often designate hot springs or hydrothermal solutions as juvenile waters, mostly on the basis of the general geological configuration or the temperature of the water alone. However, as geochemical data accumulated it became apparent that juvenile waters are extremely rare, at least in those portions of the lithosphere presently accessible for water studies. Even waters in areas of recent volcanic activities are for the most part meteoric in origin as evidenced by isotope data.

To classify waters on the basis of chemistry is rather difficult, because of the great number of ions which may occur in natural waters. Fortunately, however, only a few of these are sufficiently common and widespread to be of practical use for the construction of a general classification scheme. The four potential anions are: bicarbonate, carbonate, chloride and sulfate; and the corresponding cations: sodium, potassium, calcium, and magnesium.

According to Chebotarev (1955), anions are assumed to be the independent ingredients while cations are the dependent variables. The major geochemical groups of water are therefore those determined by the occurrence and prevalence of anions. On this basis one may distinguish between three major categories of natural waters, i.e., (1) bicarbonate waters, (2) sulfate waters, and (3) chloride waters. If two of the anions are far in excess of the third, one may speak, for example, of bicarbonate-sulfate water or sulfate-chloride water, always putting the common anion in front.

The terms "fresh water" and "salt water" are frequently employed. The upper boundary for fresh water is 1 per cent salinity. This is about the maximum salt concentration tolerated by the natural fresh water fauna and flora. The salt limit for human consumption is ~ 0.5 per cent, though a few instances are known where waters up to 0.8 per cent salinity were used for human consumption without noticeable damage to health. Waters having a salt content between 1 and 3.5 per cent are called salinized water. The upper value corresponds to the salinity of the ocean. Waters beyond this concentration are known as brines.

3. Chemistry of Subsurface Waters

Large quantities of waters are continuously extracted from the hydrosphere during the deposition of sedimentary materials. Most of the buried water occupies the pore spaces of sediments and some of it may be structurally incorporated in certain minerals. Recent muds may contain up to 80 per cent water by volume, but upon compaction of the strata the water will be gradually expelled to the next environments. The speed by which the water is released from the original bed rock in the course of diagenesis is not only a function of overburden pressure; it also depends on parameters such as mineral composition, texture, and structure of the sediment. The hydraulic gradient controls the direction of flow.

Studies on subsurface waters are a challenging research topic in the area of sediment geochemistry. In a broad sense, water in a sedimentary rock formation displays a role analogous to magmatic fluids in crystalline rocks. Both types of fluids represent the mobile phase and act as the universal solvent, carrier and transporter of material from one spot to the other. The solid rock compounds as a whole must be considered stationary when compared to the agility of their interstitial waters. This in turn suggests that connate water will interact with the surrounding mineral and organic matter and will not preserve indefinitely its chemical makeup as fixed at the time of deposition. Consequently, there will be considerable changes concerning the nature and the concentration of solutes in the water. Similarly, meteoric waters will pick up or release materials during their migration through the rock strata.

Regarding the formation waters, at first the clue was believed to lie in the type and distribution pattern of electrolytes. One objective of such studies was to evaluate the possibility of using the chemical characteristics of certain subsurface waters as a key to the chemistry of the ancient sea. However, as information on these waters accumulated, it became evident that they had been severely altered in composition as a result of a variety of physical and chemical processes, as, for example, ion filtration and reduction and dissolution of rock materials. They no longer reflected the chemistry of the original water during deposition.

The interest in studies of subsurface waters then shifted in the direction of using the postdepositional characteristics of the waters as a tool for the understanding of reactions taking place during diagenesis, i.e. dolomitization, silicification and extraction, migration and accumulation of hydrocarbons. For details and a review on this subject, see DeSitter (1947), Durov (1948, 1961), Wyllie (1955,1958), McKelvey et al. (1957), Chave (1960), von Engelhardt (1960, 1961), Siever et al. (1961), Siever (1962), McKelvey and Milne (1962), Knetsch et al. (1962), Degens and Chilingar (1964), Rainwater and White (1958), Chilingar (1956), Rittenberg et al. (1963), Ayers et al. (1952), and Wright et al. (1957).

It has been pointed out that juvenile water is uncommon in environments at or close to the earth's surface. Thus, practically all water in the upper few miles of the lithosphere is either meteoric or connate in origin or represents a mixture of both. From a geochemical point of view, it is quite important to be certain whether one is dealing with meteoric or connate water. Therefore, any criterion to distinguish between these two major types of water would be valuable.

Meteroic water has an average of only a few hundred ppm salts compared to 35,000 ppm in connate water. Furthermore, sea water is uniform in chemical composition whereas meteoric water can vary considerably. But as soon as water is in contact with mineral and organic matter reactions and interactions take place that may cause

(1) desalting of water, (2) concentration of salt, or (3) preferential increase or decrease of one or the other of the dissolved mineral and organic species. This diagenesis or metamorphosis of a water is often so pronounced that its chemistry no longer reflects the original chemical composition at the time of deposition or infiltration, respectively.

Diagenesis of meteoric water: Precipitations will pick up some of the salts already in the atmosphere from sources such as sea spray, dust, or atmospheric CO_2. But most of the dissolved matter is obtained when the waters seep into the soil. Micro-organisms and decaying organic matter play an important part in these processes by supplying, for instance, CO_2 to the reacting system. Following the diagenesis in a soil, meteoric waters may be geochemically altered when they percolate through the underlying rock formation. The old saying by Plinius that "Tales sunt aquae, qualis terra per quam fluunt" (waters take their nature from the strata through which they flow) carries indeed a profound meaning.

On the continents, in areas where precipitation is abundant, the turnover of migrating meteoric water in subterranean water basins or ground water tables is relatively rapid. This implies that the time of reaction with the sediment or soil is kept at a minimum. In contrast, in desert regions, where recharge and subsurface migration of water is comparatively slow and over long distances, water will stay longer in contact with the surrounding rock strata. Consequently, the chemical alteration is more severe. Very often, if time allows and if the rock formation is favorable, a chemical stratification pattern can develop in the sense that the more saline water will occupy the deepest and the less saline water the highest level of a subterranean water reservoir (Chebotarev, 1955).

Diagenesis of connate water: Microbial activity and decaying organic matter unquestionably will leave some imprint on the chemical spectrum of interstitial waters entrapped in marine muds. But most of the geochemical alteration will be brought about during the subsequent compaction and partial dehydration of the marine sediment.

Information on connate water is largely obtained from studies of deeply buried "fossilized brines," most of them associated with petroleum reservoirs. It has to be emphasized that all of these waters are derived from highly permeable sediments such as sandstones and certain carbonates. Thus, we know very little of the geochemistry of water present in shales. With the recent advancement in pressure and dilution techniques for extraction of water from clay minerals and shales (von Engelhardt, 1961; von Engelhardt and Gaida, 1963; Siever, 1962; Rieke et al., 1964), hydrogeochemical data may soon be obtained from less permeable rock materials.

Fossilized brines of salinities up to 300 per mil are considered to be accumulations of connate waters. Criteria for the marine origin of these waters are their geologic relations to the source strata, which in most instances can be identified as marine beds as well as the chemical relationship to present day ocean water. There are, however, certain differences in the chemical composition relative to modern sea water. Generally, there is a much higher concentration of electrolytes. Also the salt spectrum is different. (Fig. 40). Particularly noteworthy are the relative depletion in magnesium and sulfate ions and the enrichment in calcium and chlorine ions (DeSitter, 1947; Chave, 1960; Eremenko, 1960; Krejci-Graf et al., 1957; and von Engelhardt, 1961). These changes can be explained by geochemical processes occurring during diagenesis. Most important of these are the interactions of interstitial water with clay minerals, and reduction and dolomitization phenomena.

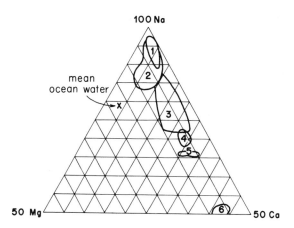

Fig. 40   Cations in petroleum brine waters of the United States. (1) Woodbine Sand, Texas (Cretaceous); (2) California (Tertiary); (3) Kansas and Oklahoma (Paleozoic); (4) Appalachian (Mississippian); (5) Appalachia (Upper Devonian); Arkansas (Jurassic) (after De Sitter, 1947; and von Engelhardt, 1960)

One may well ask what mechanism caused the enormous salt concentration, since sea water has a salinity of only 35 per mil (Table 12). There are two possibilities: either by earlier evaporation in a surface environment, or by compaction of sediments during their burial, with the connate water being squeezed out. Experiments by von Engelhardt (1961) and Rieke et al. (1964) have shown that clays upon compaction (0 to 200 psi) release water enriched in electrolytes relative to the original interstitial water, whereas a gradual increase in pressure from 200 psi up to 200,000 psi yields water that exponentially decreases in electrolytes (Figs. 41 and 42). Considering that the waters expelled at the initial stages of diagenesis at some pressure below approximately 200 psi are apparently only slightly enriched in salinity (10 to 20 per cent) relative to mean ocean water, this mechanism cannot account for a salinity of up to 30 per cent, as found in quite a few fossilized brines. A more effective mechanism must have operated during diagenesis to produce these salinities.

It has been proposed by Wyllie (1955), Ellis (1954), Davis (1955), McKelvey et al. (1957), and recently by von Engelhardt (1961) and

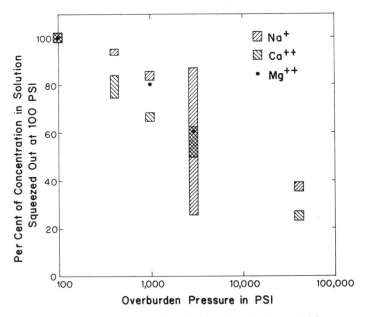

Fig. 41   Sodium, calcium, and magnesium ions in interstitial waters of recent marine sediments off California (Santa Cruz Basin) squeezed out at various overburden pressures (after Rieke et al., 1964)

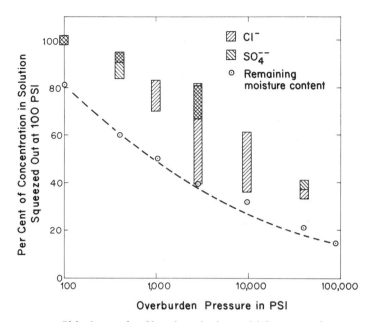

Fig. 42   Chlorine and sulfate ions in interstitial waters of recent marine sediments off California (Santa Cruz Basin) squeezed out at various overburden pressures. Dashed line represents remaining moisture content (after Rieke et al., 1964)

Bredehoeft et al. (1963) that buried waters may be subjected to ion-filtration by charged-net clay membranes. (The filtration of salt solutions through charged-net clay membranes has been suggested as a mechanism for producing fresh water from saline water.)

Shale beds in situ may be considered to be ideal membrane electrodes. The most suggestive argument for this assumption is the observed uniformity of a "shale baseline" on "spontaneous potential" logs found in drill holes in every part of the world (Wyllie, 1955). A quantitative theoretical treatment of the electrochemical properties of clays is given by the theory of membrane behavior of Meyer-Sievers-Teorell (Davies, 1955), which, according to calculations based on the SP curve (spontaneous potential) of e-logs, approximates the behavior of shales in situ in the earth. A comprehensive mathematical treatment of this phenomenon has been presented by Wyllie (1955), Bredehoeft et al. (1963) and Degens and Chilingar (1964).

The general consensus is that during compaction of clay-containing sediments salts are filtered and accumulate in the formation water retained in the strata. The process of salt removal or concentration depends on the large excess charge permanently attached to the clay membrane which prevents the passage of ions of the same charge. In other words, the separation is due to the electrical properties rather than to the size of the electrolyte. This process yields a lower salt level in the filtrate as compared to the original solution. Thus, the salt is filtered by virtue of its electrolytic dissociation and the electric properties of the clay membrane.

Inasmuch as not only the inorganic electrolytes but also the dissolved organic molecules are affected by the outlined filtration mechanism, the natural concentration of hydrocarbons and the subsequent formation of oil droplets and crude oils may be reasonably explained (p. 298).

4. Isotopic Composition of Natural Waters

The variation of the isotopic composition of natural waters is another useful parameter for the purpose of classification. Deuterium and oxygen-18 concentrations in meteoric surface waters vary by about 43 and 5.6 per cent, respectively, and are linearly related (Friedman, 1953; Epstein and Mayeda, 1953; Epstein, 1959; Daansgard, 1953, 1961; and Craig, 1961a, 1961b). The comparison of the O^{18}/O^{16} and D/H ratio shows that atmospheric precipitation normally follows a Raleigh process at liquid-vapor equilibrium. The atmospheric Raleigh process also explains why at higher altitudes and latitudes fresh waters become isotopically progressively lighter whereas tropical samples show very small depletions relative to mean ocean water (Fig. 43).

A linear isotope relationship between deuterium and oxygen-18 concentration, however, does not exist when the water is formed under non-equilibrium conditions. For example, in a dry climate (desert), a re-evaporation of falling raindrops may increase the fractionation factors, especially for the oxygen isotopes. Any process of free evaporation is governed by kinetic factors (Craig et al., 1963; Ehhalt et al., 1963a; Merlivat et al., 1963). This will cause certain deviations from the linear deuterium-oxygen-18 pattern normally produced by Raleigh condensation in the clouds at liquid-vapor equilibrium.

Isotope measurements of a large number of ocean waters indicate that most of them fall within a narrow range, namely less than 1 per cent for δD and 1 per mil for δO^{18}. Evaporation processes, however,

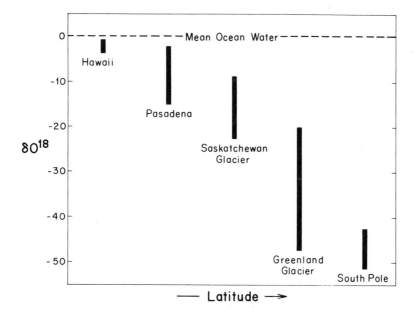

Fig. 43 O^{18}/O^{16} ratio of selected meteoric water samples (after Epstein and Sharp, 1959; Epstein and Mayeda, 1953; and Epstein, unpublished data)

strongly affect the isotope composition since they cause a preferential depletion in the lighter isotopes which become enriched in the vapor phase. The remaining water consequently will be heavier, i.e., highly saline waters generally have the greatest D and O^{18} content.

Stable isotopes may perhaps tell whether the high salinities in connate waters are a result of syngenetic evaporation or of diagenetic ion filtration. In contrast to evaporation processes, compaction and filtration by charged-net clay membranes should not noticeably influence the isotope ratios of the participating water, particularly in cases of the oxygen isotopes where the mass differences are small. These processes are relatively slow and, since only one phase is participating, no fractionation is produced when equilibrium is reached. In this connection it is noteworthy that hydrochemical studies within the same aquifer (Nubian Series of the Western Egyptian Desert) on the effect of long-range migration on the O^{18}/O^{16} ratio indicate that oxygen isotopes apparently are not fractionated during subsurface transportation over periods of about twenty to thirty thousand years and migration distances up to 700 miles (Knetsch et al., 1962).

Figure 44 shows that the δO^{18} values of high saline connate waters associated with petroleum deposits do, as expected, not deviate appreciably from the δO^{18} of modern sea water (Degens et al., 1964). Deviations from this mean value in some of the samples into the negative range of δO^{18} are always well correlated to a decrease in salinity. This feature can easily be explained by effects of dilution with isotopically lighter meteoric water during the migration of the brine, or perhaps later-stage infiltrations as a result of a change in the geological setting by uplift, denudation, or other phenomena.

It is reasonable to conclude that the brines are former sea waters if we assume that the O^{18}/O^{16} ratio of the ocean waters has remained more or less unchanged, at least since Cambrian time. This assumption is supported by isotope work of Clayton and Epstein (1958) according to which it is difficult to assign to marine waters of the past O^{18}/O^{16} ratios which are much different from those of the modern sea. Moreover, preserved calcareous fossils of late Paleozoic age have δO^{18} values similar to those of present-day calcareous marine shells (Compston, 1960), which in turn suggests that the oceans indeed must have stayed isotopically fairly uniform for a considerable geologic span of time.

The similarity between isotope characteristics of the brines and modern sea water leads immediately to the conclusion that the concentration of the inorganic salts has not been accomplished by evaporation. It probably occurred by processes of compaction and and ion-filtration by charged–net clay membranes. It is tentatively suggested that isotope data may serve as an indicator for the relative proportions of meteoric and connate water within a given water sample.

Aside from the stable isotopes, the radioactive tritium produced by cosmic radiation, thermonuclear weapons and nuclear industries is also very useful for a number of hydrological, meteorological, and geological problems (Libby, 1959; Begemann and Libby, 1957; Begemann and Friedman, 1959; Gonsior et al., 1963; Ehhalt et al., 1963b; and others). The title of the paper by Begemann and Libby (1957), "Continental water balance, ground water inventory and storage time, surface ocean mixing rates, and world-wide water circulation patterns from cosmic-ray and bomb tritium," well illustrates the wide variety of hydrological problems that can be tackled by tritium analyses.

Another potential radioisotope tracer is carbon-14. The activity of the dissolved carbonate fraction in the sea and in certain fresh

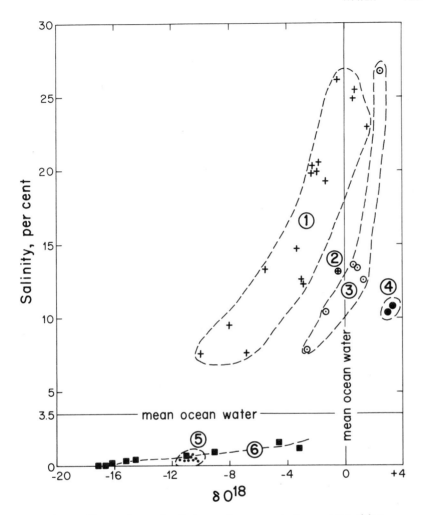

Fig. 44 Comparison of salinity and oxygen isotope composition in waters associated with marine and freshwater petroleum deposits. (1) Cambrium-Ordovician, Oklahoma; (2) Devonian, Oklahoma; (3) Pennsylvanian, Oklahoma; (4) Tertiary, Texas; (5) Cretaceous, Colorado; and (6) Tertiary, Utah. (after Degens et al., 1964)

waters can be used for the age dating of water samples as old as about forty thousand years (Münnich, 1957, 1963; Münnich and Vogel, 1962; Broecker et al., 1960, 1961; Bien et al., 1960; Brinkmann et al., 1959). These studies have added considerably to the understanding of the circulation pattern and mixing rates of ocean waters and the storage time of subterranean fresh waters.

5. Origin of the Hydrosphere

Hypotheses on the origin of the hydrosphere fall into two principal categories: (1) the primitive ocean had about the same water volume as the modern sea or (2) water gradually accumulated by leakage from the earth's interior over geological periods of time.

Uncertainty also exists concerning the chemistry of the ancient sea. Some investigators believe that salts have gradually accumulated to the present value of 3.5 per cent; others assume that steady-state conditions were already reached in late Pre-Cambrian time. According to another group, the chemical spectrum of the Pre-Cambrian sea was significantly different from the present sea. For instance, it was assumed that the primitive ocean was undersaturated with respect to $CaCO_3$ due to an excess of CO_2, and that the Ca/Mg ratio was considerably lower.

It is not the objective of this chapter to evaluate critically and adequately the pros and cons of the individual hypotheses. The data on which most ideas are based are for the most part too controversial and speculative to allow a brief and therefore uncritical presentation. However, an excellent attempt to state the problem has been made by Rubey (1951, 1955).

Gases

A variety of gases of organic and inorganic origin have been found in sediments and subsurface waters. Abundant and widespread are carbon dioxide, ammonia, hydrogen sulfide, hydrogen, atmospheric air, and the gaseous hydrocarbons among which methane is the most prominent one.

Gases may have a physical and chemical effect on sediments. In unconsolidated sediments, for example, transportation of matter can be accomplished; also, gas produced markings are rather common.

It may be pointed out that the marks of gas bubbles are often mistaken for organic markings, and similarly bubble imprints are easily confused with raindrop imprints. Compressed gas accumulations in petroleum deposits and subsurface water reservoirs may speed up the flow of oil and water. In both instances, gas is the main agent to lift these liquids to the earth surface.

Among all the gases recognized in sediments, carbon dioxide has the greatest effect on the geochemistry of sediments. Detailed information on the activity of CO_2, however, is difficult to obtain, because carbon dioxide is part of the calcium carbonate system. The most significant source for carbon dioxide in sediments is micro-organisms and decaying organic matter. On the other hand, gases such as hydrogen and methane can be utilized by micro-organisms as a source of energy during various life processes.

The formation of gas in the sediments is most extensive in the early stages of diagenesis. A great portion of the gas will certainly escape into the surface waters or the atmosphere, but some gases are partially retained and eventually contribute to oil field gases, or they become dissolved in the interstitial waters. Some may even be fixed to the sediments in the form of sulfides and carbonates or will be associated with the detrital matrix. Consolidated sediments are mostly poor in gases although some gases may be entrapped as so-called "air bubbles." The major sources for gas after organic activity and decay has passed its climax are the various radioactive decay products such as argon and helium. Under certain conditions they may be tightly fixed to the parent material and can be used in some instances (glauconites, authigenic feldspars) for radioactive age determinations.

A recent review on the occurrence and activities of gases in sediments has been given by Cloud (1960).

Petroleum

Liquid crude oil represents the most important mobile organic phase in sediments. During migration petroleum may extract some of the organic solvent soluble constituents from a sediment. For the most part these increments are hydrocarbons, pigments and related compounds. But free sulfur may also be obtained in this manner. Little is known, however, of the effect of petroleum on the mineral matter of a sediment, or of the influence the mineral matter may exercise on the migrating petroleum. For details on the origin of petroleum see page 288.

Selected References

Ayers, M. L., R. P. Dobyns, and R. Q. Bussel, "Resistivities of Water from Subsurface Formations." North Texas: Petrol. Engineer, B-36, (1952).

Begemann, F. and W. F. Libby, "Continental Water Balance, Ground Water Inventory and Storage Times, Surface Ocean Mixing Rates, and World-wide Water Circulation Patterns from Cosmic Ray and Bomb Tritium." Geochim. et Cosmochim. Acta, **12** (1957), 277–296.

Begemann, F. and I. Friedman, "Tritium and Deuterium Content of Atmospheric Hydrogen." Z. Naturforsch., **14a** (1959), 1024.

Bien, G. S., N. W. Rakestraw, and H. E. Suess, "Radiocarbon Concentration in Pacific Ocean Water." Tellus, **12** (1960), 436–443.

Bredehoeft, J. D., C. R. Blyth, W. A. White, and G. B. Maxey, "Possible Mechanism for Concentration of Brines in Subsurface Formations." Bull. Amer. Assoc. Petrol. Geol., **47** (1963), 257–269.

Brinkmann, R., K. O. Münnich, and J. C. Vogel, "C¹⁴ — Altersbestimmung von Grundwasser." Naturwissenschaften, **46** (1959), 10–12.

Broecker, W. S., R. D. Gerard, M. Ewing, and B. C. Heezen, "Natural Radiocarbon in the Atlantic Ocean." J. Geophys. Research, **65** (1960), 2903–2931.

Broecker, W. S., R. D. Gerard, M. Ewing, and B. C. Heezen, "Geochemistry and Physics of Ocean Circulation." In *Oceanography,* edited by M. Sears, Amer. Assoc. Adv. Sci., Publ. No. **67** (1961), 301–322.

Chave, K. E., "Evidence on History of Sea Water from Chemistry of Deeper Surface Waters of Ancient Basins." Bull. Amer. Assoc. Petrol. Geol., **44** (1960), 357–370.

Chebotarev, I. I., "Metamorphism of Natural Waters in the Crust of Weathering." I, II and III.: Geochim. et Cosmochim. Acta, **8** (1959), 22–48; 137–170; and 198–212.

Chilingar, G. V., "Durov's Classification of Natural Waters and Chemical Composition of Atmospheric Precipitation in USSR: A Review." Trans. Amer. Geophys. Union, **37**, 193–196.

Clayton, R. N. and S. Epstein, "The Relationship between O¹⁸/O¹⁶ Ratios in Coexisting Quartz, Carbonate, and Iron Oxides from Various Geological Deposits." J. Geol., **66** (1958), 352–373.

Cloud, P. E. Jr., "Gas as a Sedimentary and Diagenetic Agent." Amer. J. Sci., Bradley Vol. **258-A** (1960), 35–45.

Compston, W., "The Carbon Isotopic Compositions of Certain Marine Invertebrates and Coals from the Australian Permian." Geochim. et Cosmochim. Acta, **18** (1960), 1–22.

Craig, H., "Isotopic Variations in Meteoric Waters." Science, **133** (1961a), 1702–1703.

Craig, H., "Isotopic Geochemistry of Volcanic Water and Steam." Science, **134** (1961b), 1427–1428.

Craig. H., L. I. Gordon, and Y. Horibe, "Isotopic Exchange Effects in the Evaporation of Water. 1. Low Temperature Experimental Results." J. Geophys. Research, **68** (1963), 5079–5087.

Dansgaard, W., "The Abundance of O^{18} in Atmospheric Water and Water Vapor." Tellus **5** (1953), 461–469.

Dansgaard, W., "The Isotopic Composition of Natural Waters with Special Reference to the Greenland Ice Cap." Medd. Groenland, **165** (1961), 120 pp.

Davis, L. E., "Electrochemical Properties of Clays." In "Proc. First Nat'l Conference Clays and Clay Techn.," Div. Mines Calif., Bull. **169** (1955), 47–53.

Degens, E. T. and G. V. Chilingar, "Diagenesis of Subsurface Waters." In *Diagenesis of Sediments,* edited by U. Larsen and G. V. Chilingar. Amsterdam: Elsevier Publishing Company, 1964.

Degens, E. T., J. M. Hunt, J. H. Reuter, and W. E. Reed, "Data on the Distribution of Amino Acids and Oxygen Isotopes in Petroleum Brine Waters of Various Geologic Ages." Sedimentology, **3** (1964).

DeSitter, L. U., "Diagenesis of Oil-Field Brines." Bull. Amer. Assoc. Petrol. Geol., **31** (1947), 2030–2040.

Durov, S. A., "Classification of Natural Waters and Graphical Presentation of their Composition." Dokl. Akad. Nauk SSSR, **59** (1948), part 1, 87–90.

Durov, S. A., 1961, *Synthesis in Hydrochemistry (Origin of Salts Composition in Natural Waters):* Knizh. Izd. Rostov. (1961).

Ehhalt, D., K. Knott, J. F. Nagel, and J. C. Vogel, "Deuterium and Oxygen 18 in Rain Water." J. Geophys. Research, **68** (1963a), 3775–3780.

Ehhalt, D., G. Israel, W. Roether, and W. Stich, "Tritium and Deuterium Content of Atmospheric Hydrogen." J. Geophys. Research, **68** (1963a), 3747–3751.

Ellis, C. B., *Fresh Water from the Ocean:* New York: Ronald Press Co., 1954.

Engelhardt, W. von, *Der Porenraum der Sedimente:* Miner. Petrogr. Einzeldarst., edited by W. von Engelhardt and J. Zemann, Berlin-Göttingen-Heidelberg: Springer Verlag, 1960.

Engelhardt, W. von, "Zum Chemismus der Porenlösung der Sedimente." Bull. Geol. Inst. Uppsala Univ., **40** (1961), 189–204.

Engelhardt, W. von, and K. H. Gaida "Concentration Changes of Pure Solutions during the Compaction of Clay Sediments." J. Sed. Petrol. (1963).

Epstein, S., "The Variations of the O^{18}/O^{16} Ratio in Nature and Some Geologic Implications." In *Researches in Geochemistry*, edited by P. H. Abelson. New York: John Wiley & Sons, Inc., 1959.

Epstein, S. and T. Mayeda, "Variation of O^{18} Content of Waters from Natural Sources." Geochim. et Cosmochim. Acta, **4** (1953), 213–224.

Eremenko, N. A., ed., *Geology of Petroleum* (Handbook) I. *Principles of Geology and Petroleum*. Moscow, Gostoptekhizdat, 1960.

Friedman, I., "Deuterium Content of Natural Waters and Other Substances." Geochim. et Cosmochim. Acta, **4** (1953), 89–103.

Gonsior, B., I. Friedman, and D. Ehhalt, "Measurements of Tritium and Deuterium Concentration in Atmospheric Hydrogen." J. Geophys. Research, **68** (1963), 3753–3756.

Knetsch, G., A. Shata, E. Degens, K. O. Münnich, J. C. Vogel, and M. M. Shazly, "Untersuchungen an Grundwässern der Ost-Sahara." Geol. Rundschau, **53** (1962), 587–610.

Krejci-Graf, K., F. Hecht, and W. Palser, "Über Ölfeldwässer des Wiener Beckens." Geol. Jahrbuch, Hannover, **74** (1957), 161–209.

Libby, W. F., "Tritium in Hydrology and Meteorology." In *Researches in Geochemistry*, edited by P. H. Abelson. New York: John Wiley & Sons, Inc., 1959, 151–168.

McKelvey, J. G. Jr. and I. H. Milne "The Flow of Salt Solutions through Compacted Clays." In "Proc. Ninth Nat'l. Conference on Clay and Clay Minerals," edited by A. Swineford. New York: The Macmillan Company, (1962), 248–259.

McKelvey, J. G. Jr., K. S. Spiegler, and M. R. J. Wyllie, "Salt Filtering by Ion-Exchange Grains and Membranes." J. Phys. Chem., **61** (1957), 174–178.

Merlivat, L., R. Botter, and G. Nief, "Fractionment Isotopique au Cours de la distillation de l'eau." J. Chim. Phys., **60** (1963), 56–59.

Münnich, K. O., "Messungen des C^{14}-Gehaltes von hartem Grundwasser." Naturwissenschaften, **44** (1957), 32–33.

Münnich, K. O., "Der Kreislauf des Radiokohlenstoffs in der Natur." Naturwissenschaften, **50** (1963), 211–218.

Münnich, K. O. and J. C. Vogel, "Untersuchungen an Pluvialen Wässern der Ost-Sahara." Geol. Rundschau, **52** (1962), 611–624.

Rainwater, F. H. and W. F. White, "The Solusphere — its Inferences and Study." Geochim. et Cosmochim. Acta, **14** (1958), 244–249.

Rieke, H. H., G. V. Chilingar, and J. O. Robertson, "High-Pressure (up to 500,000 psi) Compaction Studies on Various Clays." Proc. XXII Internat. Geol. Congr. New Delhi, India, 1964.

Rittenberg, S. C., K. O. Emery, J. Hülsemann, E. T. Degens, R. C. Fay, J. H. Reuter, J. R. Grady, S. H. Richardson, and E. E. Bray, "Biogeochemistry of Sediments in Experimental Mohole." J. Sed. Petr., **33** (1963), 140–172.

Rubey, W. W., "Geologic History of Sea Water: An Attempt to State the Problem." Bull. Geol. Soc. Amer., **62** (1951), 1111–1148.

Rubey, W. W. "Development of the Hydrosphere and Atmosphere, with Special Reference to Probable Composition of the Early Atmosphere." In *Crust of the Earth,* ed. A. W. Poldervaart (New York: Geol. Soc. Amer., 1955), Special Paper **62** (1955), 631–650.

Siever, R., "A Squeezer for Extracting Interstitial Water from Modern Sediments." J. Sed. Petr., **32** (1963), 329–331.

Siever, R., R. M. Garrels, J. Kanwisher, and R. A. Berner, "Interstitial Waters of Recent Marine Muds off Cape Cod." Science, **134** (1961), 1071–1072.

Wright, J., D. Pearon, E. T. Kurt, and J. W. Watkins, "Analyses of Brines from Oil Productive Formations in Oklahoma." Bureau of Mines, Rep. Invest. **5325**, U. S. Department of Interior (1957).

Wyllie, M. R. J., "Role of Clays in Well Log Interpretation." In "Proc. First Nat'l. Conference Clays and Clay Minerals," Div. Mines, Calif., Bull., **169** (1955), 282–305.

Wyllie, M. R. J., "Some Electrochemical Properties of Shales." Science, **108** (1958), 684–685.

5

Organic Geochemistry

Concepts of Biogeochemical Studies

Sediments are the principal depositories of posthumous organic debris throughout the earth's history. The quantity carried in natural waters in the molecular-dispersed or particulate state is comparatively small. Trace amounts of organic chemicals may also be found in crystalline rocks; even meteorites, in particular the carbonaceous chondrite variety, contain a wide spectrum of "bio" chemical constituents.

There is no doubt that all terrestrial and extraterrestrial sources of organic matter have to be considered and evaluated in studies concerning the primordial synthesis of organic molecules and the origin of life. Nevertheless, our interest during the forthcoming discussions will be mainly focused on the presentation and interpretation of biochemical data of recent and ancient sediments, soils, and natural waters.

Hunt (1962) determined the amount of organic matter in more than 1000 rock specimens collected from 200 formations in 60 major sedimentary basins. Shales averaged 2.1 per cent, carbonates 0.29 per cent (Gehman, 1962), and sandstones 0.05 per cent. From these data and the figures reported by Weeks (1958) on the total volume of sediments and the ratio of shales to carbonates to sandstones, it has been calculated that the organic matter entrapped in sediments runs about 3.8×10^{15} metric tons; the overwhelming part, that is 3.6×10^{15} metric tons, is present in the shales. In other words, most of the organic matter occurs in a finely disseminated state and is associated with fine-grained sediments. For comparison, the coal deposits of the world have been estimated at about 6×10^{12} metric tons. This is 1/500th of the disseminated organic matter. Estimates of the ultimate primary petroleum reserves run to 0.2×10^{12} metric tons. This is only 1/16,000th of the total organic matter entrapped in sediments.

In order to illustrate more vividly the ratio of inorganic to organic matter the following generalized picture is offered. From an evaluation of the total thickness of sedimentary materials that have been formed and deposited over the last 3 to 4 billion years, it can be assumed that a sediment layer of approximately 1000 meters around the earth's surface has been laid down. Roughly 2 per cent of this layer, namely $\sim$20 meters, is organic, the rest is inorganic in nature. Of this 20 meter organic part, coal comprises $\sim$5 cm and crude oil only a little more than 1 mm. The rest represents the finely disseminated organic matter in shales, limestones, and sandstones.

For comparison, the amount of dissolved organic substances in the sea is only a few milligrams per liter (Goldberg, 1961). Fresh waters and some interstitial waters may carry considerably higher quantities, but relative to the total mass of the ocean, their volume, and consequently the total amount of organic matter present, is small.

The total amount of organic matter that can be expected in various rocks and natural waters is reasonably well known. More interesting from a geochemical point of view, however, would be a knowledge of the precise chemical nature and distribution pattern of individual organic species and a general understanding of processes and mechanisms that are responsible for the preservation, alteration, or destruction of organic matter throughout geological history.

Over the past three decades much has been learned of the quantitative distribution of biochemical constituents in marine and fresh water sediments, and their dependence upon the type of sediment and the depositional environment in terms of pH, Eh, or salinity. These studies have evolved far beyond the estimates of total organic carbon and nitrogen to the isolation and measurement of specific kinds of organic matter, for example the amino acids, hydrocarbons, sugars, and porphyrins. It became evident that the former theory of the instability of certain "perishable" organics such as proteins, carbohydrates or fats had to be revised.

More than 500 organic constituents have so far been extracted from sediments, soils, and natural waters. This number does not include all the individual organic chemicals that have been isolated from coal tars and crude oils. This is, in essence, the research product of the last 15 years. Due to the spontaneous increase of activity in the field of organic geochemistry and analytical chemistry, it takes no great ingenuity to predict that more organic compounds, in addition to the 500 compounds already known, will be identified in the near future.

Critics have stated that organic geochemistry has very little to offer for a better understanding of geological and paleontological problems. This is an erroneous statement. There is a wide range of exciting problems that can be tackled by means of organic geochemical studies. For example, there is the opportunity of a direct approach to hitherto inaccessible problems, such as the sequence of the origin of the key components of life through a study of Mohole-type cores from the deep sea (Rittenberg et al., 1963) or well-preserved drill-core sediments available on the continents. A study of the mechanism of silicification and calcification in biological systems (Glimcher, 1960) is another challenging topic which will eventually assist in understanding evolutionary trends in the history of the earth. Hydrocarbon generation and accumulation, coal formation, post-depositional microbial activities, diagenetic stabilities of organic molecules, nature and origin of extraterrestrial organic matter, condensation phenomena, and interactions of organic and inorganic materials (i.e., "organo-clays") are a few additional areas of biochemical research which have great potentialities in the fields of geology, paleontology, and related sciences.

From the published data it can be inferred that most of the biochemical alteration of organic matter takes place in the environment of deposition and during early stages of diagenesis, i.e., at a time when microbes and burrowing organisms are still active in soils and sediments. During the later stages of diagenesis, when organic activity in the strata has more or less ceased, alteration of organic matter predominantly proceeds in the direction of slow nonbiological maturation processes or geographical redistribution of organic molecules, such as are observed during the migration of hydrocarbons.

Much has still to be learned about the distribution pattern and fate of organic constituents in present day environments, modern shell materials, soils, and recent sediments before we can hope to find the key to the organic spectrum of ancient rocks. To investigate some of the most challenging areas of biogeochemical research, namely the synthesis of organic matter in the early stages of the earth or other planets, and the origin and biochemical evolution of life, one first has to know what kind of organic molecules can survive early and late diagenesis, and which ones are merely products of diagenesis.

Classification of Organic Substances

In order to evaluate alterations in biochemical compounds following the death of plants and animals, one naturally has to be acquainted with the major types of organic components that build up the plant and animal kingdom. Besides water, which constitutes about two-thirds of all living matter, four types of organic compounds are the principal building-blocks of all plant and animal organisms. These are the (1) proteins, (2) carbohydrates, (3) lipids, and (4) pigments. A fifth group, the lignins, generally only occur in more highly organized plants, in which they are common and widespread. Derivatives of these and some other organic constituents are known also; however, they represent only minor fractions. For example, only rarely do hydrocarbons make up more than 50 ppm of living materials on a dry weight basis.

The ratios of the four or five principal organic constituents can fluctuate considerably from one organism to the other. Some organisms are rich in proteins (algae), others in carbohydrates (trees). Furthermore, the type of protein, carbohydrate, or lipid can vary between different biological species. However, biological variations of this type are of minor importance considering the similarity that exists in the basic pattern of biological macromolecules. Summarizing, one can say that the fundamental biochemical structure of plants and animals is surprisingly uniform.

Biochemical studies are concerned with the functions and the distribution of organic constituents in present-day organisms. Organic geochemical studies investigate the fate that these materials undergo in the course of deposition and diagenesis. However, with the progress achieved in the field of organic geochemistry it has been discovered that certain reactions that take place in sediments and interstitial waters long after burial can only be explained in biochemical terms. This observation implies that an understanding of principal biochemical processes is essential for the intelligent interpretation of quite a few geochemical phenomena (Jones and Vallentyne, 1960; Lindblom and Lupton, 1961).

During maturation of sediments and waters some of the major organic compounds from the plant and animal kingdom can be drastically reduced or even eliminated with time. In contrast, other compounds which are quantitatively of minor importance in the life cycle of organisms can become concentrated relative to the metastable organic fraction. A third group of organic materials can be generated de novo in the environment of deposition and diagenesis. This change in the biochemical composition of organic debris can be a result of the action of micro-organisms and burrowing animals, or of slow inorganic maturation processes.

Since most organic compounds found in sediments and natural waters reflect to some degree the chemical and structural make-up of former living things, a geochemical classification of organic matter should not be very different from the biochemical one. Even compounds generated during diagenesis bear some structural resemblance to former living matter.

A tentative classification scheme of organic end-members, previously proposed by Degens and Reuter (1963), has been adapted, in a modified form (Fig. 1). As progress in the field of organic geochemistry continues, there will certainly come a time in the not too distant future where changes have to be made in the way of adding new organic groups and dropping familiar names such as kerogen or humic acids. For the moment, however, this scheme covers to some degree the major and characteristic organic fractions known from recent and ancient sediments and natural waters. In addition, this classification model allows the presentation of data in a geochemically organized manner.

1. Amino Compounds

This chapter deals with the biogeochemistry of substances which feature interaction between amino and carboxylic acid functions.

These compounds fall into three major categories, namely free amino acids, peptides and proteins, and various amino acid containing non-proteinaceous polymers.

Most of the naturally occurring amino acids have a primary amino group in α-position in relation to the carboxylic acid function. In a few cases a secondary amino group is found elsewhere in the molecule; occasionally a single amino group is present in ω-positions. With the exception of glycine, all natural amino acids which are incorporated in proteins have a center of asymmetry at the α-position and are optically active (L–series).

Based on the number of amine and carboxyl groups present in the structure, amino acids can be classified as neutral (one carboxyl, one amino group), acidic (two carboxyl, one amino group), and basic (one carboxyl, two amino groups). There are other chemical and structural properties of amino acids — for instance, the presence of sulfur, of aromatic groups, or of pyrrolidine rings — which characterize them in one way or another. Some of the more common amino acids are listed in Table 14.

In peptides and proteins, amino acids are joined together by amide linkages. Arbitrarily, peptides are generally defined as polyamides of amino acids possessing molecular weights of less than 10,000, whereas proteins are those amino acid condensates exceeding this number.

The chemical nature of peptides and proteins is a function of the number and kind of amino acids and their sequential arrangement. In many of the peptides and proteins the peptide chains have an α-helix arrangement, which is a coiling of the chain in a manner such as to develop hydrogen bonds between the amide hydrogens and the carboxyl groups that are four peptide bonds apart (Fig. 45).

Proteins and peptides are the principal sources of amino acid compounds found in sediments and natural waters. Whereas structurally intact proteinaceous matter has only a fair chance of "survival" over geological periods of time, amino acids, the building blocks of all proteins and peptides, have proved to be relatively stable.

Outstanding experimental work on the thermal stability of proteins and their individual amino acids has been done by Vallentyne (1957b, 1964), Conway and Libby (1958), and Abelson (1959). Their data indicate that proteins are most likely hydrolyzed in an aqueous environment within hundreds or thousands of years, but that some of the released free amino acids are stable over millions of years under low temperature conditions. Among the most stable amino acids reported are glycine, alanine, and glutamic acid, whereas serine and threonine appear to be thermally unstable.

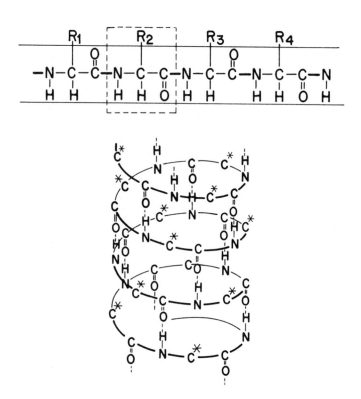

Fig. 45 Protein structure. Simple structural principles; variety of chemical reactivity (after Calvin, 1961)

Recently it was found that radiocarbon-dated shells of *Mytilus californianus* ranging in age from 400 to 5500 years, as well as specimens from an upper Pleistocene marine terrace, show a significant decrease in total organic matter when compared with recent *Mytilus* carbonate shells (Hare, 1962). This agrees with the statement on the rapid depolymerization of proteins which was made earlier by Abelson and Vallentyne. However, the sequence of stability of amino acids was not necessarily the same as predicted from the thermal decomposition studies. Next to alanine, serine was the most stable amino acid (Fig. 46). Other factors besides those considered by the experimental workers apparently are effective in nature (i.e., oxidation and re-polymerization or recondensation).

The occurrence of intact proteins or peptides has until now been reported only from shells and bones from the Pleistocene upwards. The bones from which Abelson (1959) isolated preserved peptide or proteinaceous substances were embedded in the La Brea tar pit in Los Angeles. This shows that certain unique geological environments sometimes "mummify" and preserve even proteins over geological periods of time.

One way to recover proteins from carbonate materials is to use a decalcifying agent such as EDTA (ethylene diamine tetra-acetic acid) or dilute organic acids. Weak mineral acids, although more effective in the dissolution of the carbonate, may partly hydrolyze the proteinaceous material. A solvent extraction, of course, would be more convenient than the above mentioned procedure, but the factors influencing the solubility of such complex substances as proteins are manifold and thus prohibit a simple solvent extraction device.

The complexity, in addition to the limited stability of proteins with geological time, makes studies of amino acids most attractive, particularly as amino acids are relatively stable; furthermore, they

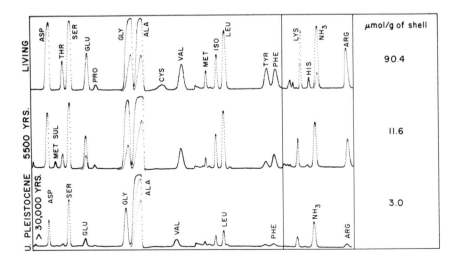

Fig. 46 Distribution of amino acids in recent and fossil shell proteins of *Mytilus californianus* (after Hare, 1962)

are water-soluble and extractable from soils and sediments. A third factor is the relative easiness of analytical identification and quantitative estimation.

In general, one may distinguish between free and combined amino acids in rock materials. In the case of natural waters, the expression "combined" is often substituted for the term "particulate" matter. Free amino acids are those that are dissolved in the water or which can be extracted with water or ammonium acetate from soils and sediments. In contrast, combined amino acids are those which require acid or alkaline hydrolysis for their final release. It has to be emphasized that the term "combined" does not necessarily imply that the material is in all instances a protein or a peptide. There is ample evidence that most of the combined amino acids in the rock strata are either part of nonproteinaceous polymers or that they are present in the adsorbed state.

Free amino acids may occur in reasonable quantities in soils and recent sediments (Jones and Vallentyne, 1960; Stevenson, 1961). In both instances the size and nature of amino acids appears to be closely related to the level of microbial activity. Paul and Schmidt (1961) and Putnam and Schmidt (1959) showed that soils low in microbial activity contain free amino acids in concentrations ranging from about 0.05 to 0.5 $\mu g/g$, whereas well populated soils may reach peak values of 100 to 200 $\mu g/g$. Most free amino acids in soils are excretary or autolytic products of micro-organisms. Some may also have been added by root excretion. The rapid destruction by micro-organisms, however, prevents large accumulations of free amino acids in soils.

Recent sediments of marine and terrestrial origin which were deposited under oxidizing conditions contain about the same amount of free amino acids as does the average soil. As the microbial activities decrease with depth of burial, so do the free amino acids. After three to five meters, the level of concentration is about 0.5 $\mu g/g$. On the other hand, recent sediments deposited in strong reducing environments offer a completely different picture. Here free amino acids constitute most of the amino acid fraction. Values in the neighborhood of a few hundred $\mu g/g$ are quite common. Furthermore, considerable fluctuations exist between the individual amino acids in systematically dug up cores (Fig. 47). A calculation of the mean value from several samples of the upper few meters of deposit and a comparison with the plankton in the sea shows a surprising uniformity

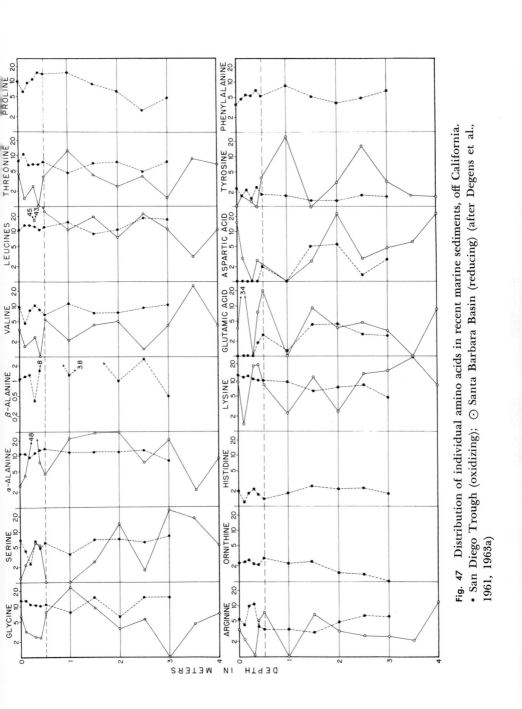

Fig. 47 Distribution of individual amino acids in recent marine sediments, off California. • San Diego Trough (oxidizing); ⊙ Santa Barbara Basin (reducing) (after Degens et al., 1961, 1963a)

of the amino acid spectrum in the different sets of samples. The following explanation is offered to account for this phenomenon.

In the initial stages of diagenesis, plankton protein supplied from the sea above becomes gradually hydrolyzed. The generated free amino acids redistribute themselves during compaction along the clay-water interface. The free amino acids are adsorbed and resorbed on clay minerals. The degree of separation between individual amino acids depends on the pH, the salinity, and temperature and pressure in the clay-amino acid-water system. The final result is the irregular distribution pattern observed in Figure 47. Low Eh values slow microbial activity; otherwise free amino acids would have been biologically eliminated. To test this, the reducing sediments were exposed for a few weeks to oxidizing conditions. As in soils and oxidizing sediments, the level of amino acids dropped sharply to a few $\mu g/g$.

Most of the ancient sediments are practically devoid of free amino acids. Exceptions are ancient shell carbonates which occasionally yield greater concentrations of free amino acids, because proteins in shell carbonates can escape microbial decomposition in the early stages of diagenesis; microbes are too large (~ 1 micron) to have access to protein films embedded in the carbonate matrix. On the other hand, in the presence of water, proteins become gradually hydrolyzed and simultaneously released to the next environments. Recrystallization, i.e., of aragonite to calcite, certainly will enhance hydrolysis, but even in well preserved carbonate shells (Fig. 46) proteins will disappear with time.

Sea and lake waters contain free amino acids in small quantities (10 to 100 $\mu g/1$) as shown by Tatsumoto et al. (1961), Rittenberg et al. (1963), and Degens et al. (1963ab). In waters of the Pacific Ocean taken off the shore of California, the concentration is uniform with depth of water (Fig. 48). It is interesting to add that there are no significant qualitative changes throughout most of the water column. Only waters taken near the ocean floor at a depth of about 4000 meters show a somewhat different amino acid pattern. Noteworthy are the high concentrations of serine, ornithine, and glycine; arginine, proline, cystine, and methionine are not present in detectable quantities. Samples near the bottom of the sea often lack acidic amino acids, and the level of basic compounds is small. This characteristic can be linked to the enhanced bacterial activity in areas near the water-sediment interface.

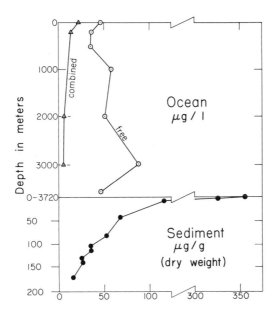

Fig. 48   Depth distribution of amino acids in ocean water (μg/l) and in the underlying sediment (μg/g dry weight) (after Rittenberg et al., 1963)

The distinction between free amino acids and particulate matter in the sea is generally based on the size of the material. For convenience, all constituents that pass a 0.4 micron filter are called free, and the others are designated as particulate matter. Actually, it seems, that some, if not all, of the amino acids in the sea that pass the micron filter are in a polymerized state and not in a chemically free form. That this assumption may be correct is indicated by the analytical difficulties encountered in the chromatographical separation of amino acids in cases where the filtrated waters have not been subjected to acidification prior to extraction of the amino acids.

Quite interesting results were obtained from filtered petroleum brine waters (< 0.4 micron filter) of Paleozoic and Tertiary ages (Degens et al., 1964b). If one adjusts the salinity of the brines to that of today's ocean waters and applies the same calculation factors to the original amino acid values, the similarities between the amino acid spectra in the fossil brines and in recent sea water become striking.

An outstanding feature is the relatively high concentration of serine and the presence of threonine, phenylalanine, and glutamic and aspartic acids in the petroleum brines. These five amino acids could not have been present in a free state if one believes that the amino acids are actually as old as the brines. Serine in particular has been shown to be thermally unstable in a free state (Abelson, 1959; Vallentyne, 1957, 1964). The only way to account for their presence in the petroleum brines is to assume that either: (1) the brines are relatively recent and not as old as their host strata, (2) the amino acids are a result of recent bacterial contamination, or (3) the amino acids occur in a combined state as a nonproteinaceous amino acid complex.

Table 14   AMINO ACIDS COMMONLY FOUND IN SEDIMENT
AND SOIL HYDROLYSATES.

BASIC AMINO ACIDS		NEUTRAL AMINO ACIDS	
Arginine	$H_2N-C-NH-CH_2-CH_2-CH_2-\overset{NH_2}{\underset{H}{C}}-COOH$, NH	α—Alanine	$CH_3-\overset{NH_2}{\underset{H}{C}}-COOH$
Histidine	$HC\!=\!C-CH_2-\overset{NH_2}{C}-COOH$, N, NH, N, H	β—Alanine	$H_2N-CH_2-CH_2-COOH$
Lysine	$H_2N-CH_2-CH_2-CH_2-CH_2-\overset{NH_2}{\underset{H}{C}}-COOH$	γ—Aminobutyric acid	$H_2N-CH_2-CH_2-CH_2-COOH$
δ-Hydroxylysine	$H_2N-CH_2-\overset{OH}{CH}-CH_2-CH_2-\overset{NH_2}{\underset{H}{C}}-COOH$	Glycine	$H-\overset{NH_2}{\underset{H}{C}}-COOH$
Ornithine	$\overset{NH_2}{CH_2}-CH_2-CH_2-\overset{NH_2}{\underset{H}{C}}-COOH$	Leucine	$CH_3-\underset{CH_3}{CH}-CH_2-\overset{NH_2}{\underset{H}{C}}-COOH$
ACIDIC AMINO ACIDS		Isoleucine	$CH_3-CH_2-\overset{H}{\underset{CH_3}{C}}\!=\!\overset{NH_2}{\underset{H}{C}}-COOH$
Aspartic acid	$HOOC-CH_2-\overset{NH_2}{\underset{H}{C}}-COOH$		
Glutamic acid	$HOOC-CH_2-CH_2-\overset{NH_2}{\underset{H}{C}}-COOH$	Proline	$\underset{N}{\overset{CH_2-CH_2}{CH_2}}CH-COOH$
AROMATIC AMINO ACIDS		Hydroxyproline	$HO-CH-CH_2$, $\underset{N}{CH_2}CH-COOH$, H
Phenylalanine	⬡$-CH_2-\overset{NH_2}{\underset{H}{C}}-COOH$	Serine	$HO-CH_2-\overset{NH_2}{\underset{H}{C}}-COOH$
Tyrosine	$HO-$⬡$-CH_2-\overset{NH_2}{\underset{H}{C}}-COOH$	Threonine	$CH_3-\overset{H}{\underset{OH}{C}}-\overset{NH_2}{\underset{H}{C}}-COOH$
Tryptophan (largely destroyed in acid hydrolysis)	⬡$-\overset{C-CH_2-\overset{NH_2}{\underset{H}{C}}-COOH}{\underset{N-CH}{\underset{H}{}}}$	Valine	$CH_3-\underset{CH_3}{CH}-\overset{NH_2}{\underset{H}{C}}-COOH$
SULPHUR AMINO ACIDS			
Cystine	$HOOC-\overset{NH_2}{\underset{H}{C}}-CH_2-S-S-CH_2-\overset{NH_2}{\underset{H}{C}}-COOH$	Methionine	$CH_3-S-CH_2-CH_2-\overset{NH_2}{\underset{H}{C}}-COOH$

The first suggestion can be ruled out for a number of geological and chemical reasons. The second hypothesis, concerning bacterial infection, can also be dismissed. An organism of about 10 microns in diameter weighs about 10^{-10}g, which would amount to about 0.5×10^{-10}g in protein. Less than 10 microbes were counted in one milliliter of brine water (by courtesy of Dr. G. Lindblom, Jersey Production Research Company). The third possibility seems to be the most probable one: most of the amino acids are believed to be packed together in some fashion to form more complex molecules. This shows up in the hydrolysis required for analytical identification. At this state of knowledge, it is, however, difficult to ascertain the chemical nature and structure of these complexes. In view of the data of Abelson (1959) and the experimental results of Vallentyne (1957, 1964), peptidic linkages between the individual monomers can be ruled out. From recent experiments (Kroepelin, 1964), it is known that amino acids obtain a higher degree of stabilization when they are associated with other compounds such as clay minerals. Another possibility is that humic acids and perhaps kerogen-type compounds act as amino acid carriers and stabilizers. The similarities in the amino acid spectra of fossilized brines and recent marine waters can mean that the amino acids in their present state of polymerization are diagenetically rather stable and that both are of the same origin. The up to tenfold increase in total amino acid concentration in the case of the ancient high-saline brines may be a result of ion-filtration along charged-net clay membranes.

Combined compounds represent the bulk of the amino acids extractable from sediments of all ages. In order to illustrate the fate of these materials in the course of diagenesis let us examine a sediment core obtained during experimental Mohole drillings (Riedel et al., 1961; Rittenberg et al., 1963). This core penetrated about 170 meters of hemipelagic ooze and covers 15 million years of earth history. In the final analysis additional organic contributions from the overlying sea will be evaluated.

It is generally agreed that the dissolved and particulate matter in the sea and in marine sediments are ultimately derived from (1) organisms living in the ocean waters or on the sea floor, and (2) terrestrial organic debris brought into the marine environment during weathering and denudation. Plankton is often mentioned as the principal progenitor material of organic matter in marine sediments. This suggestion is certainly correct for sediments deposited under shallow marine conditions. However, with increase in water depth there is progressively less chance for the preservation of planktonic materials, as shown by Krey (1961), Bogorov (1958), Cushing (1959), and others. Actually, plankton produced at or near the surface of the ocean is recycled within the upper few hundred meters of the mixed layer, and upon death of the organisms only a small percentage eventually settles to the sea floor as organic detritus (tripton). Tripton and its attached organic nutrients serve as the principle food supply for all filter feeding animals, including burrowing animals and micro-organisms.

In view of the enormous turnover of organic materials within the upper few hundred meters of the ocean, the relative consistency of the "free" amino acid spectrum throughout a vertical profile of 4000 meters comes as a surprise. Apparently, the present organic activity in the sea seems to leave no significant imprint on the free amino acid pattern. The particulate matter in the ocean, on the other hand, changes in a systematic fashion from the top to the bottom of the sea. The basic, acidic, and aromatic amino constituents decrease gradually to be replaced by neutral components, particularly the metabolically related serine and glycine. This process may be explained by the action of bacteria which are known to thrive on the organic detritus which is slowly settling downward (Jannasch, 1954).

A comparison of the distribution of amino acids in the upper sediment layers and the immediately overlying waters reveals several interesting features. Arginine, lysine, and β-alanine account for about 40 per cent of all the amino acids present in the sediments, whereas these compounds are virtually absent from the dissolved and particulate matter in the ocean. On the other hand, ornithine and serine make up approximately 40 per cent of the free and combined amino acids in the sea but account for less than 5 per cent of the total in the surface sediment.

This biochemical relationship strongly suggests that a great portion of the proteinaceous material present in the sediment is generated in situ by micro-organisms and burrowing animals. Ornithine, which is relatively abundant in the sea, is the most likely source for arginine. Many organisms are capable of producing arginine from ornithine and aspartic acid by way of cittrulline and arginosuccinic acid in the course of the urea cycle. The lysine may be formed in the sediment by de novo microbial synthesis; more cannot be said at this point. β-alanine may arise from metabolic decarboxylation of aspartic acid which is one of the dominant amino acids in the over-lying water. In soils it is also observed that the level of β-alanine is directly related to microbial activity.

The amino acid concentration sharply decreases with depth of burial (Fig. 48). Amino acids biogenically produced at or near the water-sediment interface gradually decrease relative to the amino acids formerly contributed by the sea. By taking an average of the first two meters and comparing it with that of the lower seventy meters of the section, the relationships plotted in Figure 49 are obtained. Ornithine, serine, glutamic and aspartic acids, the leucines, threonine, and glycine are diagenetically more stable than the rest of the amino acids. It is of great significance that these are the same amino acids that have been found in petroleum brine waters from the Paleozoic and up. It is conceivable that the highly metastable arginine and tyrosine are altered into ornithine and serine, respectively. The last reaction would yield an additional benzene ring.

Inasmuch as the Mohole-type environments represent predominantly oxidizing conditions and, furthermore, as the rate of sedimentation is relatively slow (1 cm/1000 years), it was considered worth while to compare two of the most strongly oxidizing and reducing basins off the shore of California, where rates of deposition are ten to 100 times larger (Emery, 1960; Emery and Bray, 1962; Degens et al., 1963b). The relationship was found to be quite revealing. The concentration of amino acids in the oxidizing San Diego Trough is higher by a factor of 5 to 10 within 1.5 meters of deposit (Fig. 50). Below this depth, reducing sediments contain relatively more amino acids. It is interesting to observe that reducing sediments do not systematically decrease or increase with depth. The values fluctuate around the 500 μg/g level. Amino acids in oxidizing sediments show a trend to diminish with depth, possibly approaching "steady state" conditions at a depth of 2.5 meters. At the much greater depth of 165 meters taken from a nearby core, the argillaceous sediment had the same concentration level of amino acids ($\sim$200 μg/g).

It has been mentioned before that the enormous fluctuations of the individual amino acid level in a reducing environment are the result of low microbial activity, generation of free amino acids by hydrolysis of tripton, and chromatographic separation along the clay-water interface (Fig. 47). Most of the fluctuations in the oxidizing San Diego Trough environment occur within the zone of biological activity. Plankton apparently serves only as a high proteina-

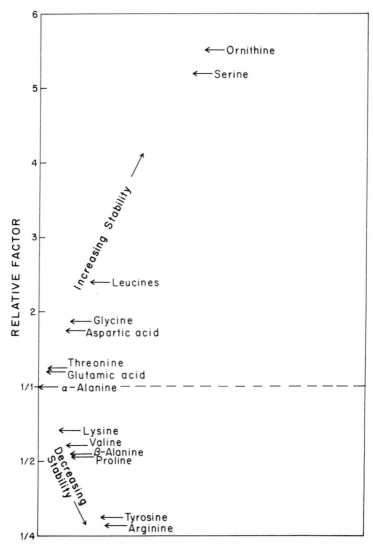

Fig. 49   Relative stability of amino acids during diagenesis; wet oxidizing environment (after Rittenberg et al., 1963)

ceous food source for organisms and as such is gradually eliminated biologically within the upper few meters of the sediment. The more or less complete disappearance of bacteria below the first meters of deposition can be linked to the depletion of biochemically available food sources supplied by plankton and various organisms living in the sediment. It is tentatively concluded that the combined amino

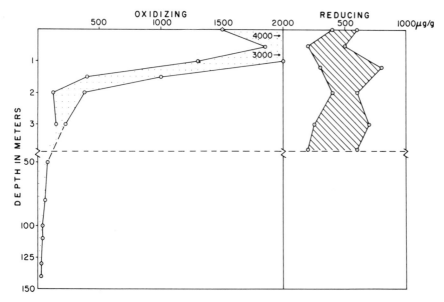

Fig. 50   Distribution of amino acids in recent marine sediments, off California. (a) San Diego Trough and Guadelupe area (oxidizing); and (b) Santa Barbara Basin (reducing) (after Rittenberg et al., 1963; Degens et al., 1961, 1963 (a), 1963 (b))

acids found at greater depth are incorporated in nonproteinaceous polymers. The bulk of the original proteins and peptides are hydrolyzed under reducing conditions and consumed under oxidizing conditions.

Amino acids are found in sediments of periods as early as the Pre-Cambrian (Abelson, 1954, 1957, 1959; Degens and Bajor, 1960; Barghoorn, 1957; Swain et al., 1958; Swain, 1961; Harington, 1962; Harington and Cilliers, 1963). Cherts and argillaceous rocks have the greatest enrichment. The data, so far, however, are too fragmentary to throw significant light on problems such as biochemical evolution of organic matter or calcifications in now fossilized biological systems.

As to the last topic, considerable information is available on the mechanism of mineralization in recent shell materials, teeth, bones, etc. (Sognnaes, 1960; Wilbur, 1960; Gross and Piez, 1960; Towe et al., 1963; Moss, 1963; Hare, 1963; Lowenstam, 1963). The deposition of inorganic crystals is a result of the type and arrangement of organic molecules in biological tissues. There is a wide range of organic matrices that may stimulate the deposition of minerals, both in the endo- and the exoskeleton (Table 15). Proteins are the most common ones, followed by carbohydrates, amino sugars, and perhaps lignins and lipids (Glimcher, 1960).

The ions essential for mineralization have to come from the body fluids of organisms. Inasmuch as precipitation does not "normally" occur in these fluids, some mechanism has to operate in or on mineralizing tissues to initiate crystallization. Furthermore, the tissues will exercise control on growth and orientation of the inorganic nucleate.

For obvious reasons, a study on the mineralization in bones and teeth is furthest advanced. Here a protein (collagen) is the major organic matrix, and hydroxyapatite is the mineral form. A collagen molecule contains more than 1000 amino acid residues per chain and is about 3000 Å long and 14 Å in diameter. The distance between residues is 2.86 Å and the repeat distance for the major helix is 86 Å (Piez, 1963) (Fig. 51). The structure is held together by hydrogen

Table 15   EXAMPLES OF BIOLOGICALLY MINERALIZED TISSUES (AFTER GLIMCHER, 1960).

Species	Tissue Mineralized	Mineral Form	Major Organic-Matrix Components
Plants	Cell wall	Calcite	Carbohydrates (Cellulose, Pectins), Lignins
Microorganisms	Exoskeleton	Amorphous Silica Calcite, Aragonite Celestite	Carbohydrates (Pectins) (?) (?)
Mollusks	Exoskeleton	Calcite, Aragonite	Protein (Conchiolin)
Arthropods	Exoskeleton	Calcite	Carbohydrate (Chitin), Protein
Vertebrates	Exoskeleton Bone Cartilage	OH-Apatite OH-Apatite	Protein (Collagen) Protein (Collagen) Carbohydrates (Mucopolysaccharides)
	Tooth Dentin Cementum Enamel	OH-Apatite OH-Apatite OH-Apatite	Protein (Collagen) Protein (Collagen) Protein (Eukeratin)

bonds and side chain interactions. Collagens are chemically characterized by a high glycine level (one third of the total) and the presence of hydroxyproline and hydroxylysine.

The role of the organic matrix in mineralization is probably to provide a set of highly specific templates which act as the sites for the nucleation of the mineral phase (Glimcher, 1960; Hare, 1963). Certain side groups in the protein matrix may concentrate cations and anions in specific positions and thus provide an appropriate initial concentration of ions to nucleate the mineral phase. Aspartic and glutamic acid side chains could provide negatively charged sites which would attract, for example, calcium ions. Similarly, the basic side chains could provide sites for the concentration of certain anions, (i.e., CO_3, HCO_3, PO_4, SO_4). A few electronmicrophotographs are presented to illustrate the mineralization pattern that can be obtained from various biological tissues (Figs. 52–54).

Only limited information is available on the chemistry of proteins associated with invertebrate calcified tissues. It seems that no one protein has the universal function which collagen has in the case of the vertebrate bone and teeth formation. There is a complex array of different proteins and other organic matrices which may stimulate the nucleation of carbonates, sulfates, silica, and even magnetite. The conflicting results by Piez (1961) and Hare (1962) on shell carbonates of different molluscs may serve as an indication of the complexities involved in the carbonate secreting systems. But systematic variations in the organic matrices of shell structures may serve as a powerful tool in comparative biochemistry. It has been shown that there are significant differences established both in total amount and type of organic matter by going from primitive to advanced species of the

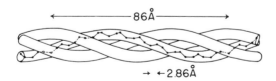

Fig. 51 A segment of the collagen structure. The tubes represent the space filled by polypeptide chains each of which extends about 3000 Å. The amino acid residues are 2.86Å apart and lie along a minor helix with a pitch of 8.6 Å (three residues per turn). Each chain is coiled into a major helix with a pitch of 86 Å. (after Piez, 1963)

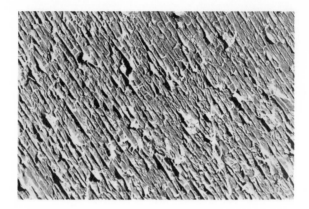

Fig. 52   Electronmicrograph of nacreous layer (aragonitic) of *Mytilus californianus* showing alternation of aragonite and protein in "brick-wall" configuration. The protein appears as "mortar". Platinum-carbon replica; magnification about 2500 (after Towe and Lowenstam, 1964; unpublished data)

same general group of animals. Thus, some calcifying tissues are more effective mineralizers than others; and concentrations may range from a few hundreds of a percent to a few percent organic matter per shell carbonate (Hare, personal communication). Most critical in determining shell morphological changes and evolutionary trends appears to be the abundance of basic, acidic and amide amino acids in the

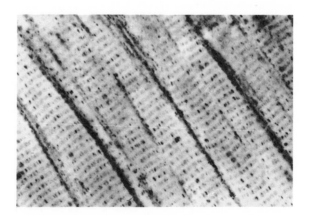

Fig. 53   Electronmicrophotograph of beginning calcification in the turkey leg tendon. Parallel rows of single apatite crystals are aligned in the direction of the fibril axis. The spacing of the rows is about 700 Å and corresponds to the collagen striations; (after Nylen et al., 1960; and Piez, 1963)

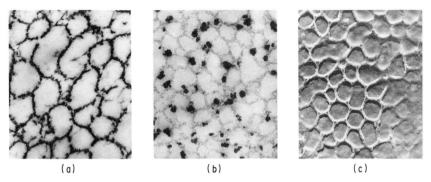

(a)   (b)   (c)

Fig. 54 Electronmicrographs of lateral radular teeth of *Cryptochiton stelleri* in various stages of development; (a) unmineralized protein, (b) nucleation of iron mineralization on protein matrix, (c) protein matrix embedded in solid magnetite of the mature tooth. (a) and (b) are epoxy embedded ultramicrotome sections, and (c) is a platinum-carbon replica; magnification about 10000 (after Towe and Lowenstam, 1964, unpublished data)

mineralized tissue. Perhaps the high content of acidic and amide residues in shell structures of gastropods can be made largely responsible for the wide variation in morphology this group of animals in particular exhibits. Also the presence of OH-proline and OH-lysine in mineralized tissues of vertebrates and the apparent lack of both amino acids in shells of a number of invertebrates may be exploited for taxonomic purposes by determining their first appearance in shell materials. As far as known, OH-proline and OH-lysine occur in phosphatized (OH-apatite) tissues.

Some insight into the formation of aragonite and calcite in shell carbonates can be obtained from the study of Hare (1963). A comparison of the compositions of the aragonite and calcite matrices of *Mytilus* shows the calcite matrices to have a consistently higher ratio of acidic to basic residues. This may indicate the presence of a mixture of protein components, one of which may be rich in the basic amino acids. That the organic matrix of some shells is indeed a mixture of different proteins has been shown by Grégoire et al. (1955), Grégoire (1961), and Tanaka et al. (1960).

Much has to be learned in the area of invertebrate mineralizations before one can hope to understand the evolution of mineralized tissues during Pre-Cambrian times. The sudden appearance of a wide spectrum of mineralized fossils at the beginning of the Cambrian is certainly a coincidence which probably has nothing to do with a spontaneous evolution. Mineralizations of tissues must have already occurred during late Pre-Cambrian times, considering the detailed mineralization pattern recorded from the first Cambrian fossils. That the earliest forms of life escaped fossilization may be linked to the metastability of their mineral parts.

2. CARBOHYDRATES

The term carbohydrates was originally coined in the belief that compounds of this class have the molecular formula $C_x(H_2O)_y$. However, there are a few exceptions to this general formula, for instance, rhamnose ($C_6H_{12}O_5$). Other compounds such as acetic acid ($C_2H_4O_2$) fit the classical formula without being a carbohydrate. Despite its somewhat misleading name, the term carbohydrate is so well rooted in literature that it is accepted in most chemical classification systems.

Chemically, carbohydrates can be defined as polyhydroxylated compounds, many of which contain aldehydic or ketonic groups or yield such groups on hydrolysis. The principal building blocks of carbohydrate chemistry are the simple sugars (monosaccharides) which contain from three to eight carbon atoms. The five- and six-carbon sugars, called pentoses and hexoses, respectively, are most abundant in nature.

All common pentoses, i.e., L-arabinose, D-xylose, D-ribose, and 2-deoxy-D-ribose, are aldehydes and should, therefore, more correctly be classified as aldopentoses. Representative aldohexoses are D-glucose, D-galactose, D-mannose, and L-rhamnose, whereas D-fructose is the only naturally abundant ketohexose.

Simple sugars (monosaccharides) can condense to low-molecular weight polymers (oligosaccharides) which may contain from two to nine simple sugars. The most frequent oligosaccharides are the di- and tri-saccharides. Combinations of more than nine simple sugar units are known as polysaccharides or high-molecular weight carbohydrates.

Approximations of the molecular structure of sugars can most conveniently be illustrated by the Haworth formulas. Five- and six-membered oxide rings which have a formal relationship to the cyclic oxides furan and pyran (Table 16) represent the basic structural pattern in most of the common sugars. The terms pyranose and furanose are defined accordingly.

Polymerization of sugars to low- or high-molecular weight carbohydrates is accompanied by O-glycosidic linkage (Table 16). Common natural oligosaccharides are sucrose, maltose, cellobiose, and raffinose;

Table 16   MOLECULAR NATURE OF REPRESENTATIVE CARBOHYDRATES
AND DERIVATIVES.

Pyran   Furan   (a)

Cellulose   (b)

Chitobiose
(Repeating unit of chitin)   (c)

abundant polysaccharides include cellulose, starch, hemicellulose, and glycogens.

Carbohydrates account for a major portion of both plant and animal residues, but they are considerably less variable and complex than proteins. That this group has been little studied from a geochemical point of view can largely be attributed to the long time lack of suitable analytical techniques. The analytical handicap is now largely being overcome as can be judged from the increased activities in the area of carbohydrate geochemistry over the last couple of years.

Carbohydrates may occur in sediments, soils, and natural waters in a free or a combined form. In the first case they are called free sugars; as such they can be both monosaccharides and oligosaccharides. By definition, free sugars are those that can be extracted from sediments with water or 80 per cent ethanol without a preceding acid hydrolysis. Combined carbohydrates may be either polysaccharides or low-molecular weight sugars which are tightly fixed in some manner to various sedimentary materials. In analogy to proteins and fixed amino acids, combined carbohydrates require an acid treatment for their final release.

When the carbohydrate complex in a soil or sediment is subjected to acid hydrolysis, dilute acids do not affect monosaccharides at all, whereas they gradually depolymerize oligosaccharides and polysaccharides, i.e., they eliminate the glycosidic bond between the monomers, and leave finally only a mixture of monosaccharides in the hydrolysis liquors. In addition, dilute mineral acids may release some or all of the sugars which are somehow associated with clay minerals and other sedimentary end-members. The rate of hydrolysis varies greatly from one carbohydrate to another. For some carbohydrates such as cellulose even strong acids are required to open effectively the glycosidic linkage between the individual monomers. Such a drastic treatment, of course, may dehydrate the naturally present or analytically produced monosaccharide, resulting in the formation of substances such as furfural or levulinic acid. The quantitative analysis of carbohydrates is, therefore, a serious enterprise, for the method must be able to split all condensed carbohydrates quantitatively to monosaccharides without affecting the initially present or artificially produced monosaccharides in the hydrolysis liquors.

Among free sugars found in recent sediments, peats and soils, are the oligosaccharides raffinose, sucrose, and maltose, and practically all of the common monosaccharides (Vallentyne, 1954; Vallentyne and Bidwell, 1956; Whitacker and Vallentyne, 1957; Plunkett, 1957; Prashnowsky et al., 1961; Mehta et al., 1961; Theander, 1952, 1954). The presence of free sugars in sediments up to 10,000 years old is rather interesting in view of the fact that free sugars are known to be easily utilized by micro-organisms as fast as they are released during decomposition. However, the amount of free sugars sharply decreases with depth of burial to zero or negligible amounts within the first few meters of deposition. On a relative basis, glucose is the most "stable" free sugar and can amount up to 1 part in 1000 of recent sediment organic matter.

Free sugars are also present in lake and ocean waters (Whitacker and Vallentyne, 1957; Degens et al., 1963a). Most abundant in the sea are glucose, galactose, and mannose, all of which seem to be evenly distributed and show no decreasing or increasing trend with water depth. Total free sugars amount to about 15 $\mu g/l$; only in sea waters taken at the immediate water-sediment interface are there higher concentrations. These are a result of the enforced bacterial activity in the upper portions of the sediment, whereby free sugars are released to the water layer above. No sugars or at best only traces of free sugars are known to occur in ancient sediments (Palacas, 1959; Rittenberg et al., 1963), an observation which has to be expected on biological (microbial utilization) and thermo-dynamical grounds (thermal instability).

Combined sugars are geochemically more rewarding, inasmuch as they represent a chemically more stable organic product. In principle, three geochemical groups of combined sugars are conceivable in a sediment (1) original plant or animal polysaccharides, (2) diagenetically formed condensates, and (3) adsorbed monomers.

Cellulose, a glucose polymer consisting of approximately 2000 to 3000 glucose units, is the most dominant polysaccharide in the continental plant kingdom, and has been the subject of detailed geochemical studies (Gothan, 1922; Hess and Komarewsky, 1928; Staudinger and Jurisch, 1939; Barghoorn, 1949; Barghoorn and Spackman, 1950; Theander, 1954). It has been isolated from sediments, i.e., lignites, as old as the early Tertiary. Noteworthy is the fact that the degree of polymerization in the Tertiary deposits is about 10 times less than in present day cellulose. Depolymerization into about ten smaller units may have been accomplished by the action of microbes; another alternative is that severe pH conditions established in a peat-bog environment may have hydrolyzed the cellulose into smaller fragments.

The most common polysaccharides under marine conditions are the alginates from seaweeds and certain "hemicellulose"-type polymers, which contain galactose, mannose, rhamnose, xylose, and arabinose as principal building blocks. Actually, the term hemicellulose is misleading, since this polymer is chemically unrelated to cellulose. Although less dominant than in land plants, cellulose also occurs in marine organisms, but there it is confined mainly to the inner wall of the cells.

The changes which transform combined sugars under marine conditions have been investigated in some detail by Rittenberg et al. (1963) and Degens et al. (1963b). The principal results are the following: Sugars in offshore California sediments range from 500 to 3000 $\mu g/g$ dry weight of sample in the most recent deposits. Within the

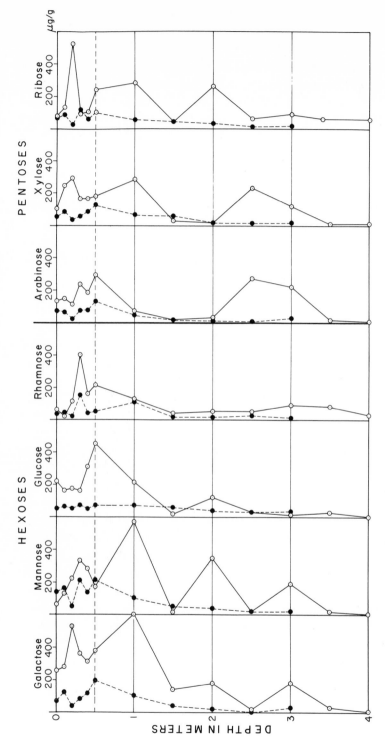

Fig. 55 Distribution of individual sugars in recent marine sediments off California. • San Diego Trough (oxidizing); ⊙ Santa Barbara Basin (reducing) (after Prashnowsky et al., 1961; Degens et al., 1963a)

first 3 to 5 meters of deposition, which is equivalent in time to a few thousand years, sugars decrease in abundance to about 100 $\mu g/g$, and after 10 meters, "steady state" values of 10 to 20 $\mu g/g$ are obtained, which extend throughout the remaining 150 meters of the studied profile (Fig. 55). This is roughly the same concentration as is reported from ancient marine sediments (Palacas, 1959). In other words, the sugar fraction of organic matter in sediments averages 5 per cent in recent deposits, 1 per cent in the upper five meters, and less than 0.1 per cent in most of the ancient sediments older than 100,000 years. This may imply that the carbohydrates in general are less stable than some of their associated organic fractions. Another alternative would be that sugars polymerize during diagenesis in such a manner that they are no longer recoverable by conventional analytical methods. The formation of resistant organic molecules may be accomplished by cross linkage of various biochemical constituents.

Another possible means of preserving carbohydrates is by formation of organo-clay complexes. The adsorption capacities of clays for sugars has been investigated by Greenland (1956), Lynch et al. (1957 a,b), and Bader et al. (1960). They demonstrated that clays adsorb sugars selectively and that the adsorption capacity for individual monomers differs from clay to clay.

Taking all sources of information on the stability of sugars into consideration, it seems most likely that in an oxidizing environment the bulk of the carbohydrates are eliminated biochemically in the early stages of diagenesis, at a time when microbes and burrowing animals are still alive in the strata. Some of the sugars may survive bacterial consumption by becoming incorporated in clay structures or by forming nutritionally unattractive polymers. Under reducing conditions, however, free sugars may become redistributed in the initial stages of compaction as a result of chromatographic separation along clay minerals (Fig. 56). Due to a prolonged interaction with the organic and inorganic phases in the sediment, the chances of formation of rather stable complexes is greatly enhanced under reducing conditions, whereas in an oxidizing environment free sugars are rapidly eliminated microbiologically. In contrast to starch, hemicellulose or alginates, cellulose seems to be one of the more stable polysaccharides under geological conditions.

The rate of decomposition of organic matter in soil has been recently studied by means of C[14]-labeled barley straw (Sørensen, 1963). Among C[14] active substances added to the soil were straw, hemicellu-

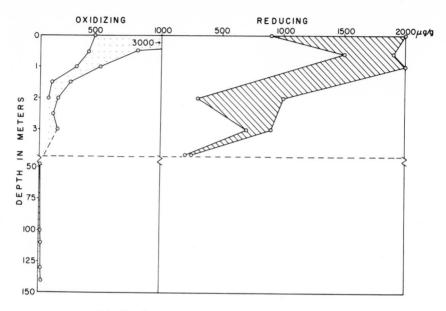

Fig. 56   Distribution of sugars in recent marine sediments, off California; (a) San Diego Trough and Guadelupe area (oxidizing), and (b) Santa Barbara Basin (reducing) (after Rittenberg et al., 1963; Prashnowsky et al., 1961; Degens et al., 1963a, 1963b)

lose, cellulose, compost, lignin, and water soluble materials extractable from straw. The rate of decay of the individual compound was measured by means of radioactive CO_2 evolved from the soil. Finally, the activities of organic extracts recovered from the soil after a period of about 100 days were measured. Ninety per cent or more of the activity initially added could be accounted for by the recovered CO_2 and the combined fractions of humic acids, fulvic acids, and humins. In Fig. 57, the values of evolved CO_2 and total organic matter — adjusted to 100 per cent — are presented. Significant differences in the rate of decomposition are established between the various organic fractions which were analyzed. It can be seen that hemicellulose is effectively reduced in contrast to lignin. It could further be demonstrated that the C^{14} incorporated in, and fixed to the soil was rather uniformly distributed between fulvic acid, humic acid, and humin. Lignin, however, left most of the activity in humic acid and humin, whereas the water soluble substances contributed little to the organic residue.

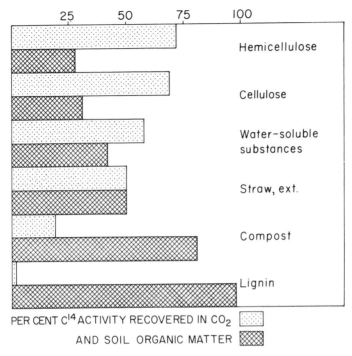

Fig. 57 Distribution of C^{14} active organic residues and carbon dioxide, recovered after about 100 days decomposition in a soil; in per cent of original input (after Sørensen, 1963)

SUGAR DERIVATIVES

This group includes a variety of compounds which are similar to the monosaccharides but differ in one way or the other from the previously discussed aldoses and ketoses. Examples are the uronic acids and the amino-sugars. Except for glycogen, the amino-sugars and glucuronic acid are the most common sugar compounds of animal and bacterial origin. Particularly the amino-sugars are geochemically interesting, inasmuch as some of the more common and resistant polysaccharides consist predominantly, if not entirely, of amino-sugar residues.

Most of the amino-sugars which occur in nature are glucosamine and galactosamine. The last monomer is also known as chondrosamine. They occur as structural components of a broad general group of substances, the mucopolysaccharides, and are known to be associated with mucoproteins as well as with smaller molecules, such as the antibiotic streptomycin. From a geological point of view, the amino-sugar polymer chitin is of great importance. Chitin is widely distributed in micro-organisms, lower organized plants, and invertebrates such as arthropods, molluscs, and nematodes, all of which date back to the early Cambrian.

Chitin, which yields glucosamine (2—acetamido—2—deoxy—D-glucose) on hydrolysis, may be regarded as a derivative of cellulose, with the hydroxyl groups replaced by acetamido residues (Table 16). Both polysaccharides serve as structural and protective materials in nature. In general, cellulose and chitin exclude each other; however, in case of the fungi there is some overlap. Most fungi have chitinous cell-walls; the rest contain cellulose, with the exception of one or two species from which both polysaccharides are reported. From the standpoint of biochemical evolution, the cellulose-chitin relationship is of great significance (Foster and Webber, 1960). Usually, chitin forms a part of rather complex biochemical systems in which carbonates, phosphates, proteins, and other organic molecules participate. For instance, it has been demonstrated by Hackman (1955) that chitin-protein complexes exist in which weak bonds between chitin and a water soluble protein are developed.

Glucosamine and chondrosamine are found in recent sediment and soil in concentrations ranging from a few hundred to a few thousand $\mu g/g$ dry material. The few data on ancient sediments show concentrations of an order of a few to a few hundred $\mu g/g$ (Rittenberg et al., 1963). The most detailed studies on hexosamines in soils are those by Stevenson (1957, 1961), Graveland and Lynch (1961), and Bremner and Shaw (1954). The data suggest that most of the mucopolysaccharides are of bacterial origin. An idea of the path of microbial destruction in soils and sediments may be obtained by analyzing the latter not only for the total amount in hexosamines, but separately for chondrosamine, glucosamine, and glucuronic acid; all three of these monomers are principal building blocks of one or the other of the mucopolysaccharides. Unfortunately, no comprehensive investigation has been made on the occurrence of these sugar derivatives in the stratigraphical column. Considering that intact chitin from wing remains of Eocene insects has been found (Aberhalden and Heyns, 1933), and that, in addition, many reports have been published on the tentative identification of chitin-type materials from arthropods, graptolites and some other invertebrates from deposits as early as the

Cambrian there is much room for future biogeochemical research in the area of mucopolysaccharides.

Other sources for sugars in soils and sediments are the glycosides, in which the sugar is associated with various hydroxy compounds. Among the natural products which occur as glycosides are many plant pigments, phenols, and steroids. Of particular importance are the N-glycosides, which are better known as ribonucleosides and deoxyribonucleosides. The non-sugar member of the glycosides will be discussed in the chapters on pigments, phenols, steroids, etc.

3. Lipids, Isoprenoids, and Steroids

This chapter deals with a group of biochemical compounds that are insoluble in water but very soluble in certain organic solvents such as ether or hydrocarbons. A reason for discussing all three substances simultaneously is their close biochemical relationship.

The basic functional groups of the lipid constituents are hydroxyl and carboxyl groups. These groups are equivalent to the hydroxyls in carbohydrates or the carboxyls in amino acids. In a broad sense, lipids can be defined as esters of long chain carboxylic acids which are usually unbranched.

Most common lipids in plants and animals are fats which are esters of glycerol; many of them exhibit the triglyceride pattern (Table 17). Like the proteins which always contain a number of different amino acids, the fats usually yield upon hydrolysis a variety

Table 17 Principal Structural Units of Lipids, Isoprenoids, and Steroids.

$$R-COO-CH_2 \qquad\qquad R-COOH \quad HOCH_2$$
$$R'-COO-CH + 3H_2O \xrightarrow{(H+)} R'-COOH + HOCH$$
$$R''-COO-CH_2 \qquad\qquad R''-COOH \quad HOCH_2$$

Neutral fat   Fatty acids   Glycerol

$$\underset{\substack{| \\ CH_2 \cdot C \cdot CH \cdot CH_2}}{CH_3}$$

Isoprene   Cyclopentanophenanthrene

of fatty acid residues; these can be saturated, unsaturated, or, as in some rare cases, may even contain branches or rings.

Saturated acids in fats may contain four (butyric acid) to twenty-six (cerotic acid) carbon atoms. However, most common are those with twelve (lauric acid), sixteen (palmitic acid), and eighteen (stearic acid) carbon atoms.

Unsaturated fatty acids usually contain sixteen or more carbon atoms; two abundant acids are palmitoleic and linoleic acid.

Waxes are lipid compounds that usually are monoesters of long chain unbranched fatty acids and alcohols. The acids may contain twenty-four to thirty-six carbon atoms, and the alcohols sixteen to thirty-six. They are often associated or mixed with steroids and unbranched hydrocarbons.

Isoprenoids are a group of substances which can be considered to be derived from isoprene (Table 17). All isoprenoids, or to use a more familiar name, "terpene hydrocarbons," are multiples of the isoprene unit C_5H_8. However, chemically speaking, the term terpene is reserved for the C_{10} compounds; those containing three isoprene units are referred to as sesquiterpenes (C_{15} compounds); those having four units are designated as diterpenes (C_{20} compounds), etc.

A great variety of terpenes are known from plants. Quite often they are the cause of the odor (essential oils) and color (carotenoid pigments) of the plant material. Important members of the isoprenoid family are vitamin A, a diterpene and building block of carotenoids, and natural rubber, which is a polyterpene.

Steroids are compounds containing the cyclopentanophenanthrene carbon skeleton (Table 17). Most are alcohols, and in this case they are often referred to as sterols. Due to their biochemical importance, the chemistry and physiological function of steroids have been thoroughly investigated. Important steroids are cholesterol, calciferol, and the sex hormones.

In the geological literature, the term lipid is often used in a much broader sense. A variety of chemically unrelated substances, such as certain heterocyclic compounds, fats, hydrocarbons, inorganic sulfur, and many others are combined and referred to as the "lipid fraction." This is done only for convenience, because all listed materials are extractable from soils and sediments by the same organic solvent system. However, inasmuch as our interest is focussed on the biogeochemistry of the individual organic molecules, only those data will be considered that give detailed information on the chemical nature of the extracted "lipid" material.

As in the case of proteins and polysaccharides, there are practically no data available on the type and distribution of condensed lipid compounds (i.e., glycerides) in geological materials. All information is based on hydrolysis products such as fatty acids or certain alcohols.

Fatty acids have been isolated from soils, recent and ancient sediments, peats, lignites, waxes, petroleum, sea and lake waters, and fossil brines (Schreiner and Shorey, 1908, 1910a, b; Tanaka and Kuwata, 1928; Goryunova, 1952; Williams, 1961; Cooper, 1962; Slowey et al., 1962; Abelson et al., 1964; Jeffrey et al., 1964). Most noteworthy is the observation that acids with odd numbers of carbon atoms are found along with those having even numbers of carbon atoms. This is in contrast to nearly all biological systems where fatty acids are even numbered (Shorland, 1954). However, before attempting to explain the odd-even distribution in sediments and waters, a few items of pertinent information on the nature and abundance of fatty acids in various geological materials will be presented.

Slowey et al. (1962) studied the fatty acid content in waters from the Gulf of Mexico. A variety of saturated and unsaturated fatty acids were identified. It was observed that fatty acids in shallow waters exhibited some similarity to the composition of planktons collected from a location nearby. Furthermore, saturation seemed to increase and chain length of the molecules seemed to decrease with increase in water depth. This biogeochemical characteristic was not reflected in the total concentration of fatty acids; the amount was more or less uniform within a water column of about 2000 meters. It was suggested that decrease in unsaturation and chain length with depth was caused by extended exposure of fatty acids to oxidizing conditions in deep waters.

Similar observations were made in Pacific Ocean waters by Williams (1961). Total concentration in fatty acids ranged between 10 and 100 $\mu g/l$. The waters resembled biological systems insofar as they had palmitic and stearic acids as the predominant acids.

In a few selected samples, Cooper (1962) presented a comparative analysis of the distribution of fatty acids in recent and ancient sediments and petroleum brine waters. Independent of age, sediments show a larger proportion of even-numbered fatty acids. Again, most common are palmitic and stearic acids. However, the relative abundance of odd-numbered acids increases with geologic time (Fig. 58). In the case of petroleum brine waters, concentration differences between neighboring odd- and even-numbered acids become very small; in addition, a nearly straight-line decrease in relative abundance from C_{14} to C_{30} acids is developed (Fig. 58).

One could think of two possibilities as to how odd-numbered fatty acids came into being. Original biological production is the first, and decarboxylation of even-numbered fatty acids during diagenesis the second alternative. Some biogenic products are known to contain small amounts of odd-numbered fatty acids (Hewitt et al., 1961). Assuming that microbial activity selectively removes even-numbered

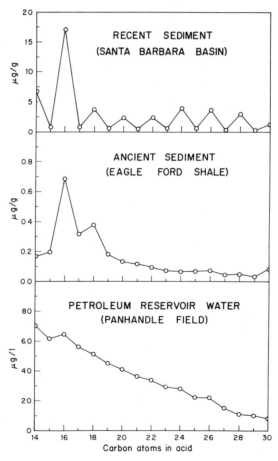

Fig. 58 Comparison of the distributions of fatty acids in a recent sediment, an ancient sediment, and in a water from a petroleum reservoir (after Cooper, 1961)

fatty acids, a relative increase in odd-numbered fatty acids can be postulated; indeed, Silliker and Rittenberg (1952) have shown that certain micro-organisms only utilize even-numbered, but not odd-numbered fatty acids. However, a selective removal of even-numbered fatty acids as a function of greater solubility can be ruled out, because waters and sediments show similar odd-even characteristics.

Although microbial activity cannot be fully excluded as a cause for the relative enrichment of odd-numbered acids in sediments and natural waters, decarboxylation seems to be a more likely explanation to account for the observed odd-even pattern. The increase in the abundance of odd-numbered acids with time apparently matches the generation of even-numbered paraffins (Bray and Evans, 1961). This parallelism suggests related processes for the formation of these acids and paraffins. Cooper (1961) proposed a relative intermediate formed by decarboxylation of a fatty acid. Intermediates of this type could yield mixtures of odd-numbered acids and paraffins as a reaction product. The odd-numbered acids produced would react similarly to form even-numbered acids and paraffins. The conversion of the naturally even-numbered carbon containing fatty acids in a sediment by chemical decarboxylation would cause the introduction, first of odd-numbered acids and paraffins and later of even-numbered paraffins.

Waxes have been isolated from peat, coals, and soils (Johnson and Thiessen, 1934; Segura et al., 1957; Meinschein and Kenny, 1957). Most of the work has been done on coal or montan waxes, as they are often called. Additional literature on this subject may be obtained by reference to Van Krevelen (1961), and Francis (1961).

Fossil waxes in peat and lignite deposits contain a variety of characteristic even- and odd-numbered fatty acids and alcohols (Cawley and King, 1945). Whereas information is plentiful on the type and concentration of wax compounds in various coals, only limited data are available on waxes in sediments. As a matter of fact, the only comprehensive study of soil waxes is that of Meinschein and Kenny (1957). The principal constituents of soil waxes are normal aliphatic acids, normal primary aliphatic alcohols, and sterols. The types of acids and alcohols show close resemblance to beeswax. Identification was based on mass spectrometric and infrared analysis of hydrogenolysis products of wax esters.

More information is available on isoprenoids in soils, sediments, natural waters, and the atmosphere. Most intensively studied so far are compounds of the carotenoid family (Trask and Wu, 1930;

Vallentyne, 1956, 1957a; Andersen and Gundersen, 1955; Fox, 1937, 1944; Erdman, 1961b; and Schwendinger and Erdman, 1963).

Plant tissues contain, on a dry weight basis, approximately 0.1 per cent carotenoids. Inasmuch as soil micro-organisms do not generally metabolize isoprenoids, a study of this class of compounds seems geochemically rewarding. The only way to eliminate isoprenoids from plant material is by volatilization into the atmosphere, or by photochemical oxidation.

Biogenically unaltered carotenoids have been extracted from terrestrial and marine sediments up to 100,000 years in age; they do not exist in older sediments. According to Schwendinger and Erdman (1963), the ratio of xanthophylls to carotenes in unconsolidated sediments is 1.3 to 3.6, compared to that of living plant materials of about 3 to 10. For xanthophylls — the oxygen-containing compounds — are disappearing at a faster rate than the carotenes — the hydrocarbon compounds. The marine sediments studied showed the highest carotenoid concentration, namely up to 800 ppm based on organic carbon. This feature is possibly a result of environmental differences: planktonic matter contains a larger percentage of carotenoid pigments.

It was suggested (Erdman, 1961; Hanson, 1959; Mulik and Erdman, 1963; Meinschein, 1961) that isoprenoids are potential sources for low-molecular weight hydrocarbons. Most significant in this respect are the data obtained by Mulik and Erdman (1963) and Day and Erdman (1963), who subjected β-carotene, dispersed in a water-sediment slurry, to a mild thermal treatment. Considerable quantities of benzenoid hydrocarbons were generated. By treating recent sediments of the Santa Barbara Basin (off the shore of California) in the same fashion, significant amounts of aromatic hydrocarbons were produced. An increase in benzenoid hydrocarbons by a factor of about 30,000 relative to an untreated control sample was obtained. Benzene, toluene, and xylenes were identified, i.e., the same type of hydrocarbons reported by Emery and Hoggan (1958) in sediment gas samples collected off the shore of California.

Considering the high quantities obtained from a mud slurry during the mild thermal treatment, there must have been other organic sources besides carotenoid pigments to account for the produced aromatic hydrocarbons. Likely precursors of benzene are polyunsaturated fatty acids. o-Xylene might arise from similar nonisoprenoid branched polyunsaturated chains. Toluene and m-xylene may originate from isoprenoids other than carotenoids, as for instance the diterpene vitamin A. The presence of greater amounts of penta-cyclic and hexacyclic compounds, possibly triterpenes, in organic soil extracts, has been demonstrated by Meinschein and Kenny (1957). Benzenoid hydrocarbons may also be generated from aromatic amino acids (phenylalanine, tyrosine) which are present in considerable quantities in recent sediments. Support for this supposition is given by the work of Hunt (personal communication), who subjected arti-ficially produced phenylalanine-clay complexes to a mild heat treat-ment. Similar benzenoid hydrocarbons as obtained by Erdman and his associates could be recovered in larger amounts.

Due to their volatile character, isoprenoids may accumulate in the atmosphere. In this connection, a controversial but interesting theory on the biogeochemical cycle of isoprenoids is worth mention-ing. According to Went (1960), 2×10^8 tons of volatile plant prod-ucts, predominantly isoprenoids, are released from living or dead organic materials to the atmosphere per year. In the absence of any mechanisms to oxidize these volatile compounds to CO_2 or water, these products will become particularized in the atmosphere. This condensation process is dependent upon sunlight and, partly, upon the presence of nitrogen oxides; it is the cause of "summer haze" in cultivated areas. Went suggests that this material, bituminous or asphaltic in nature, is removed from the air by precipitation and will be added to the organic matter in soils and sediments.

A variety of organic compounds which are steroids or resemble the steroids structurally, are found in coals (Murchison and Jones, 1964), waters, sediments, and soils. Most thoroughly studied are resins such as amber, kauri, or colophony. They are plant exudates and are associated with many coals; they can also occur as detrital constituents in sediment deposits (e.g., the Baltic Sea). The skeletal structure of two typical resin acids, abietic and dextropimaric acids, shows strong resemblance to that of sterols. It may be pointed out that some of the resinous materials also contain isoprenoids.

Among steroids reported from recent sediments and natural waters are the animal-derived cholesterol and the closely related phytosterols (Schreiner and Lathrop, 1911, 1912; Trask and Wu, 1930). Especially noteworthy is the presence of vitamin D_2 (calciferol) in view of its importance in biological mineralization processes.

In summarizing all geochemical data on fossil lipids, isoprenoids, and steroids, it becomes apparent that our information is rather lim-ited. A total of less than a hundred reliable analyses is all that has been published on these constituents. This small number which includes specimens from all over the world, different environments, and throughout the stratigraphical column, is certainly not sufficient. More work is urgently needed in this area in order to throw light on features such as the stability and fate of lipid compounds, or to unravel the principal pathways of hydrocarbon formation.

4. HETEROCYCLIC COMPOUNDS

Heterocyclic organic compounds contain elements other than carbon in their ring system. Among hetero-atoms of importance are oxygen, nitrogen, and sulfur. Heterocyclic compounds with elements such as the halogens, phosphorus, or silicon as part of their ring structure have not yet been fully investigated. Of particular biological importance are the aromatic members.

Some essential heterocycles have already been discussed earlier, namely the amino acids which have nitrogen-containing ring systems, and the carbohydrates that can be classified as oxygen heterocycles.

The ring size of heterocyclic compounds may range from 3 to 10. Numbering of the ring starts with the hetero-atom and proceeds so as to give substituents the lowest numbered positions. If several hetero-atoms are present, oxygen takes precedence over sulfur and sulfur over nitrogen for the number one position. The five- and six-membered ring compounds are the most significant ones, both from the biological and the geochemical point of view. It is for this reason that only the five- and six-membered heterocycles will be considered here; a few of the more characteristic monocyclic and polycyclic members are listed in Table 18.

A number of natural products are related to (1) pyrolle (hemoglobin, chlorophyll, vitamin B_{12}); (2) indole (tryptophan, some alkaloids: strychnine, indigo); (3) purine (adenine, guanine, some alkaloids: caffeine); (4) pyrimidine (thymine, cytosine, uracil, thiamine); (5) pyridine, quinoline, and isoquinoline (vitamin B_6, some alkaloids: nicotine, quinine, morphine); (6) pyran (some plant pigments: flavons, anthocyanins); (7) pteridine (vitamin B_{10}).

A great number of heterocycles has been isolated from coals and petroleum. The nitrogen members received particular attention, largely because of their detrimental effect on the storage stability of petroleum products and their poisoning effect on catalysts. In addition, coal tars and crude oils serve as a potential base for the industrial

Table 18   Representative Heterocycles
From Sediments, Coal Tars,
and Crude Oils.

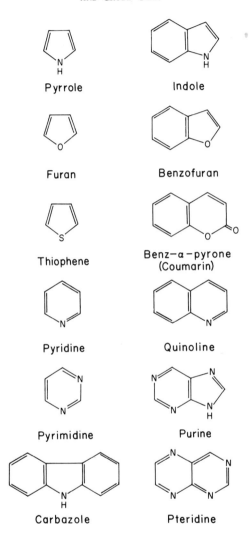

Pyrrole   Indole

Furan   Benzofuran

Thiophene   Benz-α-pyrone
(Coumarin)

Pyridine   Quinoline

Pyrimidine   Purine

Carbazole   Pteridine

production of many heterocyclic compounds such as pyridine, carbazole, acridine, quinoline, and many others.

The use of heterocycles as a help in solving the petroleum problem, or in understanding the formation of coals, has been recognized
in recent years. Pyrolle compounds which are structurally similar to
chlorophyll and hemin (Fig. 59) were among the first organic con-

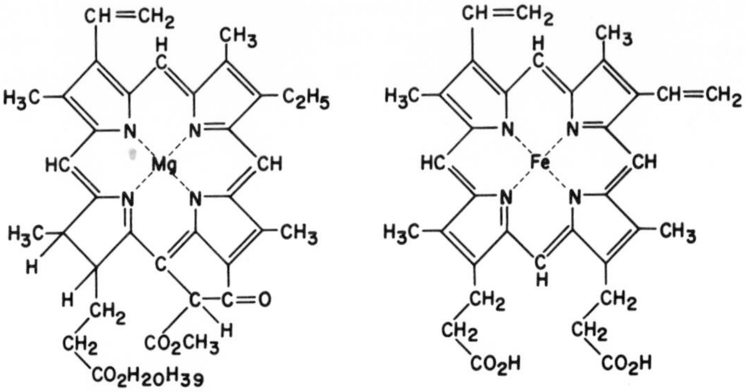

Fig. 59 Molecular structure of chlorophyll and hemin

stituents extracted from bituminous sediments to be thoroughly studied from a geochemical point of view. It was Treibs (1934, 1936) with his classical papers on the distribution of porphyrins in various geological materials who, for the first time, drew attention to the immense research potentialities in the area of biogeochemistry. His discoveries definitely led to a better understanding of processes responsible for the formation of petroleum.

Porphyrins in bituminous materials are preferentially complexed with either vanadium or nickel. Fossil porphyrins with other metals, for instance, uranium, or the metal-free chlorins, are comparatively less frequent. In contrast, recent sediments contain chlorin pigments but lack porphyrins.

It is generally agreed that most of the porhpyrins in sediments are derived from chlorophyll and, to a lesser extent, from hemin or its derivatives. For this reason, it is of interest to understand the mechanism by which the chlorophyll molecule, a dihydroporphyrin, is diagenetically altered to a metal-complexed porphyrin. Various suggestions have been made as to the most likely alteration mechanism (Groennings, 1953; Dunning et al., 1954; Vallentyne and Craston, 1957; Orr and Grady, 1957; Hodgson and Baker, 1957; Orr et al., 1958; Hodgson et al., 1960; Blumer and Omenn, 1961; Blumer, 1950, 1962ab).

According to some authors, alteration of original chlorophyll may proceed by the direct replacement of magnesium by another metal. The other alternative involves a two-step process; in the first step magnesium is expelled which releases a free chlorin pigment, and in the second step the "secondary" chlorin is re-complexed with a metal. Geological data (Orr et al., 1958; Vallentyne and Craston, 1957; Rittenberg et al., 1963) as well as experimental data (Hodgson and Hitchon, 1959; Blumer and Omenn, 1961; Lamort, 1956) indicate that chlorophyll is easily converted to pheophytine. Actually, pheophytine is the predominant chlorin pigment in recent sediments and concentrations may range from 1 to 100 ppm.

The conversion of chlorins into porphyrins may be accomplished by the reduction of the vinyl ($-CH=CH_2$) into an ethyl group ($-C_2H_5$), and by the elimination of the carbonyl group. This reduction causes dehydrogenation at positions 7 and 8 with the simultaneous formation of another ethyl group, thus converting the chlorin to a porphyrin pigment. There are two ways conceivable in which pheophytin is altered to a metal-complexed porphyrin. In the first case, reduction and dehydrogenation of the chlorin precedes the metal complexation; in the second case, the metal is introduced into the chlorin structure prior to the porphyrin formation. Neither free porphyrins nor vanadium and nickel intermediates are known from recent sediments. There is a "missing link" between pheophytin in recent, and metal porphyrins in ancient sediments. Experimental data by Hodgson et al. (1960), showing how easily chlorins can be altered to metal-complexed chlorins, may speak for the second alternative. It is noteworthy that nickel apparently complexes more readily with the chlorin than vanadium. The complexity and sometimes reversibility of the reactions involved in the chlorin-porphyrin system has been clearly demonstrated by Blumer and Omenn (1961) in studies of uncomplexed chlorins of Triassic age.

The ratio of hydrocarbons to pyrolle compounds in recent reducing sediments is mostly less than 10:1, compared to 10,000:1 in crude oils. Diagenetic generation of hydrocarbons or a preferential loss of pigments, or both factors, may be responsible for the observed distribution pattern in crude oils. A positive redox potential may favor the elimination of pigments from the strata, as can be inferred from the general low pigment concentration in recent oxidizing sediments when compared to their reducing counterparts. The hydrocarbon/ pigment ratio in oxidizing sediments is generally higher by a factor of 10 and more than observed in reducing sediments.

For reasons of thermal stability vanadium and nickel are the two heavy metals most likely to become associated with porphyrins. The quantities of both elements necessary to complex all available chlorins presented in recent sediments can easily be obtained from one or the other of the surrounding sediment materials. For example, clay minerals contain an average of 100 to 200 ppm of vanadium and 10 to 100 ppm of nickel; sedimentary sulfides and the organic fraction are highly enriched in both elements in concentrations up to 1000 ppm. Iron and manganese oxides and hydroxides are known for their ability to scoop up trace elements such as vanadium and nickel in amounts up to 1000 ppm (Krauskopf, 1955; Keith and Degens, 1959). Iron manganese hydroxides and oxides are rather unstable in reducing environments where conditions apparently are most favorable for a porphyrin formation. It can be inferred that in the early stages of diagenesis significant amounts of nickel and vanadium may be released from various sedimentary end-members to the next environments.

The ratio of nickel and vanadium porphyrins can fluctuate strongly from one formation to the other. Perhaps future studies will show the usefulness of porphyrins for stratigraphic correlations. The ease of extraction and isolation from the remainder of the inorganic and organic matter and the well-developed analytical techniques may eventually encourage porphyrin studies on a large scale.

Tryptophan is the main parent compound for indole acids, neutral indoles, indoxyls, and other metabolic breakdown products such as kynurenine. A great variety of indoles are reported from crude oils (Lochte, 1952; Sauer et al., 1952). The total yield in indoles and other nitrogen heterocycles, including carbazoles, pyrolles, quinolines, and pyridines, may range from about 0.001 to 0.1 per cent of the petroleum. Information on the type and distribution of indole compounds in sediments and soils is still lacking. However, a number of unidentified indole compounds have been reported from recent sediments (Degens et al., 1963a). In view of the metabolic importance of indoles and their apparent stability — as can be seen from their presence in crude oils — a careful geochemical examination might be rewarding.

The occurrence of purine and pyrimidine bases in soils and peats has been established by various investigators (Schreiner and Shorey, 1910ab; Schreiner and Lathrop, 1912; Shorey, 1913; Bottomley, 1917; Wrenshall and McKibbin, 1937; Wrenshall and Dyer, 1941; Adams et al., 1954; Anderson, 1958, 1961). The types of bases are characteristic of deoxyribonucleic acid (DNA, Fig. 60) and, to a lesser extent, of ribonucleic acid (RNA). That there are more bases derived from

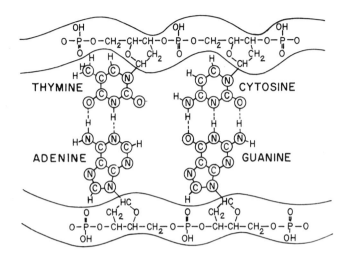

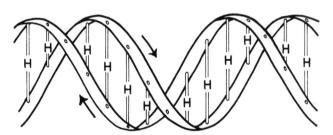

Fig. 60 Molecular drawing of components of deoxyribonucleic acid (DNA) and double helix model (after Calvin, 1961)

DNA or related polynucleotides than bases released from RNA is certainly due to the analytical preparation of the soil samples. In most instances, only the "humic acid" fraction of a soil was studied. Inasmuch as RNA — in contrast to DNA — is degraded in alkali and not extracted along with humic acids, bases of RNA should be looked for in the fulvic acid fraction.

The total values for the bases adenine, guanine, cytosine, and thymine range from about 10 to 60 μmoles/100 g soil. This accounts for up to 1 per cent of the total soil nitrogen. The proportions of the bases indicate that they were originally polynucleotides which were derived mainly from bacterial DNA. The bacterial origin is inferred from the fact that cytosine and guanine are in excess of thymine and adenine, respectively (Anderson, 1961).

Although humic acid fractions are easy to analyze for the bases of the purines and pyrimidines, more attention should be given to analyses of the total organic matter, since molecules which have shorter chains than DNA, as well as the RNA derivatives, are not necessarily part of the humic acid fraction and thus may escape detection. The concentrations reported in the literature, therefore, can only be regarded as minimum values.

In addition to the above mentioned bases, uracil and the two oxypurines, hypoxanthine and xanthine, have been isolated from soils and sediments (Schreiner and Shorey, 1910ab; Schreiner and Lathrop, 1912; Anderson, 1961; Prashnowsky et al., 1961; Prashnowsky, 1963). Uric acid, which is a major metabolic product, has not yet been detected, but it is expected to be one of the more common purines in geological materials.

Some important vitamins are heterocyclic compounds; those isolated from natural waters, soils, and sediments include thiamine (vitamin B_1), riboflavin (vitamin B_2), nicotinic acid (vitamin B_6), folic acid (vitamin B_{10}), cyanocobalamin (vitamin B_{12}), and biotin (vitamin H) (Hutchinson, 1943; Lilly and Leonian, 1938; Roulet and Schopfer, 1950; Schmidt and Starkey, 1951; Hutchinson and Setlow, 1946; Burkholder and Burkholder, 1956; Droop, 1955).

Benzo derivatives of the pyrones (coumarins, flavones), as well as the anthocyanins, have not been geochemically investigated. It is conceivable that the first constituents, like β-carotene, may become degraded to benzenoid hydrocarbons upon thermal treatment. They are very reactive and may polymerize with other materials. The occurrence of flavinoids and related heterocyclic substances has recently been reported by Swain and Venteris (1964).

Summarizing, it can be said that certain heterocyclic compounds have been isolated from geological materials. With the exception of the porphyrins, however, our knowledge concerning origin, stability, and eventual use of heterocycles for the interpretation of geological phenomena is rather poor. Judging from their biological abundance and their structure, heterocyclic compounds can be assumed to be stable and widespread in both recent and ancient sediments; they certainly deserve to be studied thoroughly.

5. Phenols, Quinones, and Related Compounds

Phenols represent a class of aromatic oxygen compounds which are of considerable importance in biological systems. They constitute the molecular framework of many plant products such as lignins and tannic substances.

Phenols are compounds having one or more hydroxyl groups directly attached to an aromatic ring (Table 19.) The reactions of the hydroxyl groups which involve breaking the O—H bonds and generating new bonds from oxygen to carbon may, for example, easily lead to the formation of esters, ethers, or methoxy derivatives.

It should be pointed out that hydroxy groups markedly modify the properties of the aromatic ring; in exchange, the aromatic ring strongly affects the reactivity of the hydroxyl groups. This interrelationship is reflected in diazo coupling reactions which involve aromatic substitution of phenoxide ions by diazonium salt and production of azo compounds. Other examples are the formation of phenolic acids and aldehydes. In general, the reaction products are rather stable due to the stability associated with the aromatic ring. In this respect phenols resemble aromatic amines.

Phenols can be oxidized, and the products obtained depend on the nature of the substituents. Polyhydric phenols with the hydroxyls in the *ortho* or *para* relationship are easily oxidized to quinones (cyclic diketones). Conversely, quinones can be reduced to the cor-

Table 19 REPRESENTATIVE DEGRADATION PRODUCTS
OF LIGNINS AND VARIOUS HUMIC MATERIALS.

Catechol   Guaiacol   Salicylic acid

Hydroquinone   Vanillin   Protocatechuic acid

Pyrogallol   Syringaldehyde   *o*-Benzoquinone

responding polyhydric phenol. Inasmuch as these reactions are sufficiently sensitive, rapid, and reversible, they may be used as a convenient oxidation-reduction system. Quinones may also come into existence via aromatic amines (i.e., aniline).

Major biological sources for quinones and aromatic oxygen compounds in organic matter found in soils and sediments are the lignins, tannic substances, aromatic amino acids and monomolecular propylphenols (-CH$_2$-CH$_2$-CH$_3$). In the living plant material the propylphenols act as respiratory chromogens and can be regarded as the most likely precursor of lignins. Recent biochemical studies have even put forward the idea that lignins are closely linked with the respiration of the cell, instead of being only physical impregnations of the maturing cell.

During soil formation and diagenesis, aromatic oxygen compounds, originally supplied by plants and animals, may undergo a number of complex chemical transformations. These alterations are either linked to microbial activity or are a result of nonbiogenic maturation processes. Eventually they lead to the formation of a variety of geochemical substances known as humic acids, hymatomelanic acid, crenic and apocrenic acids (fulvic acids), humic substances, humin, ulmin, and kerogen, to name just a few of the more commonly used terms. A great many additional terms are known from the geological and soil science literature; unfortunately, most of these are unaccompanied by precise chemical definitions.

All of the listed organic geochemical compounds refer to certain organic fractions obtained by specific analytical extraction techniques. In most instances, a knowledge of the molecular structure is lacking, or at best, is based on hypotheses. Nevertheless, inasmuch as quite a few of these terms are frequently used in the literature, often with different connotations, it seems appropriate to include some of them in the following discussion. This naturally requires some explanation regarding the probable molecular structure, in order to be able to evaluate in what respect, for example, humic acids differ from fulvic acids or kerogen from humin.

The most thorough and up-to-date survey on soil organic matter in general, and on phenols, quinones, and their derivatives in particular, is that by Kononova (1961). This study also discusses major processes responsible for the transformation of biogenic substances within the soil environment. Furthermore, the interrelationship between inorganic and organic matter receives thorough consideration. The bibliography includes more than 800 titles, most of which are concerned with humic materials in soil deposits.

Whereas soil scientists have successfully traced the origin and fate of soil organic matter, especially that of aromatic oxygen compounds and their derivatives, this area of organic geochemical research has been nearly completely ignored by sedimentologists. Only crude oils and coals have been investigated for a number of aromatic oxygen compounds. In the past, biogeochemical research was primarily directed towards an understanding of hydrocarbon genesis and accumulation, and the identification of trace constituents such as hormones, vitamins, enzymes, and the like. It was only recently (Himus, 1951; Himus and Basak, 1949; Takahashi, 1935; Forsman and Hunt, 1958 a,b; Breger and Deul, 1956; Breger and Brown, 1962; Deul, 1956; Breger, 1960) that high-molecular weight aromatic oxygen compounds received some biogeochemical attention. This material, known as kerogen, constitutes the so-called "insoluble organic matter." It should be emphasized that kerogen accounts for more than 95 per cent of the total organic matter that has come to rest or has been formed in sediments of all ages and environments. In the past it has not been easy to identify kerogen analytically; this may explain why so little is known of this substance. Some of the difficulties have recently been overcome, and new concepts of the structure of kerogen-type materials have since emerged.

In order to follow the path of kerogen formation, it is essential first to become familiar with certain chemical aspects of soil organic matter. Emphasis will be placed on the recognition of intermediate reaction products that may link kerogen to its ultimate biogenic source. In addition, possible transformation mechanisms will be discussed.

One of the major alteration products obtained during the decomposition of biogenic materials is humic acid. This term is rather loosely defined in the geological literature and is often used for a number of different products. In this connection, humic acids are regarded as the 0.3N NaOH extractable organic fraction that precipitates upon acidification. Hymatomelanic acid is the ethanol soluble part of this fraction. More difficult is the attempt to characterize humic acids in precise chemical or structural terms. Based on the concepts largely developed by Russian and German schools (Odén,

1919; Fuchs, 1931; Kononova, 1961; McLaren, 1963), the fundamental chemical and structural pattern of humic acids appears to
be as follows:

Humic acids are high-molecular weight compounds of complex
nature. The molecular weight may range from a low of 1000 to a
high of 50,000 (Flaig, 1958; Kononova, 1961). The smaller the molecule, the more rigid the linkage of the humic acids with their associated mineral matter. Sakun (1942) has demonstrated that the low-
molecular weight humic acids are the ones which are present in true
ionic solution and most actively interact with clay minerals. Equivalent weights of humic acids have been determined by Pommer and
Breger (1960a,b).

The ratio of carbon:oxygen:hydrogen:nitrogen is about 55:35:5:5.
This ratio may fluctuate within certain limits and depends on parameters such as type of soil and sediment, organic source, age of the
material, or degree of aromatization. Most of the nitrogen forms an
integral part of the humic acid molecule and is not simply a con-
taminant, as often stated.

In a structural sense, humic acids can be looked upon largely
as condensation products of phenols, quinones, and amino compounds. Other biochemicals such as sugars or heterocyclic compounds
(i.e., indoles, purines, pyrimidines, and pyrolle derivatives) participate
in the formation of humic acids; however, their contributions are
considerably smaller. It is conceivable that the presence of carbohydrates accounts for the reducing capacities of humic acids.

The number of structural units, the mode of monomer arrangement, and the type of linkage established in the humic acid molecule
are not yet fully understood. From the present state of knowledge,
it seems most reasonable to assume that $-O-$, $-NH-$, $= N-$, and perhaps $-S-$ linkages, are the more important ones. Aromatic rings may
also be linked by two methylene bridges; the linking unit can then be
described as a hydroaromatic ring. By destructive distillation, prolonged alkaline or acid hydrolysis, and other analytical means, many
of the individual building blocks of humic acids can be recovered
(Dragunov, 1948; Bremner, 1949, 1951, 1955, 1958; Hayashi and
Nagai, 1955; Savage and Stevenson, 1961; Lynch et al., 1957;
Kononova, 1961). Especially noteworthy are the high yields in aromatic oxygen compounds and quinone derivatives (Dragunov, 1948).
The aromatic nature of humic acids has been clearly established by
a great number of investigators. The close similarity in structure has

led many scientists to favor lignins as the ultimate source of humic acids. However, there are other possible biogenic precursors such as tannic substances and microbial propylphenols from which humic acids may have obtained their aromatic compounds.

Nonaromatic humic acids which resemble browning reaction products may also be encountered in nature. They may develop by way of amino acids and sugars. Little is known concerning their structural composition and stability.

The ratio of aliphatic to aromatic structures determines important physical-chemical properties of the humic acid molecule. Increase in aromaticity, for instance, decreases the hydrophilic characteristics of humic acids. The degree of aromatization is generally reflected in the carbon/hydrogen ratio of the humic material.

Hymatomelanic acid, the ethanol soluble part of the humic acid fraction, apparently represents a simpler form of humic acid (molecular weight about 800), and perhaps, in part, resin acids. Basically, however, no major chemical difference can be discerned between the alcohol soluble and non-soluble parts of the humic acid fraction; their separation into independent groups of compounds seems arbitrary.

In the case of fulvic acids, too, structural similarity to humic acids seems to be established. Fulvic acids can be defined as the NaOH extractable organic compounds that stay in solution upon acidification. In a chemical sense, however, fulvic acids show a prevalence of aliphatic side groups and a lower abundance of aromatic units (Kononova, 1956, 1961; Jenkinson and Tinsley, 1960). The high solubility of fulvic acids in aqueous solutions can probably be linked to the greater abundance of aliphatic side groups when compared with humic acids.

Humic substances that cannot be extracted from the soil by alkali treatment and organic solvents are generally called humins. Humins closely resemble humic acids, both chemically and structurally. But in contrast to humic acids, humins are not released from the soil by means of alkali extraction; this may have something to do with their tight fixation to the mineral part of the soil. Khan (1945, 1957) and Zyrin (1948) demonstrated that an alternate acid-base treatment will bring practically all humins into solution in the form of humic acid type materials. Humic acids obtained by this means exhibit only slight chemical differences as against humic acids recovered by the normal 0.3N NaOH extraction procedure. They are only slightly higher in hydrogen and oxygen and lower in nitrogen and carbon compared to the corresponding 0.3N NaOH extractable humic acids (Fig. 61).

From the data available on humic compounds in soils it appears that there are no major structural differences between humic acids,

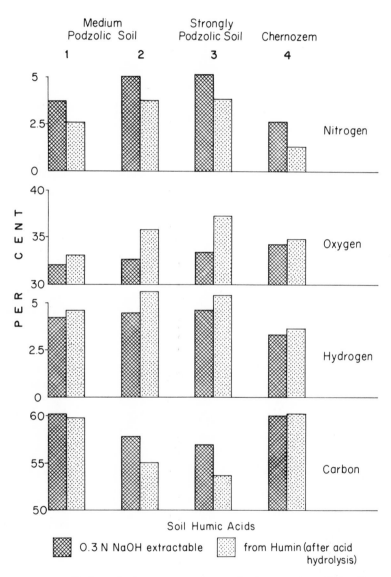

Fig. 61 Carbon, hydrogen, oxygen, and nitrogen in soil humic acids (after Kononova, 1961; Khan, 1945; and Zyrin, 1948)

humins, and other humic constituents. All are high-molecular weight condensation products which largely have phenols, quinones, and amino compounds (amino acids, urea, etc.) as their principal building blocks. Type and ratio of these constituents may, of course, vary to a certain degree. This will result in differences in extraction characteristics, chromatographic behavior, or solubility.

Unconsolidated sediments of marine and continental origin also contain significant amounts of humic acids. In some instances, this fraction constitutes 50 per cent or more of the total organic matter present in the rock material (Degens et al., 1963a,b). In view of their abundance and chemical composition, humic acids have to be considered as one of the more promising source materials for the "insoluble organic matter" present in ancient sediments.

Kerogen isolated from sediments by hydrofluoric-acid-treatment (Forsman and Hunt, 1958a,b) appears as a very fine soft powder varying in color from dark brown to black. Carbon, hydrogen, oxygen, nitrogen, and possibly sulfur, are the major constituent elements. All these elements form an integral part of the kerogen molecule. The C:H:O:N: ratio averages about 81:7:10:2 (Fig. 62). The amount of sulfur cannot be quantitatively estimated because of sulfide contaminations.

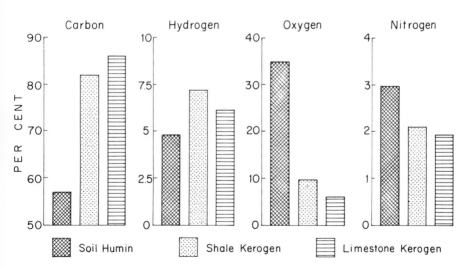

Fig. 62 Carbon, hydrogen, oxygen, and nitrogen in soil humin and kerogens (after Kononova, 1961; Forsman and Hunt, 1958 a, 1958 b; Khan, 1945; and Zyrin, 1948)

Upon hydrogenolysis (Forsman and Hunt, 1958a), soluble products were obtained, i.e., asphaltics, hydrocarbons, and O-N-S compounds, in yields ranging between 18 and 87 per cent. These geochemical data, however, are not sufficient to construct a model of the kerogen molecule, because products of hydrogenolysis will differ considerably in chemistry from the original structural constituents. This type of approach so far only gives some insight into the readiness or reluctance of the kerogen components to become hydrogenated.

In analogy to humic acid analysis (Khan, 1945), Degens and Hunt (1964) subjected kerogens to alternate acid-base treatments for longer periods of time. A wide spectrum of components, e.g., phenols, amino acids, or amino-sugars were released; the yield increased with the duration of hydrolysis. Although this treatment may partially or completely eliminate, or even alter, some of the original building blocks, one is probably still dealing with the chemically unaltered kerogen units in the case of most amino acids and phenols. In comparing kerogen and humic acid hydrolysates the similarity of the released constituents is rather striking. In the case of the amino acids, there is no basic difference between a kerogen and a humic acid hydrolysate (second extract) (Fig. 63). That the first humic acid extract shows a somewhat more complex pattern can be attributed to adsorption phenomena: most of the the initially recovered amino acids are only loosely attached to the humic acid molecule. The structurally incorporated amino acids, as obtained during the second hydrolysis, require a more rigid hydrolysis and for longer periods of time.

Most noteworthy is the presence of urea, serine, taurine, cysteic acid, and the glycine/alanine ratio. This range of products suggests that humic acids as well as kerogens incorporate a great number of metabolic substances which most likely are of microbial origin. Inasmuch as urea is slowly degraded during hydrolysis, its role in kerogen formation cannot be completely evaluated at present. But considering the fact that urea and, for example, polyfunctional amides, may condense with aldehydes to form stable resins (plastics), this may serve as an implicit indication of the potential role of urea in the origin of kerogen-type materials. The increase in ammonia with length of hydrolysis may perhaps be linked to the deamination or breakdown of amines such as urea. Cysteic acid is most likely derived from either cystine or cysteine, and taurine from the decarboxylation of cysteic acid. In aqueous solutions, phenols react most actively with compounds such as cysteine (-S- linkage), which substitute in positions

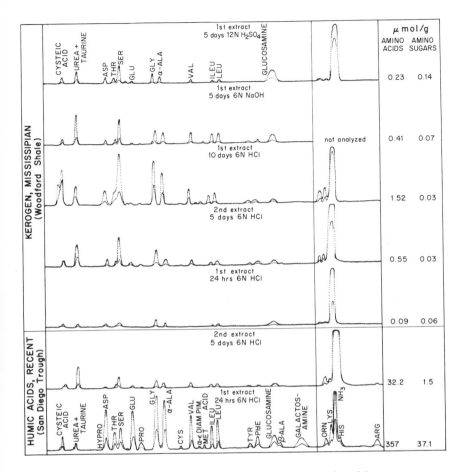

Fig. 63 Amino acids and amino sugars in humic acid and kerogen hydrolysates. Ion-exchange elution chromatogram (after Degens and Hunt, 1964)

ortho or *para* to the hydroxyl group. It is conceivable that some of the organic sulfur is present in the form of such combinations. The high yield in serine can be a result of the chelating characteristics of this amino acid. Some of the serine could possibly have been derived from tyrosine which also can be regarded as a potential precursor of low-molecular weight benzenoid hydrocarbons.

More than twenty different phenolic constituents are known from both the humic acids and kerogens. Abundant in particular are vanillin, p-hydroxybenzaldehyde, syringaldehyde, guajacol, or the corresponding phenolic acids (Morrison, 1958; Coulson et al., 1959; Kononova, 1961; Degens et al., 1963a,b). The same phenolic constituents have also been recognized in microbial (Henderson, 1955) or analytical (Brauns, 1952) degradation products of lignins. In the past, this relationship was interpreted to mean that humic acids are merely alteration products of lignins, unaccompanied by major structural changes. This viewpoint seems to be invalid. Instead, it is more likely that during decomposition lignins undergo a series of severe biochemical and chemical modifications, resulting in the production of monomolecular aromatic oxygen compounds. Upon oxidation of phenols the formation of quinones can be initiated. Both phenols and quinones may subsequently take part in a condensation reaction with other simple organic molecules such as amino acids, urea, sugars, or heterocyclic compounds to form the nucleus of the humic acid molecule.

Aside from lignin, other sources of aromatic oxygen compounds or quinone derivatives are conceivable, i.e., tannic substances, aromatic amino acids and amines, and microbial propylphenols. However, there is so far no simple criterion to distinguish between the various phenolic precursor materials of humic acids.

There are so few data concerning the chemical and structural composition of kerogen, that one can only attempt to outline a tentative model. On this basis, kerogen appears to be a denatured form of humic acid. The loss in oxygen and nitrogen, and the gain in carbon, when compared to the elemental composition of humic acids may be linked to dehydration, decarboxylation, loss of methoxyl and carbonyl groups, and deamination phenomena. Due to the resulting increase in aromatic structures, the organic residue becomes less soluble in aqueous media. The tight fixation with the associated mineral matter by ion exchange or chemisorption will further enhance the stability of the organic residue and may partly account for the poor extraction characteristics which this material exhibits when treated with mineral acids or bases. Upon an increase in metamorphosis or upon heat treatment, the total yield in nitrogen, oxygen, and hydrogen gradually declines; in its final stage the kerogenous material seems to acquire the characteristics of graphite.

The chemical nature of kerogen appears to depend largely on four parameters, namely: (1) the chemical composition and molecular size of the original humic acid molecule, (2) the redox potential, particularly in the early stages of diagenesis, (3) the thermal history of the host rock, and (4) the type of sediment in terms of mineral composition and water content.

With regard to the first parameter, i.e., the chemistry of the humic acid molecule, certain fluctuations are observable even in present day environments. For example, the ratio of aliphatic to aromatic compounds, or the type of individual monomers may vary from one humic acid to the other. Although most humic acids are metabolically related to micro-organisms, the original biochemicals as supplied by plants and animals will to a certain extent influence the chemistry of the metabolic end product called humic acid, humin, kerogen, etc. The paleontological record shows ample evidence for the wide variation in plant and animal species throughout the stratigraphical column. It is for this reason that humic acids, for example, of the Cambrian time are expected to be markedly different from those formed earlier or later in the history of the earth. Very promising in this respect are phenols and quinones, because lignins and tannic substances came rather late in the evolution of biochemicals. The limited number of phenols present in Pre-Cambrian kerogens when compared to Recent or Tertiary kerogens may be a result of this biochemical phenomenon.

The redox potential at the time of formation and during the early stages of diagenesis is of critical importance for the phenol-quinone relationship in humic acids. As soon as the molecular framework of the humic acid molecule is established, Eh seems to exercise only minor control on the structural pattern. An increase in aromaticity will favor electrophilic substitution in which sulfur components, e.g., cysteine, may easily develop sulfur-bridges in positions *ortho* or *para* to the hydroxyl groups of phenols. The amount of sulfur in the organic residue may perhaps serve as criterion of the redox potential at the time of deposition. It should be emphasized that humic acids and kerogens are stable forms under reducing as well as oxidizing conditions. To associate black shales with reducing environments, as is frequently done by geologists, has no justification whatsoever. Shales high in organic matter are common in anaerobic as well as in perfectly aereated basins of deposition.

Very little is known of the "sensitivity" of kerogen molecules, i.e., their response to heat and pressure. The few data available so far suggest that temperatures in the neighborhood of a few hundred degrees C are necessary before some of the kerogen constituents are released or decomposed in measurable quantities. Kerogen present in a rock wall (Pierre shale, Cretaceous) about 15 cm away from a one-meter igneous dike, still contains measurable amounts of amino acids in concentrations only about 5 to 10 times less than in the normal shale (Fig. 64). Aromatic oxygen compounds appear to not be affected at all. The effect lower temperatures may have on the molecule during a period extending over millions of years cannot be evaluated at present.

The importance of the fourth parameter, the association with mineral matter, has already been stressed in detail. Since sediments lose water during compaction in significant amounts, it is conceivable that this will result in a complete or partial dehydration of the humic acid or kerogen molecule.

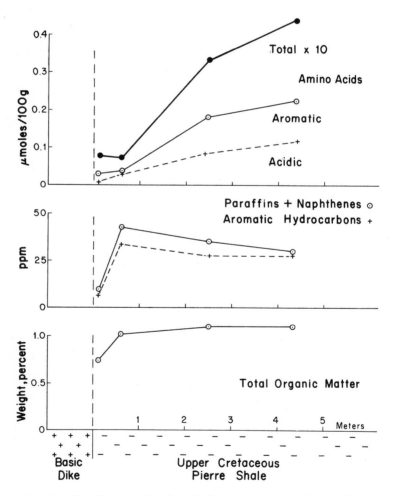

Fig. 64 Distribution of various hydrocarbons and amino acids in the wall rock of a basic dike; Upper Cretaceous Pierre Shale (after Hunt, 1962; and Degens and Hunt, 1964)

6. HYDROCARBONS, ASPHALTS, AND ALLIED SUBSTANCES

Bituminous substances can be grouped into the carbon disulfide soluble and insoluble organic constituents. The major types of bituminous compounds, both those which occur in nature and those which are produced synthetically can be obtained from Figure 65. The classification scheme is adapted from Abraham (1960, 1961, 1962a,b) and Hunt (1963). In principle, it distinguishes between bitumens and pyrobitumens. The expression "pyrobitumens" implies that the material is produced by a thermal treatment. In this connection only the hydrocarbons in petroleum, soils, and sediments, and the various asphaltic bitumens and pyrobitumens will be considered.

(a) *Hydrocarbons.* Compounds of the elements hydrogen and carbon are called hydrocarbons. The classification of hydrocarbons is based on the structural arrangement of the carbon atoms; one generally distinguishes between the following types: (1) alkanes, (2) cycloalkanes, (3) alkenes, (4) cycloalkenes, (5) alkynes, and (6) arenes.

Open-chain or acyclic hydrocarbons without double or triple bonds represent the so called alkanes or saturated paraffin hydrocarbons. They follow the general formula C_nH_{2n+2}. Two types occur: (a) the straight-chain or normal hydrocarbons, e.g., n-butane $CH_3\text{-}CH_2\text{-}CH_2\text{-}CH_3$, and (b) the branched chain hydrocarbons, e.g.,

$$CH_3$$
$$|$$
isobutane $CH_3\text{-}CH\text{-}CH_3$.

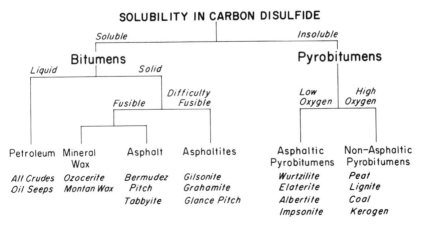

Fig. 65 Terminology and classification of naturally occurring bituminous substances (after Abraham, 1960; and Hunt, 1963)

Cycloalkanes are hydrocarbons with a one-ring structure following the general formula C_nH_{2n} (Table 20). Their names are formed by adding the prefix *cyclo* to the name of the corresponding *n*-alkane which has the same number of carbon atoms as the ring.

Table 20 CLASSIFICATION OF HYDROCARBONS (STRUCTURAL FORMULAS OF SIMPLE EXAMPLES).

CLASS	EXAMPLE	FORMULA
Alkanes (paraffins)	methane	CH_4
	n-butane	$CH_3-CH_2-CH_2-CH_3$
	isobutane	$CH_3-\underset{\underset{CH_3}{\mid}}{CH}-CH_3$
Cycloalkanes* (cycloparaffins)	cyclobutane	
	cyclohexane	
Alkenes	ethylene	$CH_2=CH_2$
	propylene	$CH_3-CH=CH_2$
	isobutylene	$CH_3-\underset{\underset{CH_3}{\mid}}{C}=CH_2$
Cycloalkenes	1,3-dimethylcyclohexene	
Alkynes	ethyne (acetylene)	$H-C\equiv C-H$
	2-butyne	$CH_3-C\equiv C-CH_3$
Arenes (aromatic hydrocarbons)	benzene	
	toluene	
	o-xylene	
	naphthalene	
	anthracene	

*cyclopentane and cyclohexane derivatives are known as naphthenes

Alkenes are open-chain hydrocarbons with one double bond (olefinic linkage); a simple member is ethylene $CH_2=CH_2$. Formerly, the term "olefins" was frequently used because these compounds yield "oily" products on treatment with chlorine or bromine. The corresponding ring hydrocarbons are known as cycloalkenes. Alkadienes, alkatrienes, and alkatetraenes, are compounds with two, three, and four double bonds, respectively.

Alkynes or acetylenes are hydrocarbons with triple bonds. Acetylene, C_2H_2, is the simplest and most important member of this class.

Arenes or aromatic hydrocarbons contain six–membered rings into which are fitted three carbon-carbon double bonds. This arrangement of double bonds in aromatic systems determines significant physical and chemical properties. In Table 20, examples for the various classes of hydrocarbons are presented.

Hydrocarbons can be synthesized by plants and animals (Chibnall and Piper, 1934; Meinschein, 1963; Smith, 1954; Erdman, 1961; Blumer, 1961; and Blumer et al., 1963). Although generally the concentrations do not exceed a few tenths or a few hundredths ppm of the living matter, some hydrocarbons, in particular pristane, can be highly concentrated in certain marine organisms (planktonic crustaceans) (Blumer et al., 1963). The concentration in this case may reach 1 to 3 per cent of the body fat. The structural similarity between pristane and phytol suggests that the former has been derived from the chlorophyll of its phytoplankton diet. The level of hydrocarbon concentration in most recent and ancient sediments is generally in the order of a few tenths to a few hundredths ppm. Only petroleum pools represent natural hydrocarbon concentrates.

There are striking similarities between hydrocarbons found in biogenic materials, soils, sediments, and crude oils. But on the other hand, there also exist pronounced differences between these compounds which makes it rather difficult to suggest a simple mechanism for the origin of hydrocarbons altogether. A detailed discussion on the origin of hydrocarbons in organisms and sediments, and the formation of petroleum, is presented elsewhere (p. 288). Inasmuch as, without question, petroleum represents the most interesting geochemical hydrocarbon mixture, a few data on the principal crude oil constituents are given below:

The composition of petroleum varies widely among the various oil producing areas throughout the world. Saturated hydrocarbons from C_1 to C_{50} make up a substantial part of the crude oils. Naphthenes (cyclopentane and cyclohexane derivatives) and aromatic hydrocarbons also constitute a significant portion of petroleum. Despite the considerable variations between paraffins, naphthenes, and aromatics from one crude oil to the other (Smith, 1952), a representative petroleum (Rossini, 1960) will yield on distillation the following fractions: (a) *gas fraction,* boiling point up to $40°C$, contains normal and branched alkanes from C_1 to C_5; (b) *gasoline fraction,* boiling point from $40°$ to $180°C$, contains normal and branched alkanes, cycloalkanes, and arenes in the C_6 to C_{10} range. The branched alkanes have higher octane numbers (anti-knock ratings) than their straight-chain isomers; (c) *kerosene,* boiling point from $180°$ to $230°C$, contains various hydrocarbons from C_{11} to C_{12}; (d) *gas oil,* boiling point from $230°$ to $405°C$, contains compounds in the C_{13} to C_{25} range; (e) *lubricants,* boiling point from $405°$ to $515°C$, C_{26} to C_{38}, commonly encountered as paraffin wax and petroleum jelly (vaseline). The distillation residues are better known as asphalts.

O-N-S compounds are present in petroleum in minor amounts. The nitrogen and sulfur levels of petroleum are of particular economic importance. Both elements are extremely undesirable because of their detrimental effect on the storage stability of petroleum products, and their poisoning effect on catalysts (in the case of nitrogen). Sulfur develops corrosive acids by oxidation during use of the oil. Some trace elements, e.g., vanadium and nickel, are so highly concentrated in crude oils that in the near future their extraction may perhaps become economically feasible.

(b) *Asphalt and Allied Substances.* Asphaltic constituents represent the dark colored nonhydrocarbon fraction of petroleum and the low oxygen organic compounds of ancient sediments. Aside from carbon, hydrogen and amounts of oxygen which are below 5 per cent, asphaltic constituents consist of nitrogen and sulfur. By definition they fall into the general group of the O-N-S compounds. Their molecular weight may range from a few hundred to a hundred thousand or more (Erdman, 1961, 1964). It is interesting to note that similar to humic substances, differences in molecular weight between asphaltic fractions of a given sediment or crude oil are not reflected in the elemental composition or the infrared characteristics. The series of fractions obtained from one sample by using the ultracentrifuge or by employing solubility tests are chemically closely related.

The majority of the asphaltic bitumens contain substances that are insoluble in low-molecular weight aliphatic hydrocarbons. The insoluble portion is called the asphaltene fraction and the soluble part the malthene fraction. The latter contains both the heavy viscous oil and asphaltic resins.

According to Abraham (1960) and Hunt (1963), bituminous substances can be put into two major classes, those which are soluble (bitumens), and those which are insoluble (pyrobitumens) in carbon disulfide (Fig. 65). The two classes may be further subdivided with respect to their phase relationship, fusibility characteristics and oxygen content. The analytical relationship of the various asphaltic constituents to kerogen, coal, and petroleum is illustrated in Figure 65. Going across the chart from left to right, the carbon hydrogen ratio increases and the solubility decreases. One can recognize the following major asphaltic materials:

Ozocerite is a mineral wax having straight chain paraffins with a few naphthenes. Montan wax is a mixture of high-molecular weight acids and esters. Asphalts are the viscous liquids or low melting bitumens (Bermudez asphalt, tabbyite). When their fusing point is higher than $230°F$, the term asphaltite is commonly used. Gilsonite, glance pitch, and grahamite are three common representative materials. The term pyrobitumens applies to species of bitumens that decompose before melting. One may distinguish between the asphaltic, e.g., wurtzilite, elaterite, albertite, and impsonite, and the nonasphaltic pyrobitumens. Peat, coals, and kerogens belong to the latter class of compounds.

The chemical and structural properties of the various asphaltic constituents have been investigated by Pfeiffer and Saal (1940), Witherspoon (1958), O'Donnel (1951), Nagy and Gagnon (1961), Abraham (1960), Erdman (1961, 1964), Brandes (1956), Hood et al. (1959). Colombo and Sironi (1961), Erdman and Ramsey (1961), Hunt (1963), and others. A structural model of the asphaltene molecule has been offered by Pfeiffer and Saal (1940). This model suggests that asphaltenes are centers of micelles (Fig. 66).

As is the case with the hydrocarbons of the gas and gasoline fraction, asphaltic constituents have never been identified as direct biogenic products; they have also not been isolated from recent sediments. It is inferred that asphalts are a product of slow inorganic maturation, generated in some fashion during diagenesis. Various alternatives have been offered as to the most likely source of asphaltic constituents.

According to Erdman (1961), the evidence for fused ring centers strongly suggests that cellulose may have been a contributor, with the more aliphatic matrix being provided by lignin. N–Heterocycles may be linked to biogenic purines and pyrimidines. Sulfur is assumed to have been supplied later in the process of genesis.

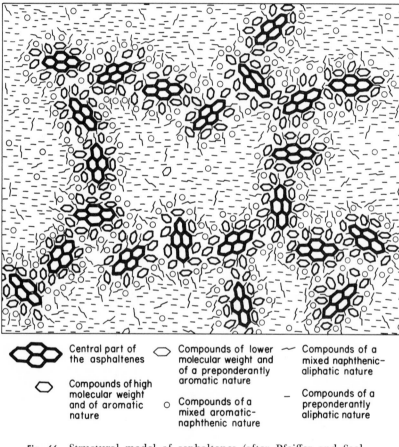

◇◇◇ Central part of the asphaltenes

◇ Compounds of high molecular weight and of aromatic nature

◇ Compounds of lower molecular weight and of a preponderantly aromatic nature

o Compounds of a mixed aromatic-naphthenic nature

⌒ Compounds of a mixed naphthenic-aliphatic nature

– Compounds of a preponderantly aliphatic nature

Fig. 66   Structural model of asphaltenes (after Pfeiffer and Saal, 1940)

Silverman (1964), on the basis of the C^{13}/C^{12} ratio, tentatively concludes that the asphaltenes are polymerization products of unsaturated compounds that developed during the generation of light paraffins from high-molecular weight parent molecules (protopetroleum hypothesis).

According to Pfeiffer and Saal (1940), the asphaltenes consist of high-molecular weight hydrocarbons of predominantly aromatic character with a comparatively low hydrogen content; they were formed by condensation and dehydrogenation of aromatic naphthenic hydrocarbons of lower molecular weight.

One of the important single factors controlling the composition and molecular structure of bitumens seems to be the salinity, as shown by a study of Hunt (1963b). With increase in salinity, the dominant molecular structure of the asphaltic materials changes from paraffin chains to aromatic rings and to chain and ring compounds high in sulfur and nitrogen. In the Uinta bitumens, the sequence ozocerite-albertite-gilsonite — and finally wurtzilite — developed with an increase in salinity.

Weathering is another significant factor for the chemical composition of asphalts. For example, whereas unweathered solid gilsonite contains only traces of oxygen, the same product when weathered yields a few per cent in oxygen. Inasmuch as this enrichment in oxygen is unaccompanied by changes in carbon, hydrogen, nitrogen, and sulfur content, the formation of stable oxygenated compounds rather than increased polymerization may be assumed.

7. MICRO-ORGANISMS

From the previous discussion it is apparent that micro-organisms play a significant part in the alteration and formation of organic matter in natural waters, soils, and sediments of all environments. They also influence to a great extent the chemical environment in terms of pH and Eh conditions. Although micro-organisms undoubtedly are the number one factor which controls the fate of organic matter in the early stages of diagenesis, it is surprising how little is known concerning their occurrence, type of population, distribution, and biochemical activities in various geological materials.

A great number of micro-organisms such as the viruses, actinomycetes, bacteria, or fungi have been found in sediments of the deepest ocean as well as in the soils of the highest mountains. They may live under aerobic or anaerobic conditions, and quite a few can even exist simultaneously in reducing and oxidizing environments. Growth of certain marine bacteria has been observed at temperatures as low as $-7.5°C$, and other forms can develop at temperature between $70°$ and $80°C$.

It is not the purpose of this chapter to illustrate in an extensive way the physiology and chemistry of micro-organisms, nor to present a classification and detailed inventory of all the various forms that have been reported from sediments, soils, natural waters, and even meteorites. The data available at present are too fragmentary and controversial to justify such an attempt. On the other hand, biological information on the various microbial species and populations and their biochemistry and physiology is so plentiful that no reasonable summary can be offered.

One of the difficulties encountered in microbial studies of geological materials is to find and use the best possible aseptic technique in the procurement and handling of samples, in order to minimize the chances of introducing contaminating bacteria from the surrounding environment. Also, the selection of the right media for incubation represents a serious problem, particularly when one is dealing with "ancient" micro-organisms.

There is no doubt that the number of microbes in soils and sediments sharply decreases with depth of burial. For example, the bacterial population in surface sediments of marine environments may amount to 100 million bacteria per gram and more. This would represent approximately 10^{-3} g of organic matter or ~ 1 mg/g of sediment. Sediments at a depth of 50 to 100 cm have considerably lower yields, i.e., a few thousand bacteria per gram of sediment. The interesting question, therefore, arises, of whether micro-organisms disappear altogether at some depth of burial beneath which sterile conditions exist, or whether they are still present in rocks as old as the Pre-Cambrian.

There have been periodic claims in the geological literature of the isolation of viable bacteria from geologic ancient materials such as coal, fossil dung, petroleum, connate waters, sulfur domes, salt deposits, various sediments, igneous rocks, and even meteorites. In many such instances the investigators have stated or implied that the bacteria had survived over the geologic ages involved. This is not the place to review these claims; it is sufficient to point out that the problem of procuring and sampling such materials aseptically is a very difficult one and, in most instances, a critical appraisal of the published work reveals gross inadequacies in the experiments.

In order to assist the interested reader in the evaluation of this problem, a selection of publications is added (Porter, 1946; Oppenheimer, 1961, 1963; Lindblom and Lupton, 1961; Zobell, 1946a,b,

1952, 1964; Baas Becking et al., 1960; Rittenberg, 1940; Rittenberg et al., 1963; Waksman et al., 1933; Sisler, 1961; Emery and Rittenberg, 1952).

It is highly problematical whether one will ever understand all of the microbial activities in sediments. But the fact that the alteration of organic matter in the early stages of diagenesis is largely controlled by the activities of micro-organisms and burrowing animals should stimulate geochemists to learn more about the functions of the living populations within the sediments and their impact on the mineral and organic matter.

Selected References

Abelson, P. H., "Organic Constituents of Fossils." Carneg. Instn. Yearbook, **53** (1954), 97–101.

Abelson, P. H., "Organic Constituents of Fossils." From *Treatise on Marine Ecology and Paleocology*, II, edited by H. S. Ladd. New York: Geol. Soc. Amer., Memoir, **67** (1957), 87–92.

Abelson, P. H., "Geochemistry of Organic Substances." In *Researches in Geochemistry*, edited by P. H. Abelson. New York: John Wiley & Sons, Inc., (1959), 79–103.

Abelson, P. H., T. C. Hoering, and P. L. Parker, "Fatty Acids in Sedimentary Rocks." In *Advances in Organic Geochemistry*, edited by U. Colombo and G. D. Hobson. New York: The Macmillan Company, (1964), 169–174.

Aberhalden, E. and K. Heyns, "Nachweis von Chitin in Flügelresten von Coleopteren des oberen Mitteleocan (Fundstelle Geiseltal)." Biochem. Z., **259** (1933), 320–321.

Abraham, H., *Asphalts and Allied Substances*. Princeton-Toronto-London: D. Van Nostrand Company, Inc., Vol. I (1960); Vol. II (1961); Vol. III (1962); Vol. IV (1962); and Vol. V (1963).

Adams, A. P., W. V. Bartholomew, and F. E. Clark, "Measurement of Nucleic Acid Components in Soil." Proc. Soil Sci. Soc. Amer., **18** (1954), 40–46.

Anderson, G., "Identification of Derivatives of Deoxyribonucleic Acid in Humic Acid." Soil Sci., **86** (1958),169–174.

Anderson, G., "Estimation of Purines and Pyrimidines in Soil Humic Acid." Soil Sci., **91** (1961), 156–161.

Andersen, S. T. and K. Gundersen, "Ether Soluble Pigments in Interglacial Gyttja." Experientia, **11** (1955), 345–348.

Baas Becking, L. G. M., I. R. Kaplan, and D. Moore, "Limits of the Natural Environment in Terms of pH and Oxidation-Reduction Potentials." J. Geol., **68** (1960), 243–284.

Bader, R. G., D. W. Hood, and J. B. Smith, "Recovery of Dissolved Organic Matter in Sea-water and Organic Sorption by Particulate Material." Geochim. et Cosmochim. Acta, **19** (1960), 236–243.

Barghoorn, E. S., "Degradation of Plant Remains in Organic Sediments." Botan. Museum Leaflets, Harvard Univ., **14** (1949), 1–20.

Barghoorn, E. S., "Origin of Life." From *Treatise on Marine Ecology and Paleoecology*, II, edited by H. S. Ladd. New York: Geol. Soc. Amer., Memoir, **67** (1957), 75–86.

Barghoorn, E. S., and W. Spackman, "Geological and Botanical Study of the Brandon Lignite, and its Significance in Coal Petrology." Econ. Geol., **45** (1950), 344–357.

Blumer, M., "Porphyrinfarbstoffe und Porphyrin-Metallkomplexe in schweizerischen Bitumina." Helv. Chim. Acta, **33** (1950), 1627–1637.

Blumer, M., "Benzpyrenes in Soil." Science, **134** (1961), 474–475.

Blumer, M., "The Organic Chemistry of a Fossil—I. The Structure of the Frigelite-pigments." Geochim. et Cosmochim. Acta, **26** (1962a), 225–227.

Blumer, M., "The Organic Chemistry of a Fossil.—II. Some Rare Polynuclear Hydrocarbons." Geochim. et Cosmochim. Acta, **26** (1962b), 228–230.

Blumer, M., and G. S. Omenn, "Fossil Porphyrins: Uncomplexed Chlorins in a Triassic Sediment." Geochim. et Cosmochim. Acta, **25** (1961), 81–90.

Blumer, M., M. M. Mullin, and D. V. Thomas, "Pristane in Zooplankton." Science, **140** (1963), 974.

Bogorov, B. G. "Perspectives in the Study of Seasonal Changes of Plankton and of the Number of Generations at Different Latitudes." In *Perspectives in Marine Biology*, edited by A. A. Buzzati-Traverso. Berkeley, California: University of California Press, 1958.

Bottomley, W. B., "The Isolation from Peat of Certain Nucleic Acid Derivatives." Proc. Roy. Soc. London, **B 90** (1917), 39–44.

Brandes, G., "Die Strukturgruppen von Erdölfraktionen; I. Mitteilung; Die Strukturgruppenanalyse mit Hilfe der Ultrarotspektroskopie." Brennstoff-Chem., **37** (1956), 263–267.

Brauns, F. E., *The Chemistry of Lignin*. New York: Academic Press, Inc., 1952.

Bray, E. E. and E. D. Evans, "Distribution of N-Paraffins as a Clue to Recognition of Source Beds." Geochim. et Cosmochim. Acta, **22** (1961), 2–15.

Breger, I. A., "Diagenesis of Metabolites and a Discussion of the Origin of Petroleum Hydrocarbons." Geochim. et Cosmochim. Acta, **19** (1960), 297–308.

Breger, I. A. and M. Deul, "The Organic Geochemistry of Uranium." U.S. Geol. Survey Prof. Paper, **300** (1956), 505–510.

Breger, I. A., and A. Brown, "Kerogen in the Chattanooga Shale." Science, **137** (1962), 221–224.

Bremner, J. M., "Studies on Soil Organic Matter. Part I. The Chemical Nature of Soil Organic Nitrogen." J. Agric. Sci., **39** (1949), 183–193.

Bremner, J. M., "A Review of Recent Work on Soil Organic Matter." J. Soil Sci., **2** (1951), 67–82.

Bremner, J. M., "Studies on Soil Humic Acids. I. The Chemical Nature of Humic Nitrogen." J. Agric. Sci., **46** (1955), 247–256.

Bremmer, J. M., "Amino Sugars in Soils." J. Sci. Fd. Agric., **9** (1958), 528.

Bremner, J. M., and K. Shaw, "Studies on the Estimation and Decomposition of Amino Sugars in Soil." J. Agric. Sci., **44** (1954), 152–159.

Burkholder, P. R. and L. M. Burkholder, "Microbiological Assay of Vitamin B_{12} in Marine Solids." Science, **123** (1956), 1071–1073.

Cawley, C. M. and J. G. King, "Ester Waxes from British Lignite and Peat." J. Soc. Chem. Ind. London, **1945** (1945), 237–242.

Chibnall, A. C. and S. H. Piper, J. Biochem., **28** (1934), 2008–2019 (quoted by W. G. Meinschein, 1963).

Colombo, U. and G. Sironi, "Geochemical Analysis of Italian Oils and Asphalts." Geochim. et Cosmochim. Acta, **25** (1961), 24–51.

Conway, D. and W. F. Libby, "The Measurement of Very Slow Reaction Rates; Decarboxylation of Alanine." J. Amer. Chem. Soc., **80** (1958), 1077–1084.

Cooper, J. E., "Fatty Acids in Recent and Ancient Sediments and Petroleum Reservoir Waters." Nature, **193** (1962), 744–746.

Coulson, C. B., R. I. Davies, and E. J. A. Khan, "Humic Acid Investigations: 3. Studies on the Chemical Properties of Certain Humic Acid Preparations." Soil Sci., **88** (1959), 191–195.

Cushing, D. H., "On the Nature of Production in the Sea." Fish. Invest. Ser., II, **22** (1959), 1–37.

Day, W. C. and J. G. Erdman, "Ionene: A Thermal Degradation Product of β-Carotene." Science, **141** (1963), 808.

Degens, E. T. and M. Bajor, Die Verteilung von Aminosäuren in bituminösen Sedimenten und ihre Bedeutung für die Kohlen-und Erdölgeologie." Glück-auf, **96** (1960), 1525–1534.

Degens, E. T. and J. M. Hunt, "Thermal Stability of Amino Compounds in Recent and Ancient Sediments, Humic Acids and Kerogen Concentrates." Intern. Meeting on Organic Processes in Geochemistry, Paris, Sept. 28–30, 1964.

Degens, E. T. and J. H. Reuter, "Analytical Techniques in the Field of Organic Geochemistry." In *Advances in Organic Geochemistry*, edited by U. Colombo and G. D. Hobson. New York: The Macmillan Company, (1964), 377–402.

Degens, E. T., J. H. Reuter, and K. N. F. Shaw, "Biochemical Compounds in Offshore California Sediments and Sea Waters." Geochim. et Cosmochim. Acta, **28** (1964), 45–66.

Degens, E. T., K. O. Emery, and J. H. Reuter, "Organic Materials in Recent and Ancient Sediments. Part III. Biochemical Compounds in San Diego Trough, California." N. Jb. Geol. Paläont. Mh. (1963), 231–248.

Degens, E. T., J. M. Hunt, J. H. Reuter, and W. E. Reed, "Data on the Distribution of Amino Acids and Oxygen Isotopes in Petroleum Brine Waters of Various Geologic Ages." Sedimentology, **3** (1964).

Degens, E. T., A. Prashnowsky, K. O. Emery, and J. Pimenta, "Organic Materials in Recent and Ancient Sediments. Part II. Amino Acids in Marine Sediments of Santa Barbara Basin, California." N. Jb. Geol. Paläont. Mh., (1961), 413–426.

Deul, M., "Colloidal Method for Concentration of Carbonaceous Matter from Rocks." Bull. Amer. Assoc. Petrol. Geol., **40** (1956), 909–917.

Dragunov, S. S., "A Comparative Study of Humic Acids from Soils and Peats." Pochvovedenie, **7** (1948).

Droop, M. R., "A Suggested Method for the Assay of Vitamin B_{12} in Sea Water." J. Mar. Biol. Assoc. U. K., **34** (1955), 435–440.

Dunning, H. N., J. W. Moore, and A. T. Myers, "Properties of Porphyrins in Petroleum." Industr. Engng. Chem., **46** (1954), 2000–2007.

Emery, K. O., *The Sea Off Southern California: A Modern Habitat of Petroleum*. New York: John Wiley & Sons, Inc., 1960.

Emery, K. O. and E. E. Bray, "Radiocarbon Dating of California Basin Sediments." Bull. Amer. Assoc. Petrol. Geol., **46** (1962), 1839–1856.

Emery, K. O. and S. C. Rittenberg, "Early Diagenesis of California Basin Sediments in Relation to Origin of Oil." Bull. Amer. Assoc. Petrol. Geol., **36** (1962), 735–806.

Emery, K. O. and D. Hoggan, "Gases in Marine Sediments." Bull. Amer. Assoc. Petrol. Geol., **42** (1958), 2174–2188.

Erdman, J. G., "Some Chemical Aspects of Petroleum Genesis as Related to the Problem of Source Bed Recognition." Geochim. et Cosmochim. Acta, **22** (1961), 16–36.

Erdman, J. G., "Geochemistry of the High Molecular Weight Non-hydrocarbon Fraction of Petroleum." In *Advances in Organic Geochemistry*, edited by U. Colombo and G. D. Hobson. New York: The Macmillan Company, (1964), 215–237.

Erdman, J. G. and V. G. Ramsey, "Rates of Oxidation of Petroleum Asphaltenes and Other Bitumens by Alkaline Permanganate." Geochim. et Cosmochim. Acta, **25** (1961), 175–188.

Flaig, W., "Die Chemie organischer Stoffe im Boden und deren physiologische Wirkung." Verhandl. II and IV. Komm. int. Bodenk. Ges., **2** (1958).

Forsman, J. P. and J. M. Hunt, "Insoluble Organic Matter (Kerogen) in Sedimentary Rocks of Marine Origin." In *Habitat of Oil,* edited by L. G. Weeks. Tulsa, Oklahoma: The American Assoc. Petrol. Geol., 1958a.

Forsman, J. P. and J. M. Hunt, "Insoluble Organic Matter (Kerogen) in Sedimentary Rocks." Geochim. et Cosmochim. Acta, **15** (1958b), 170–182.

Foster, A. B. and J. M. Webber, "Chitin." In *Advances in Carbohydrate Chemistry.* New York-London: Academic Press, Inc., **15** (1960), 371–393.

Fox, D. L., "Carotenoids and Other Lipoid-Soluble Pigments in the Sea and in Deep Marine Mud." Proc. Natl. Acad. Sci. U. S., **23** (1937), 295–301.

Fox, D. L., D. M. Updegraff, and D. G. Novelli, "Carotenoid Pigments in the Ocean Floor." Arch. Biochem., **5** (1944), 1–23.

Francis, W., *Coal, Its Formation and Composition.* London: Edward Arnold (Publishers) Ltd., 1961.

Fuchs, W., *Die Chemie der Kohle.* Berlin: Springer Verlag, 1931.

Gehman, H. M. Jr., "Organic Matter in Limestone." Geochim. et Cosmochim. Acta, **26** (1962), 885–897.

Glimcher, M. J., "Specificity of the Molecular Structure of Organic Matrices in Mineralization." In *Calcification in Biological Systems,* edited by R. F. Sognnaes, Amer. Assoc. Adv. Sci., **64** (1960), 421–487.

Goldberg, E. D., "Marine Geochemistry." Annual Rev. Phys. Chem., **12** (1961), 29–48.

Gothan, W., "Neue Arten der Braunkohlenuntersuchung, IV." Braunkohle, **21** (1922), 400–401.

Goryunova, S. V., "Characterisation of Dissolved Organic Substances in Water of Glubokoe Lake." Trudy Inst. Mikrobiol., Akad. Nauk S.S.S.R., **2** (1952), 166–179 (cited from: Chem. Abstr., **47,** 8293h).

Graveland, D. N. and D. L. Lynch, "Distribution of Uronides and Polysaccharides in the Profiles of a Soil Catena." Soil Sci., **91** (1961), 162–166.

Grégoire, C., "Structure of the Conchiolin Cases of the Prisms in *Mytilus edulis linne.*" J. Biophys. Biochem. Cytol., **9** (1961), 395–400.

Grégoire, C., G. Duchâteau, and M. Florkin, "La Trame Protidique des Nacres et des Perles." Ann. Inst. Ocean., **31** (1955), 1–36.

Greenland, D. J., "The Adsorption of Sugars by Montmorillonite. I. X-ray Studies. II. Chemical Studies." J. Soil. Sci., **7** (1956), 319–334.

Groennings, S., "Quantative Determination of the Porphyrin Aggregate in Petroleum." Analyt. Chem., **25** (1953), 938–941.

Gross, J. and K. A. Piez, "The Nature of Collagen. I. Invertebrate Collagens." In *Calcification in Biological Systems,* edited by R. F. Sognnaes, Amer. Assoc. Adv. Sci., (1960), 395–409.

Hackman, R. H., "Studies on Chitin. III. Adsorption of Proteins to Chitin." Australia J. Biol. Sci., **8** (1955), 530–536.

Hanson, W. E., "Some Chemical Aspects of Petroleum Genesis." In *Researches in Geochemistry,* edited by P. H. Abelson. New York: John Wiley & Sons, Inc., (1959), 104–117.

Hare, P. E., "The Amino Acid Composition of the Organic Matrix of Some Recent and Fossil Shells of Some West Coast Species of *Mytilus.*" Ph.D. Thesis, California Inst. Tech., Div. Geol. Sci., 1962.

Hare, P. E., "Amino Acids in the Proteins from Aragonite and Calcite in the Shells of *Mytilus californianus.*" Science, **139** (1963), 216–217.

Harington, J. S., "Natural Occurrence of Amino Acids in Virgin Crocidolite Asbestos and Banded Ironstone." Science, **138** (1962), 521–522.

Harington, J. S. and J. J. Le R. Cilliers, "A Possible Origin of the Primitive Oils and Amino Acids Isolated from Amphibole Asbestos and Banded Ironstone." Geochim. et Cosmochim Acta, **27** (1963), 412–418.

Hayashi, T. and T. Nagai, "The Components of Soil Humic Acids. 2. The Chromatography of Humic Acids." J. Fac. Agric. Tottori Univ., **2** (1955), 55 (cited: Kononova, M. M., 1961).

Henderson, M. E. K., "Release of Aromatic Compounds from Birch and Spruce Sawdusts during Decomposition by White-rot Fungi." Nature, **175** (1955), 634–635.

Hess, K. and A. Komarewsky, "Über Isolierung und Nachweis von Cellulose in Torf." Z. angew. Chem., **41** (1928), 541–542.

Himus, G. W., "Observations on the Composition of Kerogen Rocks and the Chemical Constitution of Kerogen." In *Oil Shale and Cannel Coal,* London: Institute of Petroleum, **2** (1951).

Himus, G. W. and G. C. Basak, "Analysis of Coals and Carbonaceous Materials Containing High Percentages of Inherent Mineral Matter." Fuel, **28** (1949), 57–65.

Hodgson, G. W. and B. L. Baker, "Vanadium and Nickel Porphyrins in Thermal Geochemistry of Petroleum." Bull. Amer. Assoc. Petrol. Geol., **41** (1951), 2413–2426.

Hodgson, G. W. and B. Hitchon, "Primary Degradation of Chlorophyll under Simulated Petroleum Source Rock Sedimentation Conditions." Bull. Amer. Assoc. Petrol. Geol., **43** (1959), 2481–2492.

Hodgson, G. W., B. Hitchon, R. M. Elofson, B. L.Baker, and E. Peake, "Petroleum Pigments from Recent Fresh-water Sediments." Geochim. et Cosmochim. Acta, **19** (1960), 272–288.

Hood, A., R. J. Clerc, and M. J. O'Neal, "The Molecular Structure of Heavy Petroleum Compounds." J. Inst. Petr., **45** (1959), 168–173.

Hunt, J. M., "Some Observations on Organic Matter in Sediments." Paper presented at the Oil Scientific Session, "25 Years Hungarian Oil," 8–13 October, 1962, Budapest.

Hunt, J. M., "Composition and Origin of the Uinta Basin Bitumens." In *Oil and Gas Possibilities of Utah, Re-evaluated,* Utah, Geol. Miner. Surv. Bull., **54** (1963), 249–273.

Hutchinson, G. E., "Thiamin in Lake Waters and Aquatic Organisms." Arch. Biochem., **2** (1943), 143–150.

Hutchinson, G. E. and J. K. Setlow, "Limnological Studies in Connecticut. VIII. The Niacin Cycle in a Small Inland Lake." Ecology, **27** (1946), 13–22.

Jannasch, H. W., "Ökologische Untersuchungen der planktischen Bakterienflora im Golf von Neapel." Naturwissenschaften, **41** (1954), 42.

Jeffrey, L. M., B. F. Pasby, B. Stevenson, and D. W. Hood, "Lipids of Ocean Water." In *Advances in Organic Geochemistry,* edited by U. Colombo and G. D. Hobson. New York: The Macmillan Company, (1964), 175–197.

Jenkinson, D. S. and Tinsley, J., "A Comparison of the Lignoprotein Isolated from a Mineral Soil and Straw Compost." Int. Symposium on Humic Acids, Proc. Roy. Dublin Soc., (1960), (quoted by Kononova, M. M., 1961).

Johnson, R. C. and R. Thiessen, "Studies on Peat. Alcohol- and Ether-soluble Matter of Certain Peats." Fuel, **13** (1934), 44–47.

Jones, J. D. and J. R. Vallentyne, "Biogeochemistry of Organic Matter—I. Polypeptides and Amino Acids in Fossils and Sediments in Relation to Geothermometry." Geochim. et Cosmochim. Acta, **21** (1960), 1–34.

Keith, M. L. and E. T. Degens, "Geochemical Indicators of Marine and Fresh-water Sediments." In *Researches in Geochemistry,* edited by P. H. Abelson. New York: John Wiley & Sons, Inc., (1959), 38–61.

Khan, D. V., "A Method of Isolating the Insoluble Fraction (Humin) from Podzolic Soils." Dokl. vsesoyuz. Akad. s. -kh. Nauk Lenina, **7-8** (1945), (quoted by Kononova, M. M., 1961).

Khan, D V.., "The Effect of Humic Substances, Mineralogical Composition and Exchangeable Cations on the Formation of Water-stable Aggregates in Chernozem Soils." Pochvovedenie, **4** (1957), 63–70.

Kononova, M. M., "The Humus of the Main Types of Soil of the U.S.S.R. Its Nature and Ways of Formation." Pochvovedenie, **3** (1956), 18–30.

Kononova, M. M., *Soil Organic Matter. Its Nature, its Role in Soil Formation and in Soil Fertility.* Translated from the Russian by T. Z. Nowakowski and G. A. Greenwood. New York-Oxford-London-Paris: Pergamon Press, Inc., 1961.

Krauskopf, K. B., "Sedimentary Deposits of Rare Metals." Econ. Geol. **50**th Anniversary Volume, (1955), 411–463.

Krey, J., "The Balance between Living and Dead Matter in the Oceans." In *Oceanography*, edited by M. Sears. Amer. Assoc. Adv. Sci., **67** (1961), 539–548.

Kroepelin, H., "Some Organic Compounds Extracted from Posidonia Shale." In *Advances in Organic Geochemistry*, edited by U. Colombo and G. D. Hobson. New York: The Macmillan Company, (1964), 165–167.

Lamort, C., "Spectrographic Study of Modification of *a* and *b* Chlorophylls under the Influence of Different Physical and Chemical Agents." Rev. Fermentations et Inds. Aliment., **11** (1956), 84–105 (cited by Hodgson, G. W., et al., 1960).

Lilly, V. G. and L. H. Leonian, "Vitamin B_1 in Soil." Science, **89** (1938), 292.

Lindblom, G. P. and M. D. Lupton, "Microbial Aspects of Organic Geochemistry." Developments in Industrial Microbiology, **2** (1961), 9–22.

Lochte, H. L., "Petroleum Acids and Bases." Ind. Engng. Chem., **44** (1952), 2597–2601.

Lowenstam, H. A., "Biologic Problems Relating to the Composition and Diagenesis of Sediments." In *The Earth Sciences; Problems and Progress in Current Research,* edited by T. W. Donnelly. Chicago: University of Chicago Press (1963), 137–195.

Lynch, D. L., L. M. Wright, and H. O. Olney, "Qualitative and Quantitative Chromatographic Analyses of the Carbohydrate Constituents of the Acid-insoluble Fraction of Soil Organic Matter." Soil Sci., **84** (1957a), 405–411.

Lynch, D. L., L. M. Wright, E. E. Hearns, and L. J. Cotnoir Jr., "Some Factors Affecting the Adsorption of Cellulose Compounds, Pectins, and Hemicellulose Compounds on Clay Minerals." Soil. Sci., **84** (1957b), 113–126.

McLaren, A. D., "Biochemistry and Soil Science." Science, **141** (1963), 1141–1147.

Mehta, N. C., P. Dubach, and H. Deuel, "Carbohydrates in Soil." In *Advances in Carbohydrate Chemistry.* New York-London: Academic Press, **16** (1961), 335–355.

Meinschein, W. G., "Origin of Petroleum." In *Italian Encyclopedia of Petroleum and Natural Gas.* Rome: University of Rome, 1963.

Meinschein, W. G. and G. S. Kenny, "Analyses of Chromatographic Fraction of Organic Extracts of Soils." Analyt. Chem., **29** (1957), 1153–1161.

Morrison, R. I., "The Alkaline Nitrobenzene Oxidation of Soil Organic Matter." J. Soil Sci., 9 (1958), 130–140.

Moss, M. L., ed., "Comparative Biology of Calcified Tissue." Ann. New York Acad. Sci., 109 (1963), 410 pp.

Mulik, J. D. and J. G. Erdman, "Genesis of Hydrocarbons of Low Molecular Weight in Organic-rich Aquatic Systems." Science, 141 (1963), 806–807.

Murchison, D. G. and J. M. Jones, "Resinite in Bituminous Coals." In *Advances in Organic Geochemistry*, edited by U. Colombo and G. D. Hobson. New York: The Macmillan Company, (1964), 49–69.

Nagy, B. and G. C. Gagnon, "The Geochemistry of the Athabásca Petroleum Deposit. I. Elution and Spectroscopic Analysis of the Petroleum from the Vicinity of McMurray, Alberta." Geochim. et Cosmochim. Acta, 23 (1961), 155–185.

Odén, S., "Die Huminsäuren." Kolloidchem. Beihft., 11 (1919), 75.

O'Donnell, G., "Separating Asphalt into its Chemical Constituents." Analyt. Chem., 23 (1951), 894–898.

Oppenheimer, C. H., "Bacterial Activity in Sediments of Shallow Marine Bays." Geochim. et Cosmochim. Acta, 19 (1960), 244–260.

Oppenheimer, C. H. ed., *Symposium on Marine Microbiology.* Springfield, Illinois: Charles C. Thomas, Publisher, 1963.

Orr, W. L. and J. R. Grady, "Determination of Chlorophyll Derivatives in Marine Sediments." Deep-Sea Res., 4 (1957), 263–271.

Orr, W. L., K. O. Emery, and J. R. Grady, "Preservation of Chlorophyll Derivatives in Sediments off Southern California." Bull. Amer. Assoc. Petrol. Geol., 42 (1958), 925–962.

Palacas, J. G., *Geochemistry of Carbohydrates.* Ph.D. Thesis, Univ. Minnesota, 1959.

Paul, E. A. and E. L. Schmidt, "Formation of Free Amino Acids in Rhizosphere and Nonrhizosphere Soil." Proc. Soil Sci. Soc., 25 (1961), 359–362.

Pfeiffer, J. P. and R. N. J. Saal, "Asphaltic Bitumen as a Colloid System." J. Phys. Chem., 44 (1940), 139–149.

Piez, K. A., "Amino Acid Composition of Some Calcified Proteins." Science, 134 (1961), 841–842.

Piez, K. A., "The Amino Acid Chemistry of Some Calcified Tissues." Ann. New York Acad. Sci., 109 (1963), 256–268.

Plunkett, M. A., "The Qualitative Determination of Some Organic Compounds in Marine Sediments." Deep-Sea Research, 5 (1957), 259–262.

Pommer, A. M. and I. A. Breger, "Equivalent Weight of Humic Acid from Peat." Geochim. et Cosmochim. Acta, **20** (1960), 45–50.

Pommer, A. M. and I. A. Breger, "Potentiometric Titration and Equivalent Weight of Humic Acid." Geochim. et Cosmochim. Acta, **20** (1960), 30–44.

Porter, J. R., *Bacterial Chemistry and Physiology*. New York: John Wiley & Sons, Inc., 1946.

Prashnowsky, A. A., E. T. Degens, K. O. Emery, and J. Pimenta. "Organic Materials in Recent and Ancient Sediments. Part I. Sugars in Marine Sediment of Santa Barbara Basin, California." N. Jb. Geol. Paläont., Mh., (1961), 400–413.

Prashnowsky, A. A., "Paläobiogeochemische Untersuchungen an Sedimenten, floristischen und faunistischen Resten verschiedenen Alters." N. Jb. Geol. Paläont. Abh., **118** (1963), 135–158.

Putnam, H. D. and E. L. Schmidt, "Studies on the Free Amino Acid Fraction of Soils." Soil Sci., **87** (1959), 22–27.

Riedel, W. R., H. S. Ladd, J. I. Tracey Jr., and M. N. Bramlette, "Preliminary Drilling Phase of Mohole Project. II. Summary of Coring Operations (Guadalupe Site)." Bull. Amer. Assoc. Petrol. Geol., **45** (1961), 1793–1798.

Rittenberg, S. C., "Bacteriological Analysis of Some Long Cores of Marine Sediments." J. Mar. Res., **3** (1940), 191–201.

Rittenberg, S. C., K. O. Emery, J. Hülsemann, E. T. Degens, R. C. Fay, J. H. Reuter, J. R. Grady, S. H. Richardson, and E. E. Bray, "Biogeochemistry of Sediments in Experimental Mohole." J. Sed. Petr., **33** (1963), 140–172.

Roulet, M. A. and W. H. Schopfer, "Les Vitamines du Sol et leur Signification." Trans. 4th Int. Cong. Soil Sci., **1** (1950), 202–203.

Rossini, F. D., "Hydrocarbons in Petroleum." J. Chem. Educ., **37** (1960), 554–561.

Sakun, N. E., "The Interaction of Humate with the Mineral Part of the Soil." Pochvovedenie, **8** (1942), (cited by Kononova, M. M., 1961).

Sauer, R. W., F. W. Melpolder, and R. A. Brown, "Nitrogen Compounds in Domestic Heating Oil Distillates." Ind. Engng. Chem., **44** (1952), 2606–2609.

Savage, S. M. and F. J. Stevenson, "Behavior of Soil Humic Acids towards Oxidation with Hydrogen Peroxide." Proc. Soil Sci. Soc. Amer., **25** (1961), 35–39.

Schmidt, E. L. and R. L. Starkey, "Soil Microorganisms and Plant Growth Substances. II. Transformation of Certain B-vitamins in Soil." Soil Sci., **71** (1951), 221–231.

Schreiner, O. and E. C. Shorey, "The Isolation of Dihydroxystearic Acid from Soils." J. Amer. Chem. Soc., **30** (1908), 1599–1607.

Schreiner, O. and E. C. Shorey, "Some Acid Constituents of Soil Humus." J. Amer. Chem. Soc., **32** (1910a), 1674–1680.

Schreiner, O. and E. C. Shorey, "Chemical Nature of Soil Organic Matter." Bull. U. S. Dept. Agricult. Bur. Soils, **74** (1910b), 5–48.

Schreiner, O. and E. C. Lathrop, "The Distribution of Organic Constituents in Soils." J. Franklin Inst., **172** (1911), 145–151 (quoted by Vallentyne, J. R., 1957).

Schreiner, O. and E. C. Lathrop, "The Chemistry of Steam Heated Soils." J. Amer. Chem. Soc., **34** (1912), 1242–1259.

Schwendinger, R. B. and J. G. Erdman, "Carotenoids in Sediments as a Function of Environment." Science, **141** (1963), 808–810.

Segura, A., J. M. A. DuLama, S. Pereira, and I. Ribas, Anales real soc. esp. fis. quim., Madrid, **53** (1957), 369 (quoted from: Francis, W., 1961).

Shorey, E. C., "Some Organic Soil Constituents." Bull. U. S. Dept. Agricult. Bur. Soils, **88** (1913), 5–41.

Shorland, F. B., "Occurrence of Fatty Acids with Uneven-numbered Carbon Atoms in Natural Fats." Nature, **174** (1954), 603.

Silliker, J. H. and S. C. Rittenberg, "Studies on the Aerobic Oxidation of Fatty Acids by Bacteria. III. The Effect of 2, 4-dinitrophenol on the Oxidation of Fatty Acids by *Serratia marcescens.*" J. Bact., **64** (1952), 197–205.

Silverman, S., "Investigations of Petroleum Origin and Evolution Mechanisms by Carbon Isotope Studies." In *Isotopic and Cosmic Chemistry,* edited by H. Craig, S. L. Miller and G. J. Wasserburg. Amsterdam: North-Holland Publishing Company, (1964), 92–102.

Sisler, F. D., "Organic Matter and Life in Meteorites." Proc. Lunar Planet. Explor. Coll., **2** (1961), 67–73.

Slowey, J. F., L. M. Jeffrey, and D. W. Hood, "The Fatty-Acid Content of Ocean Water." Geochim. et Cosmochim. Acta, **26** (1962), 607–616.

Smith, H. M., "Composition of United States Crude Oils." Ind. Engng. Chem., **44** (1952), 2577–2585.

Smith, P. V., "Studies on Origin of Petroleum: Occurrence of Hydrocarbons in Recent Sediments." Bull. Amer. Assoc. Petrol. Geol., **38** (1954), 377–404.

Sognnaes, R. F., ed., *Calcification in Biological Systems.* Amer. Assoc. Adv. Sci., **64** (1960), 511 pp.

Sorensen, H., "Studies on the Decomposition of C^{14}-labeled Barley Straw in Soil." Soil Sci., **95** (1963), 45–51.

Staudinger, H. and I. Jurisch, "Über makromolekulare Verbindungen; über den Polymerisationsgrad der Cellulose in Ligniten." Papier-Fabr., (Tech.-Wiss. Teil), **37** (1939), 181–184.

Stevenson, F. J., "Investigations of Aminopolysaccharides in Soils: 2. Distribution of Hexosamines in Some Soil Profiles." Soil Sci., **84** (1957), 99–106.

Stevenson, F. J., "Some Aspects of the Distribution of Biochemicals in Geologic Environments." Geochim. et Cosmochim. Acta, **19** (1961), 261–271.

Swain, F. M., A. Blumentals, and N. Prokopovich, "Bituminous and Other Organic Substances in Precambrian of Minnesota." Bull. Amer. Assoc. Petrol. Geol., **42** (1958), 173–189.

Swain, F. M., "Limnology and Amino-Acid Content of Some Lake Deposits in Minnesota, Montana, Nevada, and Louisiana." Bull. Geol. Soc. Amer., **72** (1961), 519–546.

Takahashi, J., "Marine Kerogen Shales from the Oil Fields of Japan." Sci. Reports Tohoku Imp. Univ., **1** (1935), 63–156.

Tanaka, J. and T. Kuwata, "Higher Fatty Acids in Petroleum." J. Fac. Engng. Tokyo Imp. Univ., **17** (1928), 293–303.

Tanaka, S., H. Hatano, G. Suzue, "Biochemical Studies on Pearl. VII. Fractionation and Terminal Amino Acids of Conchiolin." J. Biochem. Tokyo, **47** (1960), 117–123.

Tatsumoto, M., W. T. Williams, J. M. Prescott, and D. W. Hood, "Amino Acids in Samples of Surface Sea Water." J. Mar. Res., **19** (1961), 89–95.

Theander, O., "Sphagnum Peat. I. Preliminary Studies on the Carbohydrate Constituents." Svensk. Kem. Tidskr., **64** (1952), 197–199.

Theander, O., "Studies on Sphagnum Peat. III. A Quantitative Study on the Carbohydrate Constituents of Sphagnum Mosses and Sphagnum Peat." Acta Chem. Scand., **8** (1954), 989–1000.

Towe, K. H., H. A. Lowenstam, and M. H. Nesson, "Invertebrate Ferritin: Occurrence in Mollusca." Science, **142** (1963), 63–64.

Trask, P. D. and C. C. Wu, "Does Petroleum Form in Sediments at Time of Deposition?" Bull. Amer. Assoc. Petrol. Geol., **14** (1930), 1451–1463.

Treibs, A., "Chlorophyll- und Häminderivate in bituminösen Gesteinen, Erdölen, Erdwachsen und Asphalten. Ein Beitrag zur Entstehung des Erdöls." Liebigs Ann., **510** (1934), 42–62.

Treibs, A., "Chlorophyll- und Häminderivate in organischen Mineralstoffen." Angew. Chem., **49** (1936), 682–686.

Vallentyne, J. R., "Biochemical Limnology." Science, **119** (1954), 605–606.

Vallentyne, J. R., "Biogeochemistry of Organic Matter. II. Thermal Reaction Kinetics and Transformation Products of Amino Compounds." Geochim. et Cosmochim. Acta, **28** (1964), 157–188.

Vallentyne, J. R., "Epiphasic Carotenoids in Post-glacial Lake Sediments." Limn. Oceanogr., **1** (1956), 252–262.

Vallentyne, J. R., "The Molecular Nature of Organic Matter in Lakes and Oceans, with Lesser Reference to Sewage and Terrestrial Soils." J. Fish. Res. Bd. Canada, **14** (1957a), 33–82.

Vallentyne, J. R., "Thermal Degradation of Amino Acids." Carneg. Instn. Yearbook, **56** (1957b), 185–186.

Vallentyne, J. R. and R. G. S. Bidwell, "The Relation between Free Sugars and Sedimentary Chlorophyll in Lake Muds." Ecology, **37** (1956), 495–500.

Vallentyne, J. R. and D. F. Craston, "Sedimentary Chlorophyll Degradation Products in Surface Muds from Connecticut Lakes." Canad. J. Bot., **35** (1957), 35–42.

Van Krevelen, D. W., *Coal. Typology-Chemistry-Physics-Constitution.* Amsterdam-New York: Elsevier Publishing Company, (1961).

Waksman, S. A., C. L. Carey, and H. W. Reuszer, "Marine Bacteria and their Rôle in the Cycle of Life in the Sea." Biol. Bull., **65** (1933), 57–79.

Weeks, L. G., "Habitat of Oil and Factors that Control It." In *Habitat of Oil,* edited by L. G. Weeks. Tulsa, Oklahoma: American Assoc. Petrol. Geol., 1958, 1–61.

Went, F. W., "Organic Matter in the Atmosphere, and its Possible Relation to Petroleum Formation." Proc. Nat. Acad. Sci., **46** (1960), 212–221.

Whitaker, J. R. and J. R. Vallentyne, "On the Occurrence of Free Sugars in Lake Sediment Extracts." Limnol. Oceanogr., **2** (1957), 98–110.

Wilbur, K. M., "Shell Structure and Mineralization in Molluscs." In *Calcification in Biological Systems,* edited by R. F. Sognnaes, Amer. Assoc. Adv. Sci., **64** (1960), 15–40.

Williams, P. M., "Organic Acids in Pacific Ocean Waters." Nature, **189** (1961), 219–220.

Witherspoon, P. A., "Studies on Petroleum with the Ultracentrifuge." Report of Investigation, **206** (1958), Illinois State Geol. Surv.

Wrenshall, C. L. and R. R. McKibbin, "Pasture Studies. XII." Can. J. Research B, **15** (1937), 475.

Wrenshall, C. L. and W. J. Dyer, "Organic Phosphorus in Soils. II. The Nature of the Organic Phosphorus Compounds. A. Nucleic Acid Derivatives. B. Phytin." Soil Sci., **51** (1941), 235–248.

ZoBell, C. E., "Studies on Redox Potential of Marine Sediments." Bull. Amer. Assoc. Petrol. Geol., **30** (1946a), 477–513.

ZoBell, C. E., *Marine Microbiology.* Waltham, Massachusetts: Chronica Botanica Co. (1946b).

ZoBell, C. E., "Bacterial Life at the Bottom of the Philippine Trench." Science, **115** (1952), 507–508.

ZoBell, C. E., "Geochemical Aspects of the Microbial Modification of Carbon Compounds." In *Advances in Organic Geochemistry,* edited by U. Colombo and G. D. Hobson, New York: The Macmillan Company (1964), 330–356.

Zyrin, N. G., "Humin of Soil Organic Matters." Vestn. moskov. Univ., **1** (1948), (cited by: Kononova, M. M., 1961).

General References

Cram, D. J. and G. S. Hammond, *Organic Chemistry.* New York-Toronto-London: McGraw-Hill Book Company, 1959.

Dyke, S. F., *The Carbohydrates.* New York: Interscience Publishers, Inc., 1960.

Hill, M. N., *The Sea; Ideas and Observations on Progress in Study of the Seas.* New York: Interscience Publishers, Inc., Vols. I and II, 1962.

Pigman, W., *The Carbohydrates. Chemistry-Biochemistry-Physiology.* New York: Academic Press, Inc., 1957.

Roberts, J. D. and M. C. Caserio, *Basic Principles of Organic Chemistry.* California Institute of Technology, private publication, 1963.

Rodd, E. H., ed., *Chemistry of Carbon Compounds, a Modern Comprehensive Treatise.* Amsterdam-New York: Elsevier Publishing Company, Vols. 1-5, 1951.

White, A., P. Handler, E. L. Smith, and DeWitt Stetten, *Principles of Biochemistry.* New York-Toronto-London: McGraw-Hill Book Company, 1959.

Distribution of Carbon Isotopes in Organic Materials

The C^{13}/C^{12} ratio in organic carbon may vary by as much as 11 per cent. Factors which may cause this variation have been considered by Wickman (1952), Craig (1953, 1954, 1957), Baertschi (1953), Bowen (1960), Park and Epstein (1961a,b), and others. From these studies it is apparent that photosynthesis has a major influence, either directly or indirectly, on the distribution of carbon isotopes in plants or animals. It is for this reason that the principal steps involved in the photosynthetic fixation of carbon will be briefly considered.

Data by Park and Epstein (1961a,b) on tomato plants grown under controlled conditions indicate that the major fractionation of carbon isotopes during photosynthesis is a two-step process and that both steps favor C^{12}. The first fractionation stage is a kinetic effect which occurs during the uptake of atmospheric CO_2 into the leaf cytoplasm. The degree of fractionation depends on a variety of circumstances; these include phenomena such as the original CO_2 concentration in the atmosphere, the speed of CO_2 absorption or back diffusion by the plant, the CO_2 respiration characteristics of the plant, and the existence or non-existence of a vascular system. The enrichment in C^{12} in the "dissolved CO_2" may be as high as 14 per mil relative to atmospheric CO_2 (Fig. 67).

The second fractionation step in favor of C^{12} takes place during the conversion of "dissolved CO_2" to 3-phosphoglyceric acid (PGA) via the carboxydismutase enzyme. In the tomato plant experiments by Park and Epstein (1961a), the observed fractionation between the bicarbonate and PGA stages amounted to about 17 per mil. Subsequent metabolism of photosynthetic products affects only the isotopic composition of a few minor constituents of the plant. For example, the chloroform-soluble or non-polar lipid fractions show some enrichment in C^{12} over the plant as a whole. As the lipid concentration becomes lower, its C^{12} content will be that much higher when compared to the plant residue, i.e., to the carbohydrates and lignins.

With this model, as proposed by the above mentioned authors, it is possible to explain, for instance, the difference between the C^{13}/C^{12} ratio of atmospheric CO_2 and plants, the difference in the C^{13}/C^{12} ratio between marine plants and land plants, or the carbon isotope variation within the plant kingdom. It is tentatively suggested that the maximum fractionation between CO_2 in the atmosphere and the photosynthetic fixed carbon in terresterial plants may be as high as ~30 per mil. The maximum difference in the C^{13}/C^{12} ratio between the dissolved CO_2 in the sea and marine algae, however, should only amount to ~17 per mil because there is no kinetic stage.

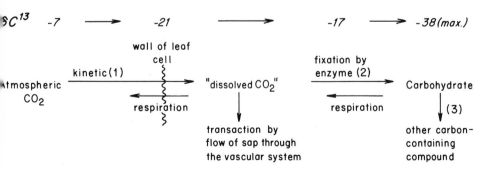

Fig. 67   Model of major carbon isotope fractionation stages during photosynthesis (after Park and Epstein, 1961a, 1961b)

C^{13}/C^{12} ratio ranges of common organic materials are presented in Figure 68. The data are largely obtained from Craig (1953), Eckelman et al. (1962), Silverman and Epstein (1958), Jefferey et al. (1955), Oana and Deevey (1960), Silverman (1962, 1963), and Landergren (1954). Marine organisms are about 10 per mil heavier than land plants. This difference can be largely attributed to the fact that during photosynthesis marine plants utilize carbonate and bicarbonate ions in the sea, whereas land plants thrive on the isotopically lighter CO_2 in the atmosphere. Fossil organic matter, i.e., coal, kerogen, and petroleum are surprisingly uniform in carbon isotope distribution. About 90 per cent of all samples investigated so far fall within the narrow range of 5 per mil. The application of this phenomenon to the petroleum, kerogen, and coal problem will be discussed elsewhere (p. 292 and p. 303).

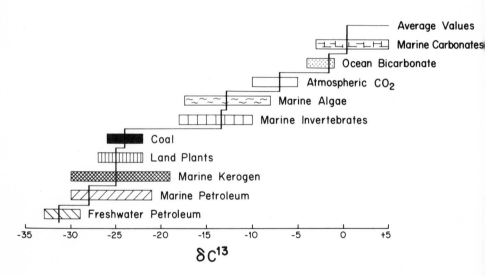

Fig. 68 δC^{13} in various types of organic matter (after Craig, 1953; Wickman, 1952; Silverman and Epstein, 1958; Eckelman et al., 1962; Silverman, 1962, 1963; and others)

Besides stable carbon isotopes, the radioactive carbon isotope C^{14} is widely used in biogeochemical studies. Some details on the geological application of C^{14} methods have previously been presented in the chapter on carbonates.

Selected References

Baertschi, P., "Die Fraktionierung der natürlichen Kohlenstoffisotopen im Kohlendioxydstoffwechsel grüner Pflanzen." Helv. Chim. Acta, **36** (1953), 773–781.

Bowen, H. J. M., "Biological Fractionation of Isotopes." Intl. J. Applied Radiation and Isotopes, **7** (1960), 261–272.

Craig, H., "The Geochemistry of the Stable Carbon Isotopes." Geochim. et Cosmochim. Acta, **3** (1953), 53–92.

Craig H., "Carbon 13 in Plants and the Relationships between Carbon 13 and Carbon 14 Variations in Nature." J. Geol., **62** (1954), 115–149.

Craig, H., "Isotopic Standards for Carbon and Oxygen and Correction Factors for Mass Spectrometric Analysis of Carbon Dioxide." Geochim. et Cosmochim. Acta, **12** (1957), 133–149.

Eckelmann, W. R., W. S. Broecker, D. W. Whitlock, and J. R. Allsup, "Implications of Carbon Isotopic Composition of Total Organic Carbon of Some Recent Sediments and Ancient Oils." Bull. Amer. Assoc. Petrol. Geol., **46** (1962), 699–704.

Jeffery, P. M., W. Compston, D. Greenhalgh, and J. DeLaeter, "On the Carbon-13 Abundance of Limestones and Coals." Geochim. et Cosmochin. Acta, **7** (1955), 255–286.

Landergren, S., "On the Relative Abundance of the Stable Carbon Isotopes in Marine Sediments." Deep Sea Research, **1** (1954), 98–120.

Oana, S. and E. S. Deevey, "Carbon-13 in Lake Waters and Its Possible Bearing on Paleolimnology." Amer. J. Sci., **258-A** (1960), 253–272.

Park, R. and S. Epstein, "Metabolic Fractionation of C^{13} & C^{12} in Plants." Plant Phys., **36** (1961a), 133–138.

Park, R. and S. Epstein, "Carbon Isotope Fractionation During Photosynthesis." Geochim. et Cosmochim. Acta, **21** (1961b), 110–126.

Silverman, S. R., "Investigations of Petroleum Origin and Evolution Mechanisms by Carbon Isotope Studies." In *Isotopic and Cosmic Chemistry*, edited by H. Craig, S. L. Miller, and G. J. Wasserburg. Amsterdam: North-Holland Publishing Company (1964), 92–102.

Silverman, S. R., "Carbon Isotope Geochemistry of Petroleum and Other Natural Organic Materials." Paper presented at the Oil Scientific Session, "25 Years Hungarian Oil," October 8–13, Budapest, 1962.

Silverman, S. R. and S. Epstein, "Carbon Isotopic Compositions of Petroleums and other Sedimentary Organic Materials." Bull. Amer. Assoc. Petrol. Geol., **42** (1958), 988–1012.

Wickman, F. E., "Variations in the Relative Abundance of the Carbon Isotopes in Plants." Geochim. et Cosmochim. Acta, **2** (1952), 243–254.

Geochemical Data and Concepts on the Origin of Organic Matter

1. Primordial "Organic" Matter

Some carbonaceous sediments are known to be 2.5 to 3.5 billion years old. From the present state of knowledge it is reasonable to assume that the very early Pre-Cambrian "organic" matter is a product of inorganic chemical synthesis. The question has frequently been asked what its most likely mode of formation could have been; a number of hypotheses have been proposed. Even more controversial and speculative is the origin and evolution of life following the synthesis of abiotic organic molecules. Recent summaries on this topic can be obtained by reference to Oparin (1957, 1960), Calvin (1961, 1964), Oró (1963a,b), Clark and Synge (1959), Florkin (1960), Horowitz and Miller (1962), Ehrensvärd (1962), and Merrill (1963).

The fundamental problem is concerned with (1) the molecular nature of the inorganic precursor materials, (2) the favorable conditions which would transform these into simple "organic" compounds, (3) the mechanism of the subsequent generation of complex macromolecules of the type presently encountered in living matter, and (4) the final creation of organisms.

Cosmochemical data (Kuiper, 1952, 1953, 1954; Middlehurst and Kuiper, 1963; Kuiper and Middlehurst, 1961; Urey, 1952; Greenstein, 1961; Swings and Haser, 1956; Jastrow and Cameron, 1963; and others) indicate that simple combinations of carbon, nitrogen, oxygen, and hydrogen are important constituents of relatively cool star atmospheres, interstellar space, comets, and cold planetary atmospheres. Based on these observations, a chemical model of the primitive earth atmosphere was proposed in which the atoms of hydrogen, oxygen, carbon, and nitrogen were present in their fully reduced or hydrogenated state (Fig. 69). Geologically, the proposed model receives support from the absence of oxidized sediments, e.g., oxides, hydroxides, and sulfates, prior to about 2 billion years ago. No evidence of such sediments has been found so far. From this it may be inferred that the free oxygen in the earth atmosphere of today has been generated in some fashion within the last 2 billion years.

If one excludes the noble gases, hydrogen is the most abundant element of the universe, followed by oxygen, nitrogen and carbon, which are from four to twenty times more abundant than silicon. One may point out that these are the same four elements of which organic matter is principally composed. In other words, living matter is a more representative sample of the universe than our dead earth (Greenstein, 1961).

Fracturing of bonds can occur following the introduction of various forms of energy such as ultraviolet light, electric discharges, radioactive minerals, or cosmic radiation into a reducing atmospheric system. The resulting high energy intermediates will recombine to intermediate stable forms (Fig. 69). Indeed, experimental studies by a great number of investigators have shown that when ionizing energy and light are introduced into specific atmospheric mixtures of the type that were supposedly present in the primitive earth atmosphere, simple "organic" molecules of biological interest accumulate. Practically all primitive monomeric molecules have been synthesized this

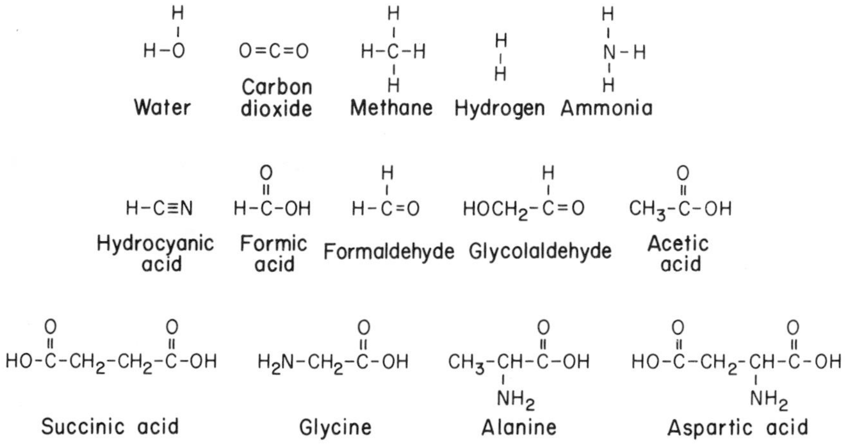

Fig. 69 Primeval and primitive organic molecules (after Calvin, 1964)

way, i.e., amino acids, sugars, and the bases of the purines and pyrimidines that constitute the building blocks of the three essential polymers of living things, namely proteins, polysaccharides, and nucleic acids (Miller and Urey, 1959; Miller, 1953, 1963; Oró, 1963a, 1963b; Oró and Kimball, 1962; Palm and Calvin, 1962; Ponnamperuma et al., 1963a; and others). Even the "energy currency" adenosine triphosphate (ATP) has been formed in a similar fashion (Calvin, 1964; Ponnamperuma et al., 1963b).

The question arises whether polymers necessary for energy and information storage and transfer can be obtained from these monomeric precursors. There is some indication that vinyl polymerization and dehydration condensation function under certain environmental circumstances, and that this gives rise to protein, nucleic acid, and carbohydrate type polymers (Calvin, 1964). The last step will bring us very close to the borderline between the living and nonliving systems. How to cross the borderline and to show the way into the well organized living world still remains a major puzzle and an exciting challenge for future research.

It has often been suggested that the primitive organic molecules of the type formed in the early earth's atmosphere floated down to the primordial ocean (Sagan, 1961). There they dissolved, interaction in the ocean occurred, and macromolecules of biological interest finally developed. From the geochemical point of view, it is more likely that most of the simple organic molecules condensed to humic acid type materials as soon as they entered the oceans. The newly formed organic condensates associated themselves with the suspended detritus (e.g., clay minerals) which in turn acted as an "organic scavenger" of the sea. As a result, the organic matter initially produced in the earth's atmosphere ended up as an organic-inorganic complex in marine sediments. Inasmuch as most clays were derived from the continents, they may have already acquired some abiotic "organic" matter from weathering solutions before entering the ancient sea as detritus.

One may ask now: What is the subsequent fate of the abiotic organic complex throughout the early stages of diagenesis? Some information on the behavior of organic molecules in strongly reducing marine sediments may be obtained by reference to Prashnowsky et al. (1961) and Degens et al. (1961). Upon natural compaction of recent marine sediments, the amount of interstitial water decreases by a factor of 3 between the surface of the sediment and a depth of about

4 meters. During compaction and dehydration of the strata a variety of biochemical constituents can be chromatographically separated along the clay-water interface. Inasmuch as the water movement during consolidation has mostly an upward trend, concentration of relatively pure organic materials can be achieved.

Clay minerals are also known to act as catalysts in the transformation of organic matter. Furthermore, it is noteworthy that in sediments of this type and environment, sulfur and phosphorus are highly abundant, as can be recognized by the presence of sulfides and phosphate nodules. In following Bernal's suggestion (1959), it is assumed that most of the crucial transformations of simple organic molecules into macromolecules of biological interest were accomplished in marine muds rather than in the ocean itself. These sediments not only provided sufficient quantities of the essential elements such as magnesium, iron, sulfur, and phosphorus, but probably also acted as catalyst, collector and purifier of organic compounds. A convenient source for magnesium and iron are, for instance, chlorites; it is interesting to note that during weathering and diagenesis of rock minerals magnesium is rather effectively mobilized. It is conceivable that upon slight compaction clay minerals and other hydrous minerals such as opaline, iron-manganese hydroxides and others can extract water from some of the adsorbed primitive organic molecules and cause the formation of biologically interesting macromolecules such as, proteins, nucleic acids, or polysaccharides. This reaction may well proceed under oxidizing conditions.

Summarizing one can say that a vast number of metabolic substances currently formed by organisms are of the same type that were once synthesized in the primitive earth atmosphere under more favorable environmental circumstances in terms of energy supply and reducing conditions. These favorable conditions no longer exist in the earth atmosphere of today, largely due to the presence of free oxygen and the existence of a protective ozone layer in the upper portions of the atmosphere. The gradual appearance of free oxygen in the earth's atmosphere is largely a result of organic activity, i.e., carbon of CO_2 is fixed by the organisms, while oxygen is released to the hydrosphere and atmosphere. To what extent cosmic radiation can contribute free oxygen from atmospheric water vapor cannot be fully evaluated at present. It is suggestive that simple biogenic (i.e., metabolic products) and abiotic molecules will eventually have humic acid type materials as their common end-product (heteropolycondensates).

Therefore, the structural and chemical differences between "biogenic" and "abiotic" humic acids are probably not too pronounced.

This statement receives some support from studies on the organic matter present in meteorites (Nagy et al., 1961; Kaplan et al., 1963; Degens, 1964). A number of biochemicals show strong resemblance to those found on earth or to those that have been synthesized in reducing atmospheres (Oró, 1963a). They lack, however, optical rotation. Since only biological systems are known to be able to separate and produce the optical isomers responsible for rotation, the absence of rotation in various organic fractions of the meteorites is suggestive of an abiogenic origin of their "organic" matter. In any event, the occurrence of organic matter in meteorites may serve as an indication that the production of organic molecules is a common feature throughout the universe. Whether life could arise on any other planet from preexisting organic matter depends only upon the general physical-chemical conditions established there.

2. PETROLEUM

Interest in the origin of oil has grown as the economic importance of petroleum has increased. Early theories favored an inorganic origin of petroleum, i.e., the formation of hydrocarbons from metallic carbides (Berthelot, 1866, 1870). Although the inorganic concept in a somewhat modernized fashion is still maintained by a few scientists (Hoyle, 1955; Robinson, 1964), geologists no longer accept this viewpoint. Instead, the present consensus is that hydrocarbons occurring in the major petroleum producing areas of the world are ultimately derived from biogenic materials. However, there is a multitude of ideas on the process of hydrocarbon genesis and petroleum accumulation. It is probably only a slight exaggeration to say that each individual connected with the field of petroleum geology has his personal theory on the origin of petroleum.

Most crude oil reservoirs occur in sediments which were deposited under shallow marine or brackish water conditions (near shore environment). In the past, this interrelationship was interpreted to mean that either marine organisms or an oceanic environment, or perhaps both factors, were essential for the formation of hydrocarbons. As more geological details were gathered on the distribution pattern of petroleum in time and space, it became evident that even sediments deposited in isolated fresh water basins and with no connection to older or younger marine deposits (e.g., Green River Formation) were capable of producing hydrocarbons. Thus, the environment in terms of fresh water versus marine was no longer regarded as the crucial factor in the generation of hydrocarbons and the final formation of crude oil.

The scarcity of economically important petroleum reservoirs associated with fresh water sediments was partly attributed to the fact that, as a result of continental weathering and denudation, fresh water sediments have less chance of survival than their contemporaneous marine counterparts. Consequently, the ratio of the total volume of fresh water deposits to the volume of time-equivalent marine sediments decreases progressively with time up to a certain point.

In addition to erosion processes, the structure and the tectonic history of marine and continental basins can differ considerably. This difference has often been used to account for the apparent ease with which petroleum is generated from a rock suite of marine origin and the general lack of crude oil formation in continental sediments. The higher percentage of clays, particularly of montmorillonites, in sediments of marine facies as compared to those deposited in fresh water environments, is a third criterion which has been used to explain the greater abundance of petroleum in marine sediments.

The various sedimentological, petrographical, and tectonic factors that control the distribution of crude oil are now relatively well understood. But there still remains a geochemical "Petroleum Problem." The crux of this problem has to do with the not-yet-settled question how hydrocarbons and the associated organic compounds in petroleum deposits were ultimately generated. The second part of this problem, which is not necessarily of secondary importance, concerns the migration and accumulation phenomena that finally led to the formation of economically important petroleum deposits.

Various theories have been advanced with regard to this two-fold problem. Since Smith (1952, 1954) for the first time isolated C^{14} active hydrocarbons from recent sediments, several outstanding papers appeared on the distribution of hydrocarbons in present day sediments: Hunt and Jamieson (1956); Judson and Murray (1956); Stevens et al. (1957); Meinschein (1959, 1961, 1963); Meinschein and Kenny (1957); Evans et al. (1957); Erdman (1961); Mulik and Erdman (1963); Day and Erdman (1963); Veber and Turkeltaub (1958); Sokolov (1959); Emery and Hoggan (1958); Bray and Evans (1961); Hunt (1962); and Dunton and Hunt (1962).

Before attempting to discuss the theories of individual investigators on the origin of oil, we present a list of criteria which eventually may help elucidate the genesis of petroleum. Any hypothesis of the formation of petroleum can be considered seriously only if it provides a reasonable explanation of the following features and facts:

(1) Formation of light hydrocarbons in the C_3 to C_{14} range which are absent from present day organisms and recent sediments; they occur in ancient sediments and constitute about 50 per cent of the average crude oil.

(2) Greater abundance of hydrocarbons in ancient sediments, when compared to recent sediments of the same lithology.

(3) General chemical similarities between all petroleums independent of their geological age; observed fluctuations in chemistry (ratio of paraffins to napththenes to aromatics) are of the same order of magnitude in crude oils taken from the same formation as they are between formations.

(4) Preference of odd- over even-numbered paraffins (C_{15} and up) in recent and, to a lesser degree, in ancient sediments, in contrast to petroleum paraffins that exhibit no preference.

(5) Formation of hydrocarbons under both fresh water and marine conditions.

(6) C^{12} enrichment in both marine kerogen and crude oil by about 6 to 10 per mil relative to living organisms with no apparent difference between the kerogen and the associated petroleum.

(7) C^{12} enrichment in the light hydrocarbon fractions up to the pentanes, and C^{13} enrichment in the benzenoid hydrocarbon fraction when compared to the δC^{13} of the whole crude oil.

(8) Identification of the biochemical composition of the source materials and simple outline of the pathway of their low temperature transformation to hydrocarbons.

(9) Time and place of hydrocarbon formation.

(10) Oil droplet formation and final accumulation of petroleum.

The first point, i.e., the origin of hydrocarbons of the gas and gasoline fraction, brings us immediately to one of the more controversial aspects of petroleum formation. Most hypotheses on this subject are related to either one of two concepts. The first theory assumes a diagenetic origin, suggesting the alteration of the original constituents, e.g., pigments, peptides, etc., or the transformation (thermal degradation) of finely disseminated kerogeneous materials. The second theory also believes in a diagenetic origin, but a hypothetical high-molecular weight crude oil, or so-called protopetroleum, is regarded as the starting material for the light hydrocarbons.

In the case of the first hypothesis, a low temperature thermal degradation of biochemical material such as isoprenes, polyunsaturated fatty acids, or amino acids, has been suggested (Erdman, 1961; Mulik and Erdman, 1963; Day and Erdman, 1963; Hunt, 1962; Abelson and Hoering, 1963). Low-molecular weight hydrocarbons may also be generated during the thermal degradation of the insoluble organic matter which in all probability contains hydrocarbon functions and some of the biochemical materials mentioned above. This reaction would take place within the source sediment; it may be catalytically influenced by the presence of clay minerals.

It was pointed out that by decarboxylation and reductive deamination amino acids could be converted into hydrocarbons (Hanson, 1959). Among the common amino acids there is a structure corresponding to every paraffinic hydrocarbon up through the pentanes. With regard to the formation of low-molecular weight aromatic compounds, certain constituents such as the carotenoids or aromatic amino acids (e.g., phenylalanine or tyrosine), could serve as a potential source material. As a matter of fact, thermal decomposition of β-carotene and phenylalanine-montmorillonite complexes will yield considerable quantities of a number of benzenoid hydrocarbons characteristic of crude oils, i.e., benzene, toluene, and xylene. Traces of these benzenoid hydrocarbons have been found by Emery and Hoggan (1958) in offshore sediments of California; they occur also in measurable quantities in most ancient sedimentary rocks. It is noteworthy that the concentration of aromatic amino acids in recent sediments can amount up to 300 ppm, which is equivalent to about 1 per cent of the total organic matter. The hypothesis therefore implies that the diagenetic transformation of former biochemical materials that have come to rest in sediments in a free or condensed form, is accomplished by simple chemical reactions such as decarboxylation, deamination, or elimination of alkyl groups. No concentration of high-molecular weight constituents in the form of a protopetroleum prior to the light hydrocarbon generation is required.

Protopetroleum formation, however, is the basic concept of the second hypothesis. Protopetroleum is regarded as an organic extract obtained from the organic debris embedded in the sediments. It is assumed to be a complex mixture of high-molecular weight organic compounds and, as such, only a petroleum precursor, inasmuch as petroleum is made up of about 50 per cent of light hydrocarbons. (Brooks, 1952; Frost, 1945; Dobryanskii, 1961; Bogomolov et al., 1960; Bogomolov and Panina, 1960; Andreev et al., 1958). Accordingly, the generation of the gas and gasoline fraction is largely accomplished after migration by thermal decomposition of the heavy hydrocarbons. The inference is that petroleum and its precursor concentrate is a dynamic mixture of chemical constituents that are subject to change throughout its post-depositional history.

The hypothesis receives its greatest support from carbon isotope studies of various crude oil fractions (Silverman, 1962, 1963ab; Silverman and Epstein, 1958). C^{13}/C^{12} ratios of narrow distillation cuts of liquid petroleum show systematic internal variations (Fig. 70), which suggest that the light hydrocarbons owe their existence to the decomposition of the associated, more complex, heavy hydrocarbons.

Both hypotheses agree insofar as the formation of light hydrocarbons is a result of thermal degradation of a more complex organic substance; this transformation is most likely catalyzed by clay min-

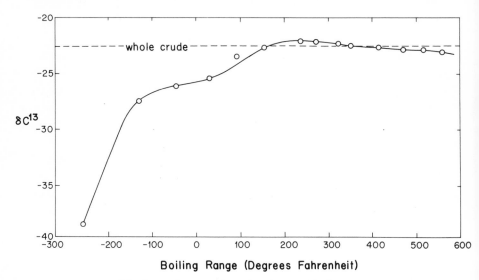

Boiling Range (Degrees Fahrenheit)

Fig. 70 δC^{13} of petroleum and gas fractions (after Silverman, 1964)

erals. It is further agreed that the organic matter of one sediment can produce all the light constituents of one crude oil during diagenesis. Disagreement is introduced with respect to the type of precursor molecules and the time and the place of the final transformation.

It was just stated that the second hypothesis receives its strongest support from the carbon isotope pattern of narrow distillation fractions of crude oils. Two major differences can be recognized; that is, the enrichment in C^{12} in the hydrocarbons up through the pentane, and the enrichment in C^{13} in the aromatic constituents when compared to the C^{13}/C^{12} ratio of the crude oil as a whole. The first hypothesis, on the other hand, points out that only hydrocarbons up through the pentanes and the benzenoid types may be obtained from the original amino acids. It is not fully understood whether this comparison between the two hypotheses has any significance at all or whether the correspondence is just fortuitous.

In this connection, a study by Abelson and Hoering (1961) on the carbon isotope fractionation between various biochemicals may be revealing. The authors observed that decarboxylation of amino acids results in a significant C^{12} enrichment of the remaining amine. For example, the carbon of the carboxyl groups of aspartic and glutamic acid is always markedly heavier (10 to 20 per mil) than the rest of these molecules. Other amino acids, for example leucine, show smaller differences, but independent of the type of organisms investigated, the carboxyl groups are found to be consistently heavier than the corresponding amine. Consequently, a light hydrocarbon generated from an amine will be enriched in C^{12} too. No studies have been undertaken on the carbon isotope relationship between the carbon in the aromatic ring and that in the aliphatic side chain of an aromatic amino acid, in order to discover whether the C^{13} enrichment in the benzenoid hydrocarbons may perhaps be accounted for in a similar fashion.

Inasmuch as the first hypothesis does not completely rule out a thermal degradation of high molecular weight hydrocarbons of the type present in crude oils or sediments, the differences between the two hypotheses become narrower. By taking all sources of information into consideration, it appears that the observed C^{12} pattern in the case of the light hydrocarbons can be interpreted as the result of mixing a number of hydrocarbons generated from various organic precursors — for example, the heavy crude oil fraction, amino acids, alkyl groups in kerogen, and others. In the case of methane which exhibits the strongest enrichment in C^{12} up to 20 permil, the contribution of biogenic sources (i.e., microbial activity) cannot be fully excluded. Bacterially produced methane is lower in δC^{13} than that of the original organic matter by as much as 75 permil (Rosenfeld and Silverman, 1959).

On the basis of the presence and similarity of hydrocarbons in the C_{15} to C_{30} range found in plant and animal materials, recent sediments, and petroleum, some writers (Smith, 1954; Baker, 1950; Meinschein, 1959, 1961) concluded that all have the same origin and are biogenic in nature, i.e., they were synthesized by the original living matter. According to this hypothesis, chemical conversions of organic matter to petroleum or significant changes in petroleum composition, do not occur during the postdepositional history of petroleum. No information is presented on the origin of the gas and gasoline fraction.

According to Vassoevich (1955) and Krejci-Graf (1960), higher organized living matter contains only small amounts of hydrocarbons (a few ppm). However, planktonic forms and micro-organisms may incorporate up to a few thousand ppm. Since both plankton and micro-organisms contribute in one way or another to the organic matter of recent sediments, hydrocarbons found there may well have been obtained overwhelmingly from these sources.

Analyses of numerous recent sediments indicate that molecules with odd numbers of carbon atoms predominate in the heavy normal paraffins in sediments of all environments (Bray and Evans, 1961). The predominance of odd-numbered hydrocarbons over those with even-numbered chains may indicate a metabolic process in which a β-keto acid has been decarboxylated and the resulting ketone has been reduced. Ancient sediments exhibit a smaller ratio of odd-to-even carbon number n-paraffins, and petroleums show no preference at all (Fig. 71). The odd-even pattern may find its interpretation by means of the data of Hunt (1961) and Jamieson and Hunt (1956) on the distribution of hydrocarbons in sediments of all ages. Ancient shales of nonpetroleum producing areas have an average hydrocarbon content of ~ 300 ppm which is about five to ten times higher than that observed in recent sediments of the same lithology. Since it is extremely unlikely that former organisms produced more hydrocarbons during their life cycle than the present forms, an increase in hydrocarbons during geologic time (recent versus ancient) can only mean that

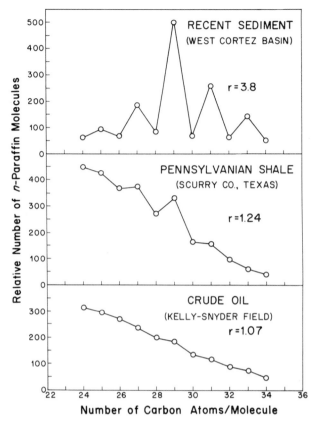

Fig. 71   *n*-Paraffin distributions for a recent sediment, a Pennsylvanian marine shale, and a Pennsylvanian crude oil; r = odd — to
even-carbon-number ratio (after Bray and Evans, 1961)

petroleum-like hydrocarbons were generated in situ from the residual
organic matter. Migration from the outside into the sediment is
also possible, but only in oil producing areas. Both processes would
dilute the original biogenic hydrocarbon mixture, and change the
distribution to give the small odd-to-even carbon number ratios observed (Fig. 71). The relationship that exists between odd-to-even
carbon number fatty acids and n-paraffins has already been presented (p. 236).

Because biogenic hydrocarbons cannot be considered as the sole
and dominant source for the hydrocarbons presently found in petroleums, one has to look for other precursor constituents as well. For
structural and chemical reasons, lipid constituents are generally con-

sidered the most likely precursor materials for the heavy hydrocarbons (Breger, 1960). According to Breger, biologic degradation and associated Diels-Alder reactions may convert fatty acids and related substances into straight-chain compounds with both odd- and even-numbers of carbon, to alicyclic compounds and even, upon dehydrogenation, into aromatic substances. Many more reaction schemes have been presented (Hanson, 1959; Erdman, 1961), all of which stress the importance of lipid materials as a feasible precursor of some petroleum hydrocarbons.

Studies on the carbon isotope distribution of various plant materials have indicated that in all cases the lipid fraction is enriched in C^{12}, compared to the whole plant, by as much as 10 per mil (Park and Epstein, 1960, 1961; Abelson and Hoering, 1961; Silverman and Epstein, 1959; Park and Dunning, 1961). This phenomenon was used by some investigators to explain the 10 per mil differences that exist between present day marine plant materials and crude oils. The theory is that the hydrocarbons we presently encounter in crude oils were generated only by the lipid fraction, i.e., the C^{12} enriched compounds. However, in view of the fact that crude oils and their associated marine kerogens never differ by more than 2 to 3 per mil and generally agree within 1 per mil (Eckelman et al., 1962; Krejci-Graf and Wickman, 1960), one must assume that either the lipid fraction produces both kerogen and oil and that the other biochemicals are diagenetically eliminated, or that other processes are responsible for this phenomenon. It has been shown earlier (p. 253) that kerogen is by no means a sole condensation product of lipids. Lipids are only a small part of the kerogen molecule. Eckelman et al. (1962) and Degens et al. (1963) assume large contributions of continental source materials to the marine environment of deposition to account at least in part for the C^{12} enrichment of marine kerogens and oils. That the limited number of fresh-water oils examined by Silverman and Epstein from the unusual Green River Formation are enriched in C^{12} by as much as 6 per mil over the average marine petroleum does not necessarily mean that all fresh-water oils are so light. It should be pointed out that the total organic matter of Green River shale is not different by more than 0.2 per mil from the oil nearby (Silverman and Epstein, 1958).

It is tentatively suggested that both terrestrial and marine organisms may directly or indirectly contribute to the organic matter of marine sediments. Microbial activity and inorganic maturation processes will alter the organic debris to such an extent that some bio-chemicals are eliminated whereas others are chemically or structur-ally modified. Although the original organic sources will frequently determine the C^{13}/C^{12} ratio of the final products, chemical transforma-tions may also produce isotope fractionation such as are observed dur-ing the decarboxylation of amino acids (Abelson and Hoering, 1961). Therefore, carbon isotope data of petroleum and organic matter have to be used rather cautiously for any interpretation regarding source, environment, or chemical transformation mechanisms.

There is some indication that geologically older oils tend to be more paraffinic than younger oils (Barton, 1934; McNab et al., 1952), and that with increasing depth of burial lighter paraffinic oils are ob-tained (McIver et al., 1963); but no crucial chemical difference has been established between the average petroleum of one formation as compared to the average oil of another formation. The processes re-sponsible for the genesis of oil must therefore have been constant for at least the last 600 million years. Since most organic matter undergoes microbial alteration in one way or another, the type of the original biological starting material seems to be relatively unimportant, as long as biochemical material is supplied to the environment of deposi-tion in sufficient quantities and in a form in which it can be utilized efficiently by the microbial population within the sediment.

At the beginning of this chapter it was pointed out that the crux of the petroleum problem centers on two phenomena: (1) the hydro-carbon genesis and (2) the hydrocarbon migration and accumulation. So far, the discussion has been focussed on the hydrocarbon genesis. Unfortunately, the data on migration phenomena are even more controversial, and no simple solution can be offered. Therefore, only a tentative model is outlined below, bearing on this problem.

Ancient sediments of all environments yield considerable quan-tities of hydrocarbons. Hunt (1961) and Jamieson and Hunt (1956) have estimated that hydrocarbons of all nonreservoir sediments of the world would produce more than 100 times as much petroleum as is estimated by Weeks (1958) to represent the world's crude oil re-serves. It is only necessary to extract small quantities of sediment hydrocarbons (though over a large area) to form petroleum pools. One may then assume, following Baker's theory (1961), that during compaction and dehydration hydrocarbons are extracted from a sedi-ment only in those quantities which are soluble in the interstitial aqueous solution. The final hydrocarbon yield will depend on the temperature, salt concentration and other chemical parameters of the water. As a general rule, increase in molecular weight will decrease the solubility of hydrocarbons in aqueous solutions; an increase in salt concentration will increase their solubility. Marine-derived formation waters are known to produce salinities up to 30 per cent as a result of ion-filtration along charged-net clay membranes (p. 191). The solubility of free hydrocarbons and related substances will naturally be affected by these processes. Oil droplet formation may be the consequence of chemical changes occurring during the migration of the formation waters through the strata. It is also conceivable that during the transition from shales to more porous sediments, i.e., sandstones and limestones or vice versa, formation waters release their hydrocarbons (Vassoevich, 1958).

The basis of this hypothesis is the high salinity of interstitial waters which promotes preferential extraction of hydrocarbons and related substances from the sediments (e.g., asphalts), and the formation of supersaturated solutions by ion-filtration along charged-net clay membranes. Under these circumstances, brines are no longer capable of holding an organic phase in solution (Degens et al., 1964a). The transition from subcapillary to capillary to supercapillary pores may also have some influence on the final oil droplet formation.

The general lack of petroleum reservoirs in closed fresh water basins can now be explained. Interstitial waters in fresh water sediments have salinities of only a few hundred ppm compared to 35,000 ppm in marine sediments. These low salinities are not sufficient to extract significant amounts of petroleum-like materials from fresh water sediments during their compaction. Moreover, ion-filtration along clay membranes cannot produce brines with salinities of the same order of magnitude as those found under marine conditions. Consequently, oil droplet formation cannot take place. Fresh water sediments will only produce petroleum in evaporation environments such as are found, for example, in the Green River Formation, and where the interstitial waters are saline. Whether they can build up extensive petroleum reservoirs depends on the size of the lake, the rate of sedimentation and the consistence of the evaporation conditions during geological time. Facies changes (fresh water — brine water — fresh water — , etc.) will mostly produce only patches of petroleum-like materials, but no extensive oil pools, because mixing of saline and fresh water will occur during compaction of the strata.

Our knowledge both of hydrocarbon genesis and of the processes

responsible for their final accumulation is still incomplete. The outlined ideas should only be regarded as a first step towards an understanding of the origin of petroleum.

3. COAL

Judging from the great number of excellent textbooks of recent
vintage in the field of coal geology and chemistry (Van Krevelen,
1961; Van Krevelen and Schuyer, 1957; Francis, 1961; Bangham,
1950; and Tomkeieff, 1954), the subject is a matter of lively concern
both under a scientific and an economic aspect. The geochemistry
and genesis of coal are also discussed by Breger (1959) and M. and
R. Teichmüller (1962, 1964).

Coal is a product of former plant debris that has undergone physical and chemical alteration throughout geological history. In the
majority of the cases, land-derived plants are precursors of coal. The
factors which cause coal formation are quite numerous; most significant in the early stages of coalification, i.e., during the humic
acid and peat stage, are microbial activities and the redox potential
in the environment of formation. Following the biochemical stage,
which results in the formation of peat deposits, slow inorganic maturation processes will eventually lead to brown coal, lignite, bituminous coal, and anthracite, respectively.

Coals are generally classified according to their rank which, in
a broad sense, is a measure of the proportions of carbon in a series
of coals. As carbon increases the rank of the coal becomes higher,
and the further the coal is removed from the composition of the
original plant material. Also the macerals which are the basic microscopic constituents of coals ("coal minerals") are helpful in petro-
logically classifying the coals. Some of the more important macerals
are vitrinite, exinite and the various forms of inertinite (Francis, 1961;
Van Krevelen, 1961).

Changes in the element composition that occur during coalification are presented in Figure 72. With increase in carbon content,
the level of oxygen drops sharply, whereas the hydrogen concentration is reduced only in the case of anthracite. Nitrogen shows a slight
increase towards the bituminous coal stage, to fall back again to the
original value in the anthracite. Inasmuch as most of the elemental
changes concern carbon and oxygen (with the latter element linked
to the periphery of the coal molecule, i.e., to hydroxyl, carboxyl,

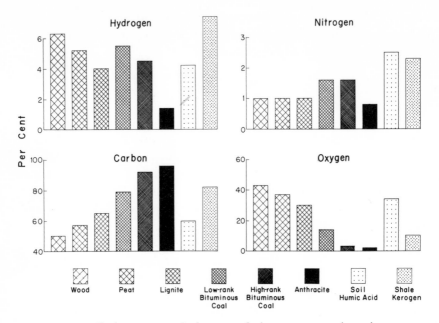

Fig. 72   Carbon, oxygen, hydrogen, and nitrogen content in various coals, humic acids and kerogens (after Khan, 1945; Kononova, 1961; Forsman and Hunt, 1958a, 1958b; Francis, 1961; and Zyrin, 1948)

and carbonyl functions), a study of the functional groups appears to be rewarding. This type of approach will also assist in outlining a structural model of coals.

Hydroxyl groups are predominantly phenolic in character; there is little evidence for alcoholic or weakly acidic hydroxyl groups (Blom et al., 1957; Friedman et al., 1961; Van Krevelen, 1961). Brown coals may contain up to 9 per cent hydroxyl oxygen, a value which is approximately maintained up to 80 per cent carbon content. Beyond that point hydroxyl oxygen rapidly decreases to less than 1 per cent at 90 per cent carbon.

Carboxyl groups are absent from bituminous and anthracite coals but represent a significant fraction in brown coals and lignites where they amount to about 5 per cent (Fuchs and Stengel, 1921; Blom et al., 1957; Van Krevelen, 1961).

Methoxyl groups are encountered only in small quantities and decrease from about 1 to 2 per cent at 65 per cent carbon down to 0.2 per cent at 80 per cent carbon.

Carbonyl groups are present in all types of coals and reach values of about 3 to 4 per cent in brown coals and fluctuate around 0.5 per cent at 83 per cent carbon and higher. Although various possibilities have been mentioned to account for the presence of carbonyl groups, it is most likely that the carbonyl groups are part of ortho-quinone systems.

In view of the fact that the sum of the above mentioned oxygen groups about equals the total oxygen content in the 70 to 90 per cent carbon range (Blom et al., 1957), it is doubtful whether any unreactive oxygen is structurally incorporated. At carbon contents over 92 per cent practically all oxygen is present in nonreactive and stable configurations. Data on oxygen functions are summarized in Figure 73.

Little is known with certainty of the nitrogen and sulfur functions in coal. Most investigators tentatively assume heterocyclic ring systems for nitrogen, and a small number of heterocyclic compounds have been isolated (e.g., nicotinic acid). Wnekowska (1959) concludes that thioether and thiophenic groups account for the organic sulfur in coals.

The bulk of the carbon is organized in aromatic nuclei which contain an average of up to three fused rings. Most frequently encountered are benzene, naphthalene, diphenyl, and phenanthrene, or their multiples (Francis, 1961). A substantial fraction of the non-aromatic carbon is arranged in hydroaromatic rings (Given, 1962, 1964).

Any one molecule of coal could theoretically contain a few or all of the listed constituents in different combinations and geometric arrangements. This could result in an array of different coals. However, inasmuch as coals are constructed from the same few building blocks, coals from all over the

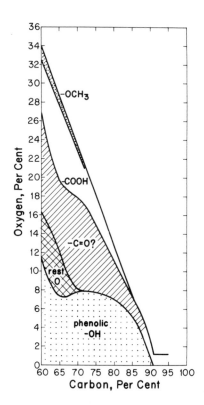

Fig. 73 Functional groups of oxygen in various coals (Krevelen, 1961; Blom et al., 1957)

world exhibit similar chemical characteristics. The suggested structure of a typical molecule of vitrinite (82% C) is presented in Figure 74.

Coal scientists agree that humic acids or humins represent the first stage in the alteration of peat towards coal. They further agree that microbial activity is largely responsible for the formation of humic acids. There is, however, still the lignin-cellulose controversy which concerns the ultimate source of the humic acid material and the intermediate reaction products. Currently the most widely accepted theory is that, although lignin is probably the major progenitor of coal or humic acid, respectively, other biochemicals such as cellulose and protein degradation products can contribute. The ratio of aliphatic to aromatic constituents in humic acids may depend on parameters such as the chemical nature of the original precursor material, the type of environment, and the metabolic pathway of the microorganisms. If, for example, wood is the only starting material, as is the case for most coals, the resulting humic acids may contain more aromatic nuclei; on the other hand, if plant or animal proteins and lipids are the major precursors, the corresponding humic acids may have a more aliphatic character.

During the subsequent stages of coalification, overburden pressure will result in the compaction and dehydration of peat, brown coal, and lignite. An increase in temperature (geothermal gradient),

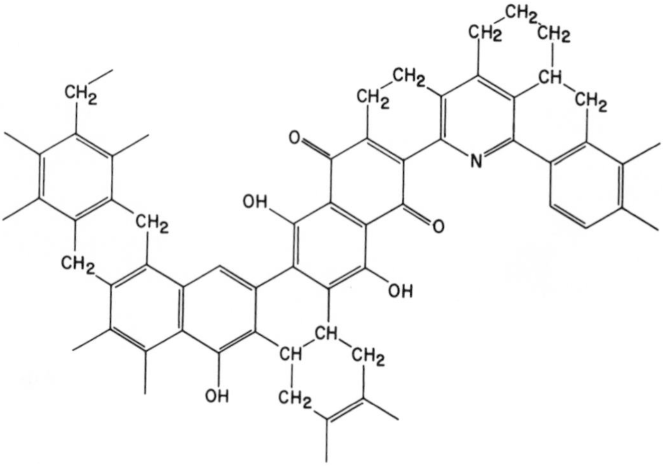

Fig. 74 Hypothetical segment of a typical molecule in a bituminous coal (after Given, 1962, 1964)

however, is the major factor in the chemical and structural alteration from peat towards anthracite (Teichmüller, M. and R., 1954, 1964; Teichmüller, 1962; Dulhunty, 1954; Huck and Karwell, 1955; Dryden, 1956; Van Krevelen and Schuyer, 1957). It is noteworthy that an increase in overburden pressure appears to slow down the reactions.

Carbon isotope studies indicate that there is no correlation between isotopic composition, degree of coalification, and geologic age of the coals. Coals of all formations show a similar isotopic composition of about -25 per mil relative to the PDB I Belemnite Standard (Craig, 1953, 1957; Wickman, 1952). It appears, therefore, reasonable to assume that no isotopic fractionation occurs during diagenesis, and that the former land plants had essentially the same isotopic composition as modern wood specimens.

In the past, considerable attention has also been given to the trace element constituents of coals. Compared to the average rock, coal can become enriched in some elements such as germanium by a factor of 100 and more. In view of the tremendous tonnage of coal mined annually, and of the concentration factor in reducing coal to ash, it is understandable that some coal ashes can provide an important source for certain trace elements. A review on this subject has been presented by Breger (1958) and Leutwein and Roessler (1954, 1955).

It was previously stated that aside from coal, kerogen also has a humic acid precursor. The question therefore arises whether kerogen is simply a finely disseminated coal, or whether its chemistry and structure differ in certain respects from those of coal. No definite answer can be offered at present for the following reason.

Coal research has been going on since the middle of the last century, and a vast amount of excellent data has accumulated. In contrast, kerogen studies have just started, and consequently the information is limited. However, from the few available data, it appears that marine kerogen has a more aliphatic character than bituminous coals of the same concentration of carbon. This feature is to some degree reflected in the nitrogen and hydrogen values which are higher in kerogen by a factor of two or three when compared to coals of the "same" rank (Fig. 72). It is tentatively concluded that the kerogen molecule contains a higher percentage of hydrocarbon (e.g., alkyl functions) and amino groups. There is also an indication that carboxyl groups, which are absent from true coals, are incorporated in marine kerogens. The presence of phenol and quinone type materials in kerogen suggests that the nuclei of the coal and kerogen molecules are similar.

Differences that in all probability exist between coal and kerogen can be a result of a number of parameters. During soil formation low-molecular weight humic acids interact more effectively with clay minerals than the high-molecular weight acids. In addition, the more soluble humic acids are preferentially carried from the soil environment to the basin of deposition. The others, staying behind, will produce humin materials. It can be inferred that the less soluble and more aromatic fraction remains on the continent and may yield coal when sufficiently concentrated. In contrast, the more aliphatic portion will be carried to the sea either in solution or via clay minerals and may produce kerogen. Another source for kerogen is the marine organic debris which is highly enriched in proteins and lipids. The resulting humic acid, as produced by the microbial population in the marine sediment, is also expected to have a more aliphatic than aromatic character. Due to the close relation with the surrounding clay minerals, organic-inorganic interactions will take place so that chemical alteration of the organic residue can be expected. One may speculate that these differences between terrestrial and marine organic residues are partially responsible for the fact that the generation of hydrocarbons proceeds predominantly under marine conditions. But additional factors have been listed (p. 288) to account for this phenomenon.

In summary, it is concluded that the formation of fossil organic matter is accomplished by a three-step process:

(1) The microbial and chemical (e.g., hydrolysis) destruction of former biochemical macromolecules such as carbohydrates, proteins or lipids in the early stages of diagenesis.

(2) The condensation of metabolic and hydrolysis products, resulting in the formation of "heteropolycondensates" (humic materials).

(3) The slow inorganic maturation of the heteropolycondensates (e.g., loss in functional groups), with thermal degradation being the number one alteration factor.

Thus, given sufficient time, all fossil organic matter is eventually reduced either to aromatic condensates resembling graphite, or to light paraffinic hydrocarbons — in particular, methane. An illustration of the main path of diagenesis or "metamorphism" of the principal organic constituents is presented in Figure 75, using O/C and H/C ratios as a convenient plot scheme.

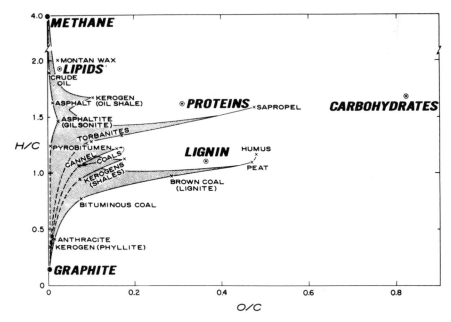

Fig. 75   Metamorphism of Organic Sediments. O/C and H/C ratios in principal biochemical and biogeochemical compounds (after Hunt, 1965).

Selected References

1. *Primordial Organic Matter*

Bernal, J. D., "The Problem of Stages in Biopoesis." In *The Origin of Life on the Earth,* Proc. First Int. Symp. Moscow, 19–24 August, 1957, eds. F. Clark and R. L. M. Synge. New York-London-Paris-Los Angeles: Pergamon Press, Inc. (1959), 38–53.

Calvin, M., *Chemical Evolution. I. From Molecule to Microbe. II. The Origin of Life on Earth and Elsewhere.* Condon Lectures, Oregon State System of Higher Education. Eugene, Oregon: University of Oregon Press, (1961), 42 pp.

Calvin, M., Chemical Evolution (preprint 1964).

Clark, F. and R. L. M. Synge, eds., *The Origin of Life on the Earth.* Proc. First Int. Symp. Moscow, 19–24 August 1957, New York-London-Paris-Los Angeles: Pergamon Press, Inc. (English-French-German Edition), 1959.

Degens, E. T., A. Prashnowsky, K. O. Emery, and J. Pimenta, "Organic Materials in Recent and Ancient Sediments, Part II. Amino Acids in Marine Sediments of Santa Barbara Basin, California." N. Jb. Geol. Paläont. Mh., (1961), 413–426.

Degens, E. T., "Genetic Relationships between the Organic Matter in Meteorites and Sediments." Nature, **202**, (1964) 1092–1995.

Ehrensvärd, G. C. H., *Life: Origin and Development.* Chicago: University of Chicago Press, 1962.

Florkin, M., ed., *Aspects of the Origin of Life.* New York-Oxford: Pergamon Press, Inc., 1960.

Greenstein, J. L., "Stellar Evolution and the Origin of the Chemical Elements." Amer. Scientist, **49** (1961), 449–473.

Horowitz, N. H. and S. L. Miller, "Modern Concepts of the Origin of Life." Fort. Chem. Org. Naturst., **20** (1962), 423–459.

Hunt, J. M., "Organic Sediments." *Encyclopedia of Earth Science,* edited by R. W. Fairbridge (1965), submitted for publication.

Jastrow, R. and A. G. W. Cameron, *Origin of the Solar System.* Proc. Goddard Inst. Space Studies. New York-London: Academic Press, Inc., 1963.

Kaplan, I. R., E. T. Degens, and J. H. Reuter, "Organic Compounds in Stony Meteorites." Geochim. et Cosmochim. Acta, **27** (1963), 805–834.

Kuiper, G. P., *The Atmospheres of the Earth and Planets.* Chicago: University of Chicago Press, 1952.

Kuiper, G. P., ed., *The Solar System;* I and II. Chicago: University of Chicago Press, Vol. I (1953), Vol. II (1954).

Kuiper, G. P. and B. M. Middlehurst, *The Solar System;* III. Chicago: University of Chicago Press, 1961.

Merrill, P. W., *Space Chemistry.* Ann Arbor: The University of Michigan Press, 1963.

Middlehurst, B. M. and G. P. Kuiper, *The Solar System;* IV. Chicago: University of Chicago Press, 1963.

Miller, S. L., "The Possibility of Life on Mars." Proc. Lunar Plan. Expl. Coll., **3** (1963), 1–7.

Miller, S. L., "A Production of Amino Acids under Possible Primitive Earth Conditions." Science, **117** (1953), 528–529.

Miller, S. L., and H. C. Urey, "Organic Compound Synthesis on the Primitive Earth." Science, **130** (1959), 245–251.

Nagy, B., G. W. Meinschein, D. J. Hennessy, "Mass Spectroscopic Analysis of the Orgueil Meteorite. Evidence for Biogenic Hydrocarbons." Ann. New York Acad. Sci., **93** (1961), 25–35.

Oparin, A. I., *The Origin of Life on the Earth*. Edinburgh: Oliver and Boyd, 1957 (translated from the Russian by A. Synge).

Oparin, A. I., *Life: Its Nature, Origin, and Development*. New York: Academic Press, 1960.

Oró, J. and A. P. Kimball, "Synthesis of Purines under Possible Primitive Earth Conditions. II. Purine Intermediates from Hydrogen Cyanide." Arch. Biochem. Biophys., **96** (1962), 293–313.

Oró, J., "Experimental Organic Cosmochemistry: The Formation of Biochemical Compounds." Proc. Lunar Plan. Expl. Coll., **3** (1963a), 9–28.

Oró, J., "Studies in Experimental Organic Cosmochemistry." Ann. New York Acad. Sci., **108** (1963b), 64.

Palm, C. and M. Calvin, "Primordial Organic Chemistry. I. Compounds Resulting from Electron Irradiation of $C^{14}H_4$." J. Amer. Chem. Soc., **84** (1962), 2115–2121.

Ponnamperuma, C., R. M. Lemmon, R. Mariner, and M. Calvin, "Formation of Adenine by Electron Irradiation of Methane, Ammonia, and Water." Proc. Nat. Acad. Sci., **49** (1963a), 737–740.

Ponnamperuma, C., C. Sagan, and R. Mariner, "Synthesis of Adenosine Triphosphate under Possible Primitive Earth Conditions." Nature, **199** (1963b), 222–226.

Prashnowsky, A., E. T. Degens, K. O. Emery, and J. Pimenta, "Organic Materials in Recent and Ancient Sediments, Part I. Sugars in Marine Sediments of Santa Barbara Basin, California." N. Jb. Geol. Paläont. Mh., (1961), 400–413.

Sagan, C., "Organic Matter and Life in Meteorites." Proc. Lunar Plan. Expl. Coll., **2** (1961), 49–54.

Swings, P. and L. Haser, *Atlas of Representative Cometary Spectra*. Louvain, Belgium: Univ. Liège Astrophys. Inst., 1956.

Urey, H. C., "On the Early Chemical History of the Earth and the Origin of Life." Proc. Nat. Acad. Sci., **38** (1952), 351–363.

2. *Petroleum*

Abelson, P. H. and T. C. Hoering, "Carbon Isotope Fractionation in Formation of Amino Acids by Photosynthetic Organisms." Proc. Nat. Acad. Sci., **47** (1961), 623–632.

Abelson, P. H. and T. C. Hoering, "Volatile Hydrocarbons from Low-temperature Heating of Sediments." Bull. Geol. Soc. Amer., Abstracts, 1963, New York Meeting.

Andreev, P. F., A. I. Bogomolov, A. F. Dobryanskii, and A. A. Kartsev, *Transformations of Petroleum in Nature.* Leningrad: Gostoptekhizdat, 1958.

Baker, E. G., "A Hypothesis Concerning the Accumulation of Sediment Hydrocarbons to Form Crude Oils." Geochim. et Cosmochim. Acta, **19** (1960), 309–317.

Barton, D. C., "Natural History of the Gulf Coast Crude Oil. In *Problems of Petroleum Geology.* Tulsa, Oklahoma: Amer. Assoc. Petrol. Geol., 1934.

Berthelot, M. P. E., "Action de la Chaleur sur la Benzine et sur les Carbures Analogues." Compt. Rend. Acad. Sci. Paris, **63** (1866), 788–793.

Berthelot, M., Méthode Universelle pour Réduire et Saturer d'Hydrogène les Composés Organiques." Ann. Chim. Phys., **20** (1870), 392–537.

Bogomolov, A. I., L. I. Khotyntseva, and K. I. Panina, "Low Temperature Catalytic Conversions of Organic Compounds in the Presence of Clays (Conversion of Stearic Acid)." Geochemical Collection, **6,** Gostoptekhizdat, Leningrad, Trudy VNIGRI, No. 155 (1960), 163–193.

Bogomolov, A. I. and K. I. Panina, "Low-temperature Catalytic Conversions of High-Molecular Naphthene Hydrocarbons from Petroleum in the Presence of Natural Clay." Zhurnal Prikladnoi Khimii, **33** (1960), 2757–2762.

Bray, E. E. and E. D. Evans, "Distribution of *n*-Paraffins as a Clue to the Recognition of Source Beds." Geochim. et Cosmochim. Acta, **22** (1961), 2–15.

Breger, I. A., "Diagenesis of Metabolites and a Discussion of the Origin of Petroleum Hydrocarbons." Geochim. et Cosmochim. Acta, **19** (1960), 297–308.

Brooks, B. T., "Evidence of Catalytic Action in Petroleum Formation." Ind. Engng. Chem., **44** (1952), 2570–2577.

Day, W. C. and J. G. Erdman, "Ionene: A Thermal Degradation Product of β-Carotene." Science, **141** (1963), 808.

Degens, E. T., G. V. Chilingar, and W. D. Pierce, "On the Origin of Petroleum Inside Fresh-water Carbonate Concretions of Miocene Age." In *Advances in Organic Geochemistry,* edited by U. Colombo, G. D. Hobson, New York: The Macmillan Company, (1964), 149–164.

Degens, E. T., K. O. Emery, and J. H. Reuter, "Biochemical Compounds in San Diego Trough, California." N. Jb. Geol. Paläont. Mh., (1963), 231–248.

Dobryanskii, A. F., *Chemistry of Petroleum.* Leningrad: Gostoptekhizdat, 1961.

Dunton, M. L. and J. M. Hunt, "Distribution of Low Molecular Weight Hydrocarbons in Recent and Ancient Sediments." Bull. Amer. Assoc. Petrol. Geol., **46** (1962), 2246–2248.

Eckelman, W. R., W. S. Broeker, D. W. Whitlock, and J. R. Allsup, "Implications of Carbon Isotopic Composition of Total Organic Carbon of Some Recent Sediments and Ancient Oils." Bull. Amer. Assoc. Petrol. Geol., **46** (1962), 699–704.

Emery, K. O. and D. Hoggan, "Gases in Marine Sediments." Bull. Amer. Assoc. Petrol. Geol., **42** (1958), 2174–2187.

Erdman, J. G., "Some Chemical Aspects of Petroleum Genesis as Related to the Problem of Source Bed Recognition." Geochim. et Cosmochim. Acta, **22** (1961), 16–36.

Evans, E. D., G. S. Kenny, W. G. Meinschein, and E. E. Bray, "Distribution of n-Paraffins and Separation of Saturated Hydrocarbons from Recent Marine Sediments." Anal. Chem., **29** (1957), 1858-1861.

Frost, A. V., "The Role of Clays in the Formation of Petroleum in the Earth's Crust." Uspekhi Khim., **14** (1952), 501–509.

Hanson, W. E., "Some Chemical Aspects of Petroleum Genesis." In *Researches in Geochemistry,* edited by P. H. Abelson. New York: John Wiley & Sons, Inc., (1959), 104–117.

Hoyle, F., *Frontiers of Astronomy.* Melbourne-London-Toronto: William Heinemann Limited, 1955.

Hunt, J. M., "Distribution of Hydrocarbons in Sedimentary Rocks." Geochim. et Cosmochim. Acta, **22** (1961), 37–49.

Hunt, J. M., "Some Observations on Organic Matter in Sediments." Paper presented at the Oil Scientific Session "25 Years Hungarian Oil," 8–13 October 1962, Budapest.

Hunt, J. M. and G. W., Jamieson. "Oil and Organic Matter in Source Rocks of Petroleum." Bull. Amer. Petrol. Geol., **40** (1956), 477–488.

Judson, S. and R. C. Murray, "Modern Hydrocarbons in Two Wisconsin Lakes." Bull. Amer. Assoc. Petrol. Geol., **40** (1956), 747–750.

Krejci-Graf, "Mikronaphtha und die Entstehung des Erdöls." Mitt. Geol. Ges., Wien, **53** (1960), 133–175.

Krejci-Graf, K. and F. E. Wickman, "Ein geochemisches Profil durch den Lias alpha (Zur Frage der Entstehung des Erdöls.)" Geochim. et Cosmochim. Acta, **18** (1960), 259–272.

Meinschein, W. G., "Origin of Petroleum." Bull. Amer. Assoc. Petrol. Geol., **43** (1959), 925–943.

Meinschein, W. G., "Significance of Hydrocarbons in Sediments and Petroleum." Geochim. et Cosmochim. Acta, **22** (1961), 58–64.

Meinschein, W. G., "Origin of Petroleum." In *Italian Encyclopedia of Petroleum and Natural Gas.* Rome: University of Rome, 1963.

Meinschein, W. G., G. S. Kenny, "Analyses of a Chromatographic Fraction of Organic Extracts of Soils." Anal. Chem., **29** (1957), 1153–1161.

Mulick, J. D. and J. G. Erdman, "Genesis of Hydrocarbons of Low-molecular Weight in Organic Aquatic Systems." Science, **141** (1963), 806–807.

McIver, R. D., C. B. Coons, M. O. Denekas, and G. W. Jamieson, "Maturation of Oil, an Important Natural Process." Bull. Geol. Soc. Amer., Abstracts New York Meeting, 1963.

McNab, J. G., P. V. Smith Jr., and R. L. Betts, "The Evolution of Petroleum." Ind. Engng. Chem., **44** (1952), 2556–2563.

Park, R. and H. N. Dunning, "Stable Carbon Isotope Studies of Crude Oils and their Porphyrin Aggregates." Geochim. et Cosmochim. Acta, **22** (1961), 99–105.

Park, R. and S. Epstein, "Metabolic Fractionation of C^{13} & C^{12} in Plants." Plant Phys., **36** (1961a), 133–138.

Park, R. and S. Epstein, "Carbon Isotope Fractionation During Photosynthesis." Geochim. et Cosmochim. Acta, **21** (1961b), 110–126.

Robinson, R. S., "The Duplex Origins of Petroleum." In *Advances in Organic Geochemistry*, edited by U. Colombo and G. D. Hobson. New York: The Macmillan Company, (1964), 7–10.

Rosenfeld, W. D. and S. R. Silverman, "Carbon Isotope Fractionation in Bacterial Production of Methane." Science, **130** (1959), 1658–1659.

Silverman, S. R., "Carbon Isotope Geochemistry of Petroleum and Other Natural Organic Materials." Paper presented at the Oil Scientific Session, "25 Years Hungarian Oil," Budapest, October 8–13, 1962.

Silverman, S. R., "Carbon Isotopic Evidence for Mechanisms of Petroleum Maturation." Geochim. et Cosmochim. Acta, (1964b) (in press).

Silverman, S. R., Investigations of Petroleum Origin and Evolution Mechanisms by Carbon Isotope Studies. In *Isotopic and Cosmic Chemistry*, edited by H. Craig, S. L. Miller, and G. J. Wasserburg. Amsterdam: North-Holland Publishing, (1964a), 92–102.

Silverman, S. R. and S. Epstein, "Carbon Isotopic Compositions of Petroleum and Other Sedimentary Organic Materials." Bull. Amer. Assoc., Petrol. Geol., **42** (1958), 998–1012.

Smith, P. V. Jr., "Preliminary Note on Origin of Petroleum." Bull. Amer. Assoc. Petrol. Geol., **36** (1952), 411–413.

Smith, P. V. Jr., "Studies on Origin of Petroleum Occurrence of Hydrocarbons in Recent Sediments." Bull. Amer. Assoc. Petrol. Geol., **38** (1954), 377–404.

Sokolov, V. A., "Possibilities of Formation and Migration of Oil in Young Sedimentary Deposits." Leningrad: Gostoptekhizdat. (1959), 59–63.

Stevens, N. P., E. E. Bray, and E. D. Evans, "Hydrocarbons in Sediments of the Gulf of Mexico." In *Habitat of Oil,* edited by J. L. Weeks. Tulsa, Oklahoma: Amer. Assoc. Petrol. Geol., 1958, 779–789.

Vassoevich, N. B., "Probleme der Erdölgenese." Angew. Geol., **4** (1958), 512–515.

Veber, V. V. and N. N. Turkeltaub, "Gaseous Hydrocarbons in Recent Sediments." Geologiia Nefti, **49** (1958), 682–686.

Weeks, L. G., "Habitat of Oil and Factors that Control it." In *Habitat of Oil,* ed. L. G. Weeks. Tulsa, Oklahoma: Amer. Assoc. Petrol. Geol., (1958).

3. Coal

Bangham, D. H., *Progress in Coal Science.* New York: Interscience Publishers, Inc., 1950.

Blom, L., L. Edelhausen, and D. W. Van Krevelen, Fuel, **36** (1957) (quoted by Van Krevelen, 1961).

Breger, I. A., "Geochemistry of Coal." Econ. Geol., **53** (1958), 823–841.

Craig, H., "The Geochemistry of the Stable Carbon Isotopes." Geochim. et Cosmochim. Acta, **3** (1953), 53–92.

Craig, H., "Isotopic Standards for Carbon and Oxygen and Correction Factors for Mass-Spectrometric Analysis of Carbon Dioxide." Geochim. et Cosmochim. Acta, **12** (1957), 133–149.

Dryden, I. G. C., "How was Coal Formed." Coke and Gas, (1956), 1–11.

Dulhunty, J. A., "Geological Factors in the Metamorphic Development of Coal." Fuel, **33** (1954), 145–152.

Francis, W., *Coal, Its Formation and Composition.* London: Edward Arnold (Publishers) Ltd., 1961.

Friedman, S., M. L. Kaufman, W. A. Steiner, and I. Wender, Fuel, **40** (1961), 33 (quoted by Van Krevelen, 1961).

Fuchs, W. and W. Stengel, 1921, (cited by Van Krevelen, 1961).

Given, P. H., "Chemicals from Coal." New Scientist, **14** (1962), 355–357.

Given, P. H., "The Chemical Study of Coal Macerals." In *Advances in Geochemistry,* edited by U. Colombo and G. D. Hobson. New York: The Macmillan Company, (1964), 39–48.

Huck, G. and J. Karwell, "Physikalisch-chemische Probleme der Inkohlung." Brennstoff-Chem., **36** (1955), 1–11.

Hunt, John M., "Organic Sediments." *Encyclopedia of Earth Sciences*, edited by R. W. Fairbridge, (1965) submitted for publication.

Leutwein, F. and H. J. Roessler, "Spurenelemente in Steinkohlenaschen." Freib. Forschungshefte, **C10** (1954), 68.

Leutwein, F. and H. J. Roessler, "Geochemische Untersuchungen an paleozoischen und mesozoischen Kohlen Mittel-und Ostdeutschlands." Freib. Forschungshefte, **C19** (1955), 956.

Teichmüller, M., "Die Genese der Kohle." Compt. Rend. Quatr. Congr. Strat. Geol. Carbonif., **3** (1962), 699–722.

Teichmüller, M. and R. Teichmüller, "Die stoffliche und strukturelle Metamorphose der Kohle." Geol. Rundschau, **42** (1954), 265–296.

Teichmüller, M. and R. Teichmüller, "The Diagenesis of Coal (Coalification)," In *Diagenesis of Sediments,* edited by G. Larsen and G. V. Chilingar. Amsterdam: Elsevier Publishing Company, 1964.

Tomkeieff, S. I., *Coals and Bitumens.* London: Pergamon Press, Inc., 1954.

Van Krevelen, D. W., *Coal. Typology-Chemistry-Physics-Constitution.* Amsterdam-London-New York: Elsevier Publishing Company, 1961.

Van Krevelen, D. W. and J. Schuyer, *Coal Science; Aspects of Coal Constitution.* Amsterdam-London-New York: Elsevier Publishing Company, 1957.

Wickman, F. E., "Variations in the Relative Abundance of the Carbon Isotopes in Plants." Geochim. et Cosmochim. Acta, **2** (1952), 243–254.

Wnekowska, L., 3rd Int. Conf. Coal Sci., Valkenburg, 1959 (cited by Van Krevelen, 1961).

6

Miscellaneous Topics

Aside from the data presented in preceding sections, there is still an enormous wealth of information in the geochemical literature which has not even been touched on here. Nobody can afford to ignore the great achievements accomplished in these so far "unnoticed" areas of geochemistry. On the other hand, it was not feasible to include them in an appropriate manner within the framework of this treatise. For this reason an arbitrary selection had to be made. Perhaps a writer who is more ambitious and courageous than the author will offer a better and broader account at some later time.

There are a great many topics which have not been duly considered in the context of this book. A few of them, taken at random, include the following:

(1) Geochemistry of major and minor elements (e.g., Green, 1959).

(2) Natural radioactivity in the atmosphere, hydrosphere, and lithosphere (e.g., Israel and Krebs, 1962; Geiss and Goldberg, 1963).

(3) Biogeochemistry of oceans, lakes, and rivers (e.g., Hill, 1963; Hutchinson, 1957; Sverdrup et al., 1946).

(4) Isotope studies of glacial ice (e.g., Epstein and Benson, 1959, Dansgaard, 1961).

(5) Ore deposits and geochemical prospecting for minerals and crude oils (e.g., Hawkes, 1959, 1963; Hawkes and Webb, 1962; Ginzburg, 1960; Kartsev et al., 1959; Amstutz, 1964; Ruckmick, 1963).

(6) Porosity/permeability studies (e.g., von Engelhardt, 1960; Aschenbrenner and Chilingar, 1960; Weyl, 1960; Murray, 1960).

(7) Geochemistry of extraterrestrial materials found in recent and and ancient sediments, soils, and glaciers (e.g. Fredriksson and Martin, 1963; Fredriksson and Gowdy, 1963; Thiel and Schmidt, 1961; Hunter and Parkin, 1961).

(8) Soil chemistry (e.g. Jackson, 1958).

(9) Synthesis of abiotic organic matter (e.g. Oró, 1963; Calvin, 1964; Horowitz and Miller, 1962; Miller and Urey, 1959).

(10) Analytical methods of inorganic and organic geochemistry (e.g., Milner, 1962; Degens and Reuter, 1962).

This list is not a complete inventory, of course; it should serve only as a reminder of the additional work that can be done in the field of low-temperature geochemistry.

Selected References

Amstutz, G. C., ed., *Sedimentology and Ore Genesis*. Amsterdam: Elsevier Publishing Company, 1964.

Aschenbrenner, B. C. and G. V. Chilingar, "Teodorovich's Method for Determining Permeability from Pore-Space Characteristics of Carbonate Rocks." Bull. Amer. Assoc. Petrol. Geol., **44** (1960), 1421–1424.

Calvin, M., "Chemical Evolution." (preprint 1964).

Dansgaard, W., "The Isotopic Composition of Natural Waters with Special Reference to the Greenland Ice Cap." Medd. Groenland, **165** (1961), 120 pp.

Degens, E. T. and J. H. Reuter, "Analytical Techniques in the Field of Organic Geochemistry." In *Advances in Organic Geochemistry*, edited by U. Colombo and G. D. Hobson. London: The Macmillan Company (1964), 377–402.

Engelhardt, W. von, *Der Porenraum der Sedimente: Mineralogie und Petrographie in Einzeldarstellungen, II.* Berlin-Göttingen-Heidelberg: Springer Verlag, 1960.

Epstein, S. and C. Benson, "Oxygen Isotope Studies." Bull. Int. Geoph. Year, **21** (1959) 9–12.

Fredriksson, K. and R. Gowdy, "Meteoritic Debris from the Southern California Desert." Geochim. et Cosmochim. Acta, **27** (1963), 241–243.

Fredriksson, K. and L. R. Martin, "The Origin of Black Spherules Found in Pacific Islands, Deep-sea Sediments, and Antarctic Ice." Geochim. et Cosmochim. Acta, **27** (1963), 245–248.

Geiss, T. and E. D. Goldberg, eds., *Earth Science and Meteoritics.* Amsterdam: North-Holland Publishing Company, 1963.

Ginzburg, I. I., *Principles of Geochemical Prospecting. Techniques of Prospecting for Non-Ferrous Ores and Rare Metals.* New York-London-Oxford-Paris: Pergamon Press, Inc., 1960.

Green, J., "Geochemical Table of the Elements for 1959." Bull. Geol. Soc. Amer., **70** (1959), 1127–1184.

Hawkes, H. E., "Dithizone Field Tests." Econ. Geol., **58** (1963), 579–586.

Hawkes, H. E., "Geochemical Prospecting." In *Researches in Geochemistry,* edited by P. H. Abelson. New York: John Wiley & Sons, Inc., (1959), 62–78.

Hawkes, H. E. and J. S. Webb, *Geochemistry in Mineral Exploration.* Harper and Row, Publishers, 1962.

Hill, M. N., ed., *The Sea. Ideas and Observations on Progress on the Study of the Seas. Vols. 2 and 3.* New York: Interscience Publishers, Inc., 1963.

Horowitz, N. H. and S. L. Miller, "Modern Concepts of the Origin of Life." Fortschr. Chem. Org. Naturst., **20** (1962), 423–459.

Hunter, W. and D. W. Parkin, "Cosmic Dust in Tertiary Rock and the Lunar Surface." Geochim. et Cosmochim. Acta, **24** (1961), 32–39.

Hutchinson, G. E., *A Treatise on Limnology, I.* New York: John Wiley & Sons, Inc., 1957.

Israel, H. and A. Krebs, eds. *Kernstrahlung in der Geophysik.* Berlin-Göttingen-Heidelberg: Springer Verlag, 1962.

Jackson, M. L., *Soil Chemical Analysis.* Englewood Cliffs, N. J.: Prentice-Hall, Inc., 1958.

Kartsev, A. A., Z. A. Tabasaranskii, M. I. Subbota, and G. A. Mogilevskii, *Geochemical Methods of Prospecting and Exploration for Petroleum and Natural Gas.* Berkeley and Los Angeles: University of California Press, 1959.

Miller, S. L. and H. C. Urey, "Organic Compound Synthesis on the Primitive Earth." Science, **130** (1959), 245–251.

Milner, H. B., *Sedimentary Petrography. I. Methods in Sedimentary Petrography*. New York: The Macmillan Company, 1962.

Murray, R. C., "Origin of Porosity in Carbonate Rocks." J. Sed. Petrol., **30** (1960), 59–84.

Oró, J., "Experimental Organic Cosmochemistry: The Formation of Biochemical Compounds." Proc. Lunar Plan. Expl. Coll., **3** (1963), 9–28.

Ruckmick, J. C., "The Iron Ores of Cerro Bolivar, Venezuela." Econ. Geol., **58** (1963), 218–236.

Sverdrup, H. U., M. W. Johnson, and R. H. Fleming, *The Oceans: Their Physics, Chemistry and General Biology*. Englewood Cliffs, N. J.: Prentice-Hall, Inc., 1946.

Thiel, E. and R. A. Schmidt, "Spherules from the Antarctic Ice Cap." J. Geophys. Res., **66** (1961), 307–310.

Weyl, P. K., "Porosity through Dolomitization: Conservation-of-Mass Requirements." J. Sed. Petrol., **30** (1960), 85–90.

7

Summary and Outlook

The information on the inorganic and organic geochemistry of sediments which has been gathered in this book gives some insight into basic problems and achievements of low-temperature geochemistry. This survey covers the fundamentals, but it is by no means comprehensive.

The emphasis on individual end-members rather than on individual types of sediments was used as a tool to present data in a meaningful and understandable form. To take the next step, namely to construct a unique "Gedankengebäude," that is an intelligent arrangement, of the multifarious information obtained from a single sediment, was not the purpose of this book. But it should be the ultimate goal for all of us who are engaged in geochemical studies of sediments.

Index of Names*

Abelson, P. H., 2, 207, 209, 214, 215, 219, 235, *267*, 291, 293, 296, 297, *307*, *308*
Aberhalden, E., 232, *267*
Abraham, H., 259, 263, *267*
Adams, A. P., 244, *267*
Adams, J. A. S., 72, *91*
Adams, J. E., 123, *129*
Adams, J. K., 147, *150*
Alderman, A. R., 118, *128*
Alexander, G. B., 74, 76, *93*
Alexander, L. T., *59*
Allen, V. T., 68, 69, *91*
Allenby, R. J., 79, *93*
Allsup, J. R., *132*, *283*, *309*
Altschuler, Z. A., 37, *56*, 141, *150*
Ames, L. L., Jr., 53, *64*, 143–45, *150*
Amirkhanov, Kh. I., 41, *56*
Amstutz, G. C., 314, *314*
Andersen, S. T., 238, *267*
Anderson, C. T., *182*
Anderson, G., 244–246, *267*
Anderson, G. M., 106, *135*
Anderson, H. V., 154, *166*
Andreev, P. F., 292, *308*
Angino, E. E., 123, *129*
D'Ans, J., 171, 173, 175, *180*
Antevs, E., 108, *129*
Arnold, P. W., 144, *151*
Arnold, R. G., 153, *166*
Arrhenius, G. O. S., 11, *12*, 54, *64*, 91, *97*, 145, 147, 149, *151*, 179, *180*, *181*

Aschenbrenner, B. C., 123, *129*, 314, *314*
Ault, W. U., 163–65, *167*
Awasthi, N., 55, *65*
Axelrod, J. M., *66*
Ayers, M. L., 187, *198*

BaasBecking, L. G. M., 27, *56*, 82, *95*, 159, *167*, 267, *268*
Bader, R. G., 229, *268*
Baertschi, P., 106, 110, *129*, 280, *283*
Bagchi, T. C., *66*
Bajor, M., 219, *269*
Baker, B. L., *272*, 273
Baker, E. G., 294, 297, *308*
Balgord, W. D., 60, *94*
Bangham, D. H., 299, *311*
Bär, A. L. S., 22, *57*
Bardossy, G., 69, *91*
Barghoorn, E. S., 219, 227, *268*
Barlow, U. H., *150*
Barnes, H. L., 153, *167*
Barnes, V. E., 118, *131*
Barshad, I., 32, *57*
Bartholomew, W. V., *267*
Barton, D. C., 297, *308*
Basak, G. C., 249, *272*
Baskin, Y., 49, *63*
Bates, T. F., 17, 31, *57*, 69, 72, *91*
Bayliss, P., 70, 71, *92*
Begemann, F., 194, *198*
Benderson, E. P., 124, *138*

* Numbers in italic denote complete citation in the References.

318

Index of Subjects*

---

* Numbers in italic denote major chapters. Numbers having # refer to subjects in tables and figures.